High Technology and the Competition State

Since its origins in 1985, the Eureka initiative has grown to rival in size and importance the European Community's collaborative research and development programmes. Industry-led and intergovernmental in design, it functions without a centralized organizational structure or source of funds.

High Technology and the Competition State is the first in-depth analysis of Eureka. John Peterson argues that Eureka is indicative of an entirely new type of policymaking, and, in some senses, a new form of government. He shows how Eureka reflects the transition to new 'competition state' public policy strategies to promote supply-side innovation. The volume breaks new ground by applying a theoretical model of 'policy networks' to explain how Eureka works in practice.

The book assesses the role of Eureka and collaborative R & D more generally in promoting the completion of the EC's internal market. It also presents findings from a comprehensive attitudinal study of industrial participants in Eureka and case studies of five individual projects.

John Peterson lectures on the European Community at the University of York. He has written widely on technology policy issues and has contributed to assessments of Eureka undertaken by the Dutch and Norwegian governments. His critical, incisive book will be of great interest to students of international business and technology, as well as policy practitioners and industrialists.

High Technology and the Competition State

An analysis of the Eureka initiative

John Peterson

London and New York

Does not the infinitude of division refer to the utterness of individuality? Does not the entireness of the complex hint at the perfection of the simple?

Edgar Allen Poe
Eureka: A Prose Poem
published 1848

First published 1993
by Routledge
11 New Fetter Lane, London EC4P 4EE

Simultaneously published in the USA and Canada
by Routledge
29 West 35th Street, New York, NY 10001

© 1993 John Peterson

Typeset in Times by Megaron, Cardiff, UK
Printed and bound in Great Britain

British Library Cataloguing-in-Publication Data
A catalogue record for this book is available from the British Library.

Library of Congress Cataloging in Publication Data
Peterson, John, 1958–
    High technology and the competition state: an analysis of the Eureka initiative / John Peterson
        p. cm.
    Includes bibliographical references and index.
    1. Research, Industrial–Europe. 2. High technology industries–Europe. 3. Technology and state–Europe. 4. EUREKA Organization.
    I. Title.
T177.E8P48 1993
607'.24–dc20

ISBN 0–415–09562–X

Contents

List of figures
List of tables
Preface
List of abbreviations

1 **High technology and the competition state**   1

2 **Partners, process and projects**   25

3 **The weight of history and origins of Eureka**   49

4 **How Eureka operates**   73

5 **Eureka and the European Community**   103

6 **The participants' view**   127

7 **Inside the projects: case studies**   161

8 **Conclusion**   198

    Appendix: Prescriptions for the re-design of Eureka   223

    Notes   226
    Bibliography   264
    Index   283

Figures

1.1 Conceptualizing policy networks   21
6.1 Size/types of Eureka participants   129
6.2 Collaborative experience prior to Eureka
     (independent survey)   131
6.3 Size/type of project leader and previous
     collaborative experience (independent survey)   134
6.4 Formal and legal organization of projects
     (independent survey)   136
6.5 Number of partners receiving public funds by
     size/type of project leader (independent survey)   138
6.6 Would the project exist without Eureka status by
     size/type of project leader (independent survey)   142

Tables

2.1 Project participation by Member States 26
2.2 Evolution of Eureka's project list (1986–88) 33
2.3 Eureka's project list (1989) 33
2.4 Eureka's project list (1992) 34
4.1 R & D spending in OECD countries 74
4.2 Business-financed R & D in OECD countries 74
6.1 Possible and actual sample sizes (independent survey) 128
6.2 Size and type of Eureka participants (official survey) 130
6.3 Number of current Eureka partners with whom project leaders had previously collaborated (independent survey) 132
6.4 How organizations became involved in Eureka 132
6.5 How project leaders found partners (independent survey) 132
6.6 Adequacy of Eureka's links to EC-funded R & D (independent survey) 136
6.7 Project size (independent survey) 136
6.8 Project leaders receiving public funds (independent survey) 137
6.9 Number of partners who receive public funds (independent survey) 137
6.10 Public funds as percentage of respondents' total and own R & D costs (independent survey) 139
6.11 Projects funded by each Member State, actual national division of project leadership, and national division of total sample (independent survey) 140
6.12 Eureka status and private finance (independent survey) 140
6.13 Would the project exist without Eureka status? 141
6.14 Would the project exist by previous experience 143
with current partners (independent survey)

6.15 Intention to participate in Eureka again 144
6.16 Intention to participate in Eureka again
cross-tabulated with previous experience with
current partners (independent survey) 144
6.17 Expected benefits of Eureka participation
(independent survey) 145
6.18 Expected benefits of Eureka participation
for large firms and SMEs (independent survey) 146
6.19 Motives for participation in Eureka (official survey) 147
6.20 Most important aspects of Eureka (official survey) 147
6.21 Effect of Eureka status on project
(independent survey) 147
6.22 Major problems experienced (independent survey) 148
6.23 Major problems experienced (official survey) 151
6.24 How governments could be more helpful
(independent survey) 151
6.25 Small and large state respondents' previous
collaborative experience with current partners
(independent survey) 151
6.26 Shares of small and large state respondents'
own R & D costs covered by public funds
(independent survey) 151
6.27 Small and large state respondents'
intentions to participate in Eureka again
(independent survey) 152
7.1 Five Eureka projects: essential characteristics 162
7.2 National direct grants to Eurotrac (1989) 169
7.3 Market shares for central office switches in Europe
(1986) 176
7.4 EC consumer electronics consumption and
share imported by product category (1989) 178
7.5 Case study findings: Eureka's added value 191
7.6 Case study findings: problems and effect of
Eureka's methodology 192
7.7 Locating Eureka projects in wider policy networks 193
8.1 European Innovation Policy: levels of analysis 209

Preface

Business before pleasure. Acronyms often are not written in full capitals (i.e. Eureka and Jessi, not EUREKA and JESSI) simply to make the text more readable. Monetary amounts are expressed in ECUs whenever possible. All interviews were conducted on a non-attributable basis. The institutional affiliations and nationalities of all interviewees are indicated whenever an interview is cited in the text. Points of information which were verified by more than two interviewees are referenced as 'numerous interviews' in endnotes, with an indication of whether interviewees were officials, industrialists or both. A list of institutions represented by interviewees is included at the end of the bibliography.

The idea of writing this book was first contemplated in Grenoble, France. Michel Chatelus, Elie Cohen, Jean-Marie Martin and Lee Schlenker stoked my interest in the project at a critical, early stage. The Annie Givelet family took me in as one of their own and shared with me the joys of their *vie quotidienne* in France.

The project entered a 'take-off phase' at the University of Essex in 1989–90, where Bob Jessop, Mel Read, Neil Robinson, Elinor Scarbrough, Gerry Stoker, Rob Stones and Eric Tannenbaum provided support and intellectual stimulation. Emil Kirchner and Hugh Ward offered valuable comments on draft chapters. Special thanks are due to Sandrine Conesa, Jane Horder, Michael Laermann and particularly Dylan Griffiths for their selfless efforts toward making the survey of Eureka participants a success. Dave, Suzy and Holly Marsh bequeathed nice meals and much love during both good times and bad.

Key sections of this study were written in a dark, noisy apartment next to the railroad tracks and 101 Freeway in Santa Barbara, California. At the University of California, Santa Barbara (UCSB), I received guidance and encouragement from Stanley Anderson, Haruhiro Fukui, Michael Gordon, Wolfram Hanrieder, Raghavan Iyer, Tom Schrock and M. Stephen Weatherford. In 1990, a period of almost overwhelming uncertainty, crucial support was offered by Cedric Robinson and John Moore. The staff at UCSB's Social Sciences Computing Laboratory – particularly Susan Banducci, Mark Schildhauer, Raoul Melendez and above all Marisela Marquez – showed limitless patience and empathy. I am especially grateful to Steve Breyman and Peter Merkl for their friendship and inspiration throughout.

As the study was completed, new colleagues at the University of York made me feel at home in what was previously a faraway place of which I knew nothing. Thanks are due to Neil Carter, Phil Cerny, Judith Evans and Linda Lofthouse. Professor Rod Rhodes believed in me when others did not or could not. Presumably, he will continue to remind me of how much I owe him.

Many Eureka officials, most of whom probably would wish to remain anonymous, provided critical assistance. However, special thanks are owed to Stephen Elton, Alistair Keddie and David Saunders of the UK Eureka office, Fleming Woldbye of the Danish Eureka office, Bjørn Henriksen of the Norwegian Eureka office and Luc Durieux, Nicholas Newman and Michel Progent of the European Commission. Pol van den Bergen and Joost de Jong of the 1991 Dutch chairmanship made me feel as if this study finally had come full circle.

The list of those who offered accommodation and companionship in between all the semi-permanent stops is long: the kind Danes at the Danish Youth Council in Copenhagen; Franz Heimel in Vienna; Leo Janssen in Amsterdam; Rob Harrison in The Hague; Yves Blanc and Sylvie Mathieu in Paris; Ulf Cronquist in Göteborg; Charles and Jacqueline Richards in Dublin; Sue Hinder and family in Manchester; Susan Painter, Claire Bannerman, Michael O'Neill, Peter Leuner and Sara Chetin in London; Sonia Garcia and Mary McKenzie in Santa Barbara; and Jim Olsen and Carrie Gear in New England. Friends in Brussels – Moya Campbell, Monica Frassoni, Rachel Kyte, Simon Nugent, Giannis Papageorgiou – must be singled out for their inspiration. Richard Doherty and Annette Schulte are more responsible than anyone else for my continued fascination with European politics. This study would be a far inferior piece of work were it not for their love and encouragement.

Above all, my family has been a source of inestimable support. Edward Peterson was generous when the chips were down. Jean Peterson showed extraordinary courage and good humour in the face of much adversity. No one would have been happier to see this book published than my late stepfather, Paul Ohman. I shall never forget his love of knowledge, Vermont and my mother.

Preface

An earlier version of this study was written as a PhD thesis at the London School of Economics. It is difficult to describe the richness of intellectual life at the LSE to anyone who has never spent time in its cramped, dingy confines. June Burnham, Marian Clarke, Mark Donovan, Peter Fysh, Desmond King, Howard Machin and especially Brendan O'Leary all played key roles in the study's successful completion. Michael Hodges of the LSE and Alan Cawson of the University of Sussex were tough, but sympathetic examiners who both contributed much to the final product as it is presented here. A special debt is owed to my long-suffering supervisor, Patrick Dunleavy. He was steadfast when all seemed lost and emerged as the real hero of the project.

Finally, Elizabeth Bomberg became a trusted colleague and a great friend while the study was being written. Just after it was finished, she became my wife. To borrow a line oft-used by the scriptwriters in Los Angeles, I simply couldn't have *written* her any better. This book is for her.

Abbreviations

AEG	*Allgemeine Elektrizitätsgesellschaft*
ANVAR	*Agence Nationale de Valorisation de la Recherche*
ASICs	Application-Specific Integrated Circuits
AT&T	American Telephone and Telegraph
BECU	billion European currency units
BMFT	*Bundesminister für Forschung und Technologie*
BREMA	British Electronic Equipment Manufacturers
Brite	Basic Research in Industrial Technologies for Europe
CAD	Computer-aided design
CECCP	*Centro Estero Camere Commercio Piedmont* (Italy)
CEN	*Comité Européen de Normalisation*
CENELEC	*Comité Européen de Normalisation Electronique*
CCIRN	Coordinating Committee for International Research Networks
CCIR	International Consultative Committee (of the International Telecommunications Union)
CEC	Commission of the European Communities
CEPT	Conference of European Post and Telecommunications administrations
CERD	European Research and Development Committee
CERN	*Centre Européen pour la Récherche Nucleaire*
CESTA	*Centre d'Etudes des Systèmes et des Technologies Avancées* (France)
CGE	*Companie Generale d'Electricité*
Cosine	Cooperation for Open Systems Interconnection Networking in Europe.
COST	Co-operation in Science and Technology
CSCE	Conference on Security and Co-operation in Europe

CTV	Colour Television
CDU	Christian Democratic Union (Germany)
DBS	Direct Broadcasting via Satellite
DG	Directorate-General (European Commission)
DM	Deutsche Marks
DRAM	Dynamic Random Access Memory
Drive	Dedicated Road Infrastructure for Vehicle Safety in Europe
DTI	Department of Trade and Industry (United Kingdom)
EBU	European Broadcasting Union
EC	European Community
ECU	European Currency Unit
EEIG	European Economic Interest Grouping
EFA	European Fighter Aircraft
EFMD	European Foundation for Management Development
EFTA	European Free Trade Association
ELDO	European Launcher Development Organization
EMRI	Eureka Management Research Initiative
EP	European Parliament
Epoch	European Programme on Climatology and Natural Hazards
ERDA	European Research and Development Agency
ESA	European Space Agency
Esprit	European Strategic Programme in Information Technologies
ES2	European Silicon Structures
ESRO	European Space Research Organization
ETSI	European Telecommunications Standards Institute
Euratom	European Atomic Energy Community
Eureka	European Research Co-ordinating Agency
Eurotrac	European Experiment on Transport and Transformation of Environmentally Relevant Trace Constituents in the Troposphere over Europe
EVCA	European Venture Capital Association
Famos	Flexible Automated Assembly Systems
FCC	Federal Communications Commission (USA)
FMS	Flexible Manufacturing Systems
FFr	French Francs
FRG	Federal Republic of Germany
GATT	General Agreement on Trade and Tariffs

GDP	Gross Domestic Product
GEC	General Electric Company (UK)
HDTV	High Definition Television
HLG	High Level Group
IBM	International Business Machines
ICs	Integrated Circuits
IEPG	Independent European Programme Group
IPRs	Intellectual Property Rights
IRDAC	Industrial Research and Development Advisory Committee
IT	Information technology
Jessi	Joint European Silicon Structures project
JET	Joint European Torus
JRC	Joint Research Centre
JVC	Japan Victor Company
MAC	Multiplexed Analogue Components
MBB	Messerschmidt Bölkow Blohm
MECU	million European currency units
MITHRA	*Matérials Intertechnologique de Haute Robot Avancée*
MITI	Ministry of International Trade and Industry (Japan)
MNCs	Multinational Corporations
MRCA	Multi-Role Combat Aircraft (Tornado)
MRT	Ministry of Research and Technology (France)
MUSE	Multiple Sub-Nyquist Encoding
NATO	North Atlantic Treaty Organization
NHK	Japanese state broadcasting organization
NLG	Dutch Guilders
NPCs	National Project Co-ordinators
NTSC	National Television System Committee
OECD	Organization for Economic Co-operation and Development
OSI	Open Standards Interconnection
PAL	Phase Alternation by Line
PHOXA	Photochemical Oxidant and Acid Deposition Model
PTT	Post, Telephone and Telecommunications
Race	Research in Advanced Communications for Europe
RA-D	Rig Automation Drilling
RAI	Italian state broadcasting organization
RARE	*Réseaux Associés pour la Recherche Européenne*

R & D	Research and Development
Science	*Stimulation des Coopérations Internationales et des Echanges Nécessaires aux Chercheurs en Europe*
SDI	Strategic Defence Initiative
SEA	Single European Act
SECAM	*Séquence à Mémoire*
SEPSU	Science and Engineering Policy Studies Unit (UK Royal Society and Fellowship of Engineering)
SME	Small or Medium-sized Enterprise
SPAG	Standards Promotion and Application Group
SPES	Stimulation Programme for Economic Sciences
SPD	Social Democratic Party (Germany)
Step	Science and Technology Programme for Environmental Protection
UK	United Kingdom
VCR	Video cassette recorder
Value	Valorization and Utilization for Europe
VLSI	Very Large-Scale Integration
ZIRST	*Zone pour l'Innovation et les Réalisations Scientifiques et Techniques* (Grenoble)

1   High technology and the competition state

Review note -

This book forms the first truly exhaustive empirical study of Eureka, a framework for pan-European collaborative research and development (R & D) projects. Eureka is transnational in that it brings together twenty-one Member States, but it exists outside the formal institutional confines of the European Community (EC). By 1992 its participants included the EC twelve, the six European Free Trade Association (EFTA) states, Turkey, the European Commission and Hungary. Eureka is 'industry-led', with firms taking primary responsibility for designing individual Eureka projects and determining their technological goals. The initiative's founding charter, or Declaration of Principles, implies that Eureka exists primarily to promote collaborative R & D which is 'downstream', 'near-market', and aims to develop 'products, processes and services having a world-wide market potential'.[1] But Eureka incorporates a very eclectic collection of projects with a diversity of goals. It has few rules of process and the role of governments is essentially confined to simple choices about which of their national participants to support with what level of public funding.

The central argument of this study is that Eureka is indicative of an entirely new type of policymaking and, more broadly, a new form of government. It brings together national administrations to pursue common goals, yet in no way does it pool national sovereignty. Eureka's minimal administrative resources mean that governments have very limited means to scrutinize projects once they are deemed suitable for 'Eureka status'. In many cases, Eureka allows private actors discretion of a sort only rarely granted to recipients of public money. From a social scientist's point of view, a hard-headed policy analysis of Eureka is long overdue, considering that the total anticipated value of all Eureka projects is roughly similar to the total value of all EC-sponsored R & D programmes.[2] From an industrialist's point of view, a dispassionate and critical analysis of Eureka is needed so that future participants in its projects know what they are getting themselves into.

This chapter begins by explaining why collaborative R & D has become a logical element in both European firm strategies and industrial policies in the 1990s. Section II sets out evaluative criteria for a policy analysis of Eureka. Collaborative R & D generally, and Eureka specifically, are placed in the context of theories of regional integration in Section III. Section IV surveys recent research on government–industry relations and introduces a model of policy networks which is used throughout the study to help explain why Eureka exists and how it works. The chapter concludes with a brief synopsis of the study's organization and major themes.

I. THE LOGIC OF COLLABORATIVE R & D

The accelerating rate of technological change in the late twentieth century poses challenges to political societies previously unknown or encountered only in vastly simpler permutations. New technologies in telecommunications, computers and transport create a more open world where boundaries originally created by nature between regions and continents diminish in importance. Competition between economic actors becomes increasingly global as new technology makes it possible to market and sell products beyond national or regional boundaries which once excluded all but 'domestic' or 'local' producers.

The accelerated rate of technological change significantly contributed to three structural changes in the international economy which had emerged in bold relief by 1985, the year Eureka was created.[3] First, the total volume of global trade across national borders increased dramatically. Its value more than doubled from $903 billion in 1975 to $1915 billion in 1984.[4] No major national economy was untouched as ratios of imports to domestic demand and exports to gross domestic product increased substantially.[5]

Second, the global pace of technology transfer across borders quickened. The declining costs of cross-border communications combined with widespread financial deregulation to make capital highly mobile. More funds became available for investment in new technologies. On the supply side, new producers – particularly in Asia – gained access to state-of-the-art production technologies, and global markets for technology-intensive products became fiercely competitive. In traditional manufacturing industries, low-wage foreign competition was no longer low-productivity competition as the process and product technology utilized by competitors from low-wage countries began to match Western standards.[6] As more firms competed to develop the next generation of the same products, product life cycles fell rapidly – from an average of eight years in the 1970s to just over two years in the 1980s – in a broad range of technology-intensive industries.[7] An innovator in microelectronics could find that the next generation of components emerged to make their present innovation obsolete six months after its discovery.

On the demand side, more rapid technology transfer meant that product demand in world markets for many 'high-tech' goods became more homogeneous across geographic regions. In order to recoup high R & D costs before products with shorter life cycles became obsolete, firms were forced to sell the largest possible volume in the shortest possible time.[8] Profits from home markets became insufficient to finance the rising costs of 'leading edge' R & D and far more firms in technology-intensive industries were forced to take on global marketing strategies.

Third, the role of the nation state as an economic actor began to change as the structure of production in the world economy became internationalized. Governments increasingly found that their macroeconomic policies succeeded or failed due to largely unpredictable and uncontrollable trends in global business cycles, trade patterns and capital and investment flows. Keynesianism gradually was abandoned as a guide to macroeconomic policymaking as governments found that traditional tools of domestic demand management could no longer control national economies, which became progressively more vulnerable to fluctuations in the wider, global economy. National welfare state systems after 1970 repeatedly approached points of crisis or 'overload'[9] due to global recessions over which national governments had little or no independent influence.

The response of the 'New Right' to the crisis of the welfare state in the 1980s – deregulation, privatization and the freeing of markets – was not confined to Thatcherite Britain or Reagan's America. Many of the same principles informed the Single European Act (SEA) which 'relaunched' the EC in the mid-1980s. Nearly all western economic policies shifted away from social welfare goals to market liberalization strategies as a response to the internationalization of markets, new competitive challenges from Asia, and changes in the nature of production and innovation.

Political economists have struggled to describe and explain these transformations with limited success. Many of the most persuasive explanations of why and how western economic strategies have changed have emerged from the new 'post-Fordist' literature. Post-Fordism's generic features are quite uncertain and many of its advocates stress that it still must be viewed primarily as an heuristic device. However, it does successfully 'capture' fundamental changes in the way in which western states and markets interact.[10]

Post-Fordism may be viewed as a new mode of macroeconomic growth. It is marked by a shift away from Fordist mass production primarily for domestic markets to flexible, differentiated production for global markets. Profit-making strategies are based less on mass production and economies of scale and more on technological innovation and 'economies of scope', or the economies gained by using the same process to produce more than one product. As Chandler observes, the acceleration of technological change has 'realigned the economies of scale and scope, often reducing minimum efficient scale and at the same time expanding the opportunities for exploiting the economies of scope'.[11] For both firms and states, post-Fordism implies a new commitment to supply-side innovation and flexibility. Firms emphasize the integration of innovation and production and the diffusion of new technologies across the range of their activities. States emphasize regional and domestic market liberalization. Yet, post-Fordism has

> the paradoxical consequence of reinforcing the state's role in promoting competition . . . The post-Fordist world is one structured through national or regional rivalries in a race for societal modernization as well as through a global production system. If this marginalizes the state's role in national-level demand management, it increases its role in managing the supply-side.[12]

As Western states have abandoned Keynesian macroeconomic principles they have developed new tools of supply-side interventionism at 'meso' and microeconomic levels. State resources increasingly are mobilized to promote favoured private sector economic activities, such as venture capital investment, technology transfer and R & D. Industrial policies have become disaggregated and more focused on promotion of individual firms or technologies instead of broad industrial sectors. Such changes are a response to the reality that national comparative advantage – 'the relative export strength of a particular sector compared to other sectors in the same nation'[13] – is increasingly blurred in an era marked by rapid technological change, the break-up of sectors into 'niche' markets, and innovations which cut across industrial sectors. In a post-Fordist world, Strange argues that 'comparative advantage tends to be firm-specific more than state-specific'.[14]

Eureka may be viewed as part of a movement toward more flexible policy tools which seek to promote what may be termed the 'competitive advantage' of firms competing in markets which have fragmented into differentiated sub-sectors. Promoting the competitiveness of indigenous firms has become a higher priority for industrialized states which, in Cerny's terms, have transformed themselves from welfare states to 'competition states'.[15] The need to balance external trade accounts while maintaining high and rising incomes has become the single most important policy priority for modern industrialized states.[16] National industrial policies have been transformed because 'the *sine qua non* of the contemporary "competition state" is rapid adjustment to shifts in competitive advantage in the global marketplace'.[17]

Achieving competitive advantage is both a matter of nurturing *technological capabilities*, or 'the skills and knowledge necessary to develop, produce and sell products', and *innovativeness*, defined as 'the actual realisation of that capacity to generate and commercialise new and better products and production processes'.[18] Governments must provide 'bridging institutions' to translate national technological capabilities into actual innovation. Firms must seek to commercialize their innovations quickly to secure 'first mover' advantages in a climate of shortened product life cycles and fiercer competition in technology-intensive industries.

The policy task for governments is highly problematical. The uncertainties involved and amount of specialized information needed are daunting. Governments lack clear guidelines or routinized institutions to guide 'innovation policy', which may be defined as 'a fusion of science and technology policy and industrial policy'.[19] Economic research, much of which tends to model the innovation process only at a high level of abstraction, provides few clues to guide policy in the real world.[20] Freeman observes:

> Formally speaking, economic theory of almost all kinds recognized that technological progress was the mainspring of economic growth, even though it showed little disposition to delve into its mysteries . . . (Yet) from Adam Smith onwards all the great economists had treated science and invention as worthy of special government blessing and promotion.[21]

Governments thus approach innovation policy with 'a precious lack of explanations and guidance for policy'.[22] However, one point is clear: promoting innovation is not simply a matter of steadily increasing public spending on R & D. A positive correlation may have existed between levels of R & D expenditure and innovation in Fordist economies, but the relationship disappeared after the global economic recessions of the 1970s.[23] Governments can no longer successfully promote technological competitiveness merely by throwing money at the problem. Innovation policies must be strategic and selective to be effective.

The point is reinforced by Strange's argument that of the four major sources of structural state power in international relations – knowledge, security, finance and production – knowledge has become the most important:

> Competition between states is becoming a competition for leadership in the knowledge structure. The competition used to be for territory, when land and natural resources were the major factors in the production of wealth and therefore the acquisition of power for the state . . . Today, the competition is for a place at the 'leading edge' (as the jargon has it) of advanced technology. This is the means both to military superiority and to economic prosperity, invulnerability and dominance.[24]

The importance of knowledge as a source of competitive advantage is evidenced by the vast increase in the knowledge 'input' into industries for which global markets are expanding most rapidly. Software and associated services now make up over 80 per cent of the cost of bringing a computer to market, whereas hardware accounted over 80 per cent in the late 1960s.[25] The world market for biotechnology has tripled since the early 1980s and the market for biotechnology-related agricultural products alone will approach $100 billion by the year 2000.[26] The average growth in sales of information technology products during the early 1980s – a time of global recession – was estimated at 14 per cent per year.[27] Markets for many advanced technology-based goods are little affected by macroeconomic cycles and are essentially recession-proof. But firms constantly must seek to innovate to remain competitive.

The knowledge input for many traditional manufacturing industries also is rising exponentially. The Chairman of Volvo claims that automating distribution, or linking sales points via telecommunications, now offers the most scope for competitive advantage in the automobile industry.[28] Automated assembly and robotics have revolutionized production in traditional 'low-tech' industries such as textiles and agricultural machinery, where firms increasingly gain competitive advantage through customization and rapid delivery rather than price. A post-Fordist world is one in which economies of scope in R & D are accentuated because innovations often may be applied to more than one product or process.[29]

More generally, as Håkansson's 'network' approach to technological change argues, the development of new knowledge increasingly emerges in exchange situations which involve different kinds of knowledge.[30] For example, Japan's competitive success in many manufacturing industries is rooted in substantial collaboration between Japanese firms working in diverse product sectors such as automotives, robotics and electronics. In these and most other technology-intensive industries, strategies increasingly need to be global, the costs of innovation are high and innovations cut across traditional divisions between industries. Firms thus seek joint ventures, collaborative agreements or subcontracting arrangements with other firms which possess complementary assets in terms of knowledge. Often, a firm's partners will be other firms who were previously considered competitors or those in industries once thought irrelevant to core business strategies. Collaborative R & D projects are one of many different types of cooperative business arrangements which involve the exchange of knowledge. But R & D is particularly ripe for collaboration because it can reduce risks and costs and promote 'multi-technological' innovation. There is thus an *economic* logic to collaborative R & D for firms in industries for which there is a high knowledge input.

For European governments, collaborative R & D fits with new competition state strategies which seek to promote rapid knowledge and technology transfer in two 'directions'.[31] First, innovation requires 'vertical' transfer, from the laboratory through developmental stages to the actual production of an innovation. Eureka is designed to promote vertical transfer by acting as a 'bridge' between the final stages of R & D just before the actual development of an innovative product or process.

Second, innovation requires 'horizontal' transfer, between local economies, private and public research structures and previously distinct industrial sectors. Horizontal transfer has taken on increased importance as a policy objective due to the multi-technological nature of innovation and the increased economies of scope associated with R & D in a post-Fordist world. The EC's internal market provides new opportunities for the horizontal transfer of knowledge and technology. With fewer barriers to the diffusion of technologies and more innovations developed collaboratively by firms of different nationalities, the hope is that European producers will assimilate state-of-the-art technologies more quickly and efficiently. Collaborative R & D programmes reflect a new consensus that, if European producers are to compete globally with their Japanese and US counterparts, they must seize on the competitive advantages which stem from having the world's largest single capitalist market as a 'home' market.

Collaborative R & D programmes also allow costs to national public purses to be reduced as governments pool their subsidies in collaborative projects. Governments thus may subsidize more different types of R & D with a given pool of public funds. Collaboration may also provide an easy way out of the 'prisoner's dilemma' governments face when they subsidize R & D in a purely national context. If the R & D of indigenous firms is subsidized, the impact may be offset by subsidies provided by other national governments to their domestic firms. The withdrawal of subsidies by one government may lead indigenous firms to withdraw from competition, thus wasting past subsidies.[32] But government can hedge their bets by subsidizing collaborative projects. Collaboration also provides an alternative to past European policies which protected 'national champion' technology producers from foreign competition and thus encouraged non-European governments to protect their own indigenous firms.[33] There is thus a distinct *policy* logic to collaborative R & D.

The interests of governments and industry are never identical in any area of industrial policy, but they often converge. A necessary if not sufficient condition for the successful launch of the project to create a barrier-free internal market in the EC by the end of 1992 was consensus among European governments and industry on its desirability. Collaborative R & D serves the interests of both inasmuch as it hastens the freeing of the internal market through its effects on supply and demand.

On the supply side, collaborative R & D encourages full exploitation of the internal market. It promotes the emergence of outward-looking European suppliers which become more aware of market opportunities beyond their national borders through contact with foreign firms. The overall 'supply' of R & D becomes more efficient: collaboration helps to eliminate duplicated R & D efforts and encourages firms to pursue more technological avenues and more distinct R & D projects.[34] Publicly supported collaborative programmes which perform a 'marriage bureau' function make it easier for firms to find partners who possess complementary assets, thus lowering information costs in the pursuit of innovation. Collaborative R & D which is product-oriented, downstream and 'near-market' may help Europe as a whole to translate its substantial technological capabilities into more actual innovativeness: a high priority for a region which traditionally has failed to commercialize its innovations.

On the demand side, collaborative R & D helps create a pan-European demand for technology-intensive products. When innovations are developed collaboratively by firms of more than one nationality, they are more likely to find a market which transcends any single state's borders. Collaboration also promotes pan-European standards for entirely new products or for products which are technically superior to existing ones. Pan-European standards help facilitate a single market for public procurement, the creation of which could generate savings of up to 17.5 billion ECU per year in the EC.[35]

Collaborative R & D and the internal market are mutually reinforcing. European firms are encouraged to conduct more R & D jointly as the internal market is freed because many disincentives to collaboration across national borders are eliminated. The EC was conceived as a free trade area without internal tariffs or quotas, and evolved into a customs union with a common external tariff. A free trade area encourages firms to exploit economies of scale and 'jump' non-tariff barriers to cross-border trade through joint production. But when national innovation policies channel public support to national champions and seek to protect them with a range of non-tariff barriers, incentives to collaborate at the R & D stage are weak. A common external tariff does not make them stronger.

An entirely new set of incentives arrives with the construction of a truly common market. Restrictions to the free movement of skilled researchers, investment and all other factors of production fall. Non-tariff barriers which prevent the cross-border marketing of jointly developed innovations are eliminated and governments gradually harmonize standards for technology-based goods. Discrimination in public procurement is gradually banned.[36]

In the past, political action has been required to overcome disincentives to conduct R & D collaboratively because the EC remained 'stuck' at the customs union stage of integration. Intergovernmental political efforts had to substitute for commercial logic. Yet, as Elliott and Wood argue, 'an intergovernmental approach will be more prone to suffer from political reversals than will commercially motivated development. Commercial ventures are to a considerable extent self-sustaining, political ventures are not'.[37] Given the internal market as a backdrop, collaborative R & D projects are more self-sustaining because stronger commercial logic underpins them. Essentially, Eureka is designed to attract political support to projects which *already* are underpinned by commercial logic.

For their part, governments require policies which can target subsidies on collaborative R & D which promises to bolster national competitive advantage while still encouraging the development of the internal market. Eureka allows governments to be strategic and selective in channelling public support to the increased number of collaborative R & D projects which logically have arisen as the internal market has been put into place. The same public money which would have funded purely national R & D before the mid-1980s has been channelled to collaborative projects which, in theory, promote the goals of the 1992 project. In short, because of its symbiotic relationship with the internal market, there is a *strategic* logic to collaborative R & D which helps explain why Eureka exists.

II. THE CASE OF EUREKA: CRITERIA FOR ANALYSIS

After its launch in 1985, Eureka attracted praise from a host of policy analysts who generally applauded its goals and methodology without attempting the complex task of analysing its operation or effectiveness.[38] Eureka is still a relatively recent initiative and seeks to develop technologies that are often many years away from marketability. It will only become possible to judge its effect on European technological competitiveness in the late 1990s.

This study thus focuses on Eureka's process, 'throughputs' and decision-making structures. If there is one goal common to all publicly supported R & D programmes, it is providing *additionality* to existing R & D efforts. Defined narrowly, additionality means that public funds or any other public resources committed should make possible R & D projects which would not exist without public support. But government-sponsored R & D programmes also may provide 'added value' to projects which would exist regardless of public support (i.e. enlarging them, accelerating their completion, etc.). At its most basic level, this study seeks to determine how much additionality and 'added value' Eureka provides to the European R & D effort. But it must also consider the extent to which Eureka targets public support to the right *kind* of projects – that is, ones which promise to enhance European technological competitiveness.

National innovation policies generally failed to promote European technological competitiveness after 1970. European market shares held fairly steady in the 1960s, but shrank markedly thereafter. By one measure, Japan's export share in global technology-intensive markets increased from 7 per cent in 1965 to 20 per cent by 1984.[39] The USA lost markets to the Japanese in the 1970s, but substantially improved its own export performance between 1980 and 1984. By 1985, European governments had become alarmed at the realization that most of western Europe's 'world-class' industries were in traditional, Fordist or 'smoke-stack' sectors such as chemicals, plastics and heavy machinery, which were subject to increasing competitive pressures from newly indus-trialized countries.[40]

Post-war national innovation policies in Europe were guided pri-marily by Schumpeterian principles, which held that large oligopolies were better able than firms in highly competitive markets to generate funds for investment in large-scale, diversified and high-risk R & D projects.[41] Innovation policies thus targeted for support large, integrated national champions such as Philips in the Netherlands, ICL in the United Kingdom (UK) and Siemens in Germany. National champion strategies served a wide range of national macroeconomic goals, such as maintaining domestic employment, investment and tax revenues. Schumpeterian innovation policies thus fit with the broader goals of Keynesian welfare states.

As Fordism declined as the dominant mode of growth in western economies, so did the importance of 'Big Science' innovations in computers, aerospace and nuclear energy. More innovations began to emerge from relatively young, small and medium-sized enterprises (SMEs). A large majority of SMEs have always engaged in small-scale production while performing no organized R & D at all. Yet, by the early 1970s, the proportion of innovations originating in SMEs began to exceed their share of total R & D expenditure.[42] Scherer concluded that in industries where patterns of technological change were the most rapid and uncertain, 'new entrants contribute(d) a disproportionately high share of all really revolutionary new industrial products and processes'.[43] SMEs accounted for only a very small percentage of the total British R & D effort, but still produced 40 per cent of all significant innovations in the UK between 1975 and 1983.[44] By the late 1980s, more than half of all patent applications filed at the German Patent Office originated from SMEs or independent inventors.[45] The significance and quality of innovations emanating from SMEs had become 'remarkably constant' in their overall economic impact over a wide range of step-level categories, from those which produced entirely new products to those which modestly improved existing ones.[46]

The potential for innovation by small or large firms differs markedly between industries. Relatively mature industries where barriers to new entrants are high, such as semiconductors or colour television, are dominated by large, oligopolistic firms because large market shares are required before firms can risk large-scale R & D projects. Here, Schumpeter's assumptions seem to apply. By contrast, as much as two-thirds of all SME innovations occur in sectors where capital intensity and development costs are low, such as scientific instruments, robotics or electronics.

Innovation patterns are often crucially dependent on the relationship between small and large firms. Much of the post-Fordist literature is preoccupied with explaining how complex interaction between large firms and SMEs in Japan has yielded innovations and led to their rapid spread and application across industrial sectors.[47] Technological breakthroughs often require large, established firms with their ample pools of finance, skilled workforces and preoccupation with basic 'cutting-edge' technologies to advance early developments. At later stages, SMEs often provide entrepreneurial drive and fast market exploitation. For example, computer hardware and software were standardized and mass-produced by large firms until the late 1960s when the needs of customers became more specialized. The subsequent development of integrated circuits and microprocessors allowed SMEs to gain entry into niche markets for minicomputers, microcomputers and peripherals. A large number of small, dynamic software firms and systems houses emerged to produce customized software and combined hardware/software packages for specific applications.[48]

Despite these changes and variations between industries, it remains generally true that 'in the economics of technological change, Joseph Schumpeter continues to reign as the undisputed godfather'.[49] But Schumpeterian principles have become outmoded as guides for innovation policies. The protection and subsidization of national champions by post-war European governments provided disincentives for new market entrants and potentially innovative SMEs to emerge. Paradoxically, incentives for large firms to innovate or seek markets beyond their national frontiers were dulled in the process. Geroski and Jacquemin attribute the European economic downturns of the 1970s and 1980s largely to the 'undue height of mobility barriers which weaken(ed) market selection, and . . . rigidities within large corporations'.[50] A key source of 'Eurosclerosis' was oligopolistic markets dominated by large firms which were too slow in initiating or responding to global changes in markets and technological change. Meanwhile, European SMEs were disadvantaged compared to their American and Japanese counterparts by government regulations, a lack of access to finance and a range of other environmental factors.[51]

The 1992 project arose in large measure due to the failure of European innovation policies to promote innovation. A new title added to the Treaty of Rome by the SEA stated that:

> The Community's aim shall be to strengthen the scientific and technological basis of European industry and to encourage it to become more competitive at an international level. In order to achieve this, it shall encourage undertakings including small and medium-sized undertakings, research centres and universities . . . it shall support their efforts to cooperate with one another, aiming, notably, at enabling undertakings to exploit the Community's internal market potential to the full.[52]

Yet, the freeing of the internal market stands to benefit primarily large firms. Past trends are illustrative. The share of gross output produced by the EC's fifty largest firms increased dramatically, first in the years after the EC's common market was originally formed, and then again between 1965 and 1979.[53]

This evidence suggests that modern European innovation policies should incorporate positive discrimination in favour of SMEs. Effective collaborative R & D programmes should target industries where incentives for collaboration are low, but the potential for collaboration to yield innovations is high, such as biotechnology, microcomputers and software engineering. Technologies in these sectors are young, basic research quickly leads to marketable products, and many SMEs compete to innovate. But small firms often lack the experience or resources needed to develop or commercialize their innovations. If firms in these sectors can be persuaded to collaborate in developing innovations, the internal market could act as a launching pad for the rapid commercialization and diffusion of innovations in Europe in advance of foreign competitors. Alternatively, if programmes simply fund R & D where technologies are relatively mature and market structures are highly concentrated, subsidies are likely to be wasted. The high costs of R & D and new profit opportunities offered by the internal market provide oligopolistic competitors in these sectors with incentives to engage in joint R & D without subsidies.

Eureka's Declaration of Principles makes explicit reference to promoting the participation of SMEs and small research institutes 'in which many of the innovative technological products and processes are initiated'.[54] A key criterion for assessing Eureka's contribution to the 1992 project must be the extent to which it promotes 'additional R & D' among European SMEs or provides added value to projects which include them in sectors where their potential for innovation is high.

However, the question of how much SMEs or large firms should be the focus of European innovation policies is complicated by recent changes in the internal structure of many multinational corporations (MNCs).[55] Management, R & D and production increasingly have been decentralized into smaller units or profit centres working in specialized product and market sectors. The new trend toward large-scale industrial organizations which are compartmentalized into smaller operating units blurs the distinction between SMEs and large firms. As Prakke argues:

> Economic research has placed an inordinate amount of importance on the differences between small and large firms. In practice, there have been much more important differences between large firms in

different competitive and cultural environments. Even the largest industrial hierarchies have been dependent on such external factors.[56]

Among these 'external factors', market structures, the availability of venture capital, patterns of diffusion and technology transfer, and norms and standards regimes are particularly critical for innovation. The 1992 programme aims to transform the competitive and cultural environment within which European firms operated prior to the SEA because the environment clearly hindered European innovation. The point here is that collaborative R & D schemes such as Eureka do not exist in a vacuum. They are broadly dependent for their success on the implementation of the 1992 project, whose goals they in turn can promote. A general criterion for evaluating Eureka's effectiveness thus must be its contribution to the 1992 project: its safeguards for ensuring that collaboration on R & D does not lead to market-sharing arrangements, its ability to attract private finance to R & D, its effects on patterns of technology transfer, and its contribution to the development of pan-European norms and standards.

Eureka's projects are designed and led by industry. Thus, it is consistent with new competition state strategies which use public policy to promote market-rational behaviour. With its minimal bureaucracy, Eureka is indicative of recent changes in the nature of public administration more generally. Public policies in the 1990s reflect 'a disposition to use the lightest bureaucratic tackle and the minimum public power necessary to deal with any specific task at hand'.[57] Even the French national economic plan now declares that 'the state should decide less, decide better, and decide faster'.[58] New types of quasi- or 'para-governmental' organizations have emerged which exist in a grey area between core executives and private associations in national settings.[59] Eureka itself exists in

> a puzzling no man's land of international organizations that fall between the received categories of subjects of public international law and non-government organizations, and indeed may be difficult to categorize in terms of [the] national versus international level.[60]

Close comparisons between Eureka and previous collaborative R & D initiatives – most of which were more rules-oriented, *dirigiste* or subject to central political control – are impossible. Eureka is designed to be flexible and non-bureaucratic. But its strict intergovernmental ethos, minimal administrative resources and scant rules of process may have efficiency costs. A final criterion for evaluating Eureka thus must be the extent to which its distinctive methodology and administrative structure help or hinder the initiative in achieving its stated goals.

III. COLLABORATIVE R & D AND EUROPEAN INTEGRATION

Economic, policy and strategic rationale lie behind the growth of European collaborative R & D programmes. But the primary reasons why Eureka is purely intergovernmental and not an EC programme are political. Despite the SEA's commitment to strengthening European technological competitiveness, it gave the EC few new powers 'to make laws and policies to meet objectives beyond that of an undistorted single market'.[61] The question of how much authority for industrial policy should be centralized at the level of the EC as the internal market is created remains highly contentious and politicized.

The EC's R & D activities, most of which are grouped together in its multiannual Framework programme, are more integrated than are most other elements of the EC's industrial policy. As Duff notes, much political entrepreneurship has been invested in expanding the EC's powers in this area:

> Unsurprisingly, the Community finds it easier to influence the growth of new industries than to regulate the decline of the old. Both the Commission and the European Parliament have fallen upon hi-tech with some relief, arguing confidently that if ever there was a case for European integration, this is it.[62]

The Framework programme has grown steadily in size and impact with funding reaching approximately 1.5 billion ECU per year for 1990–94. But R & D spending still accounts for only about 3.5 per cent of the EC's budget and a slightly higher share of the combined total of separate national efforts. France, Germany and the UK each continue to spend upwards of 2 billion ECU annually on purely national programmes.[63]

The Commission has insisted that the guiding principle of the EC's innovation policy should be 'variable geometry', or the notion that each Member State should participate in EC initiatives to the extent that their technological and financial resources permit them. The argument is that the collective goal of enhancing European technological competitiveness means that EC innovation policy cannot be all things to all Member States: 'It is important that the efforts of certain countries to make progress should not be blocked by others which have not yet attained a similar level of technology or do not wish to make the effort involved'.[64] The Commission also maintains that if innovation policy is to serve the collective goals of the internal market, it must be scaled up, with centralized structures developed for medium-term strategic planning and the management of programmes to develop specific technologies.

Yet, collective goals have little impact when political decisions are made on the Framework programme's budget and general priorities. Negotiations within the Council of Ministers remain arduous, acrimonious and marked by staunch defence of purely national interests. *Juste retour* – the idea that each state should receive benefits in proportion to its budgetary contribution – is still the guiding principle of the Framework programme. The Commission has accommodated this principle in its R & D programmes only with great difficulties.

The 1992 project has not produced a fundamental pooling of national sovereignty in innovation policy. The development of Eureka, which is in many respects merely an extension of purely national innovation policies, reinforces the point that national prerogatives remain jealously guarded. The idea of a common European interest in innovation policy exists mostly in the rhetoric of the Commission and the SEA's architects.

Existing theories and models of regional integration do not explain recent developments in European innovation policies very adequately. After the Community's resurgence in the mid-1980s, many analysts argued that the leading post-war theory, neofunctionalism, was worth resurrecting.[65] Neofunctionalism assumed that integration would proceed exponentially as successful common policies in technical, apolitical sectors would require common policies in separate but related sectors due to technical pressures. Newly integrated policies in turn would hasten the transfer of authority to pan-European institutions to manage them.

Technological collaboration is a highly technical area of policy. However, Commission proposals for new collaborative schemes have never been approached by Member States as apolitical, 'functional' items distinct from wider debates about political integration. As Williams suggests:

> Technological collaboration seems . . . to have special ramifications for political integration. This follows from the fact that it, and the industrial linkages to which it gives rise, often impinge on sensitive prestige questions and on national security, and around both of these areas complex psychological halos form all too easily.[66]

Most successes in post-war European collaboration have been launched intergovernmentally and have been external to the EC. Few have had discernible effects on wider patterns of political integration. Williams concludes that technological collaboration is often 'self-encapsulating', with its activities confined to a single sphere and few if any demands by actors for further integration.[67] Neofunctionalism implies that successful technological collaboration should 'spill over' to hasten integration of political arrangements for organizing them. But collaborative R & D requires political consensus before it can proceed more than it acts to create such consensus over time. Political arrangements were needed, and were derived only after highly politicized negotiations, before either Eureka or the Framework programme could proceed. Eureka has not evolved into a centralized agency for funding 'near-market' R & D, nor has the Framework programme done much to accelerate the development of a common European industrial policy. As applied to collaborative R & D, neofunctionalism thus appears to have reversed the independent and dependent variables.

As alternatives to neofunctionalism, intergovernmental theories of European integration argue that 'EC politics is the continuation of domestic policies by other means. Even when societal interests are transnational, the principal form of their political expression remains national'.[68] Hoffmann's seminal work on intergovernmentalism argued that governments would refuse to do more than coordinate purely national policies in areas of 'high politics', or those which 'go beyond purely internal economic problems', such as foreign policy or defence.[69] Only in economic and technical areas of 'low politics' would centralized, integrated policymaking be possible.

Eureka is designed to promote collaborative R & D activities which are justified by commercial criteria and is designed to be as free from wider political influences as possible. But decisionmaking within Eureka is only very marginally integrated. The initiative is marked by competing political imperatives and distinct national interests, and remains bound up in concerns for national prestige, technological independence and competitive advantage. Eureka, like the Framework programme, contains elements of both 'high' and 'low' politics. Collaborative R & D falls between these two stools more generally.[70]

The point is that 'macro-level' theories of regional integration have not predicted or explained meso-level developments in European innovation policy very effectively. Moreover, meso-level models of industrial policy, which focus on national structures and categorize states as 'strong' or 'weak' according to their relative ability to impose public goals on private industry, are of limited use when both states and industrial firms increasingly interact on a transnational level. Besides, the EC is not a 'state'.

Explaining Eureka and the Framework programme in theory means taking account of the development of new transnational arenas for the intermediation of private and public interests. At a basic level, these arenas have emerged due to rising levels of economic interdependence between European national economies, industrial sectors and individual firms. Keohane and Nye define interdependence as the extent to which decisions taken by actors in one part of a system affect (intentionally or unintentionally) other actors' decisions elsewhere in the system.[71] Rising interdependence at multiple levels of analysis has produced clear pressures for common policies. At a macroeconomic level, the 1992 project was given substantial impetus by a general realization amongst EC political classes in the early 1980s that European national economies were so interdependent that they would either thrive or stagnate together in an increasingly globalized economy. At a meso-level, the erosion of European competitiveness in global markets for technology-intensive products gave rise to the notion that common programmes were needed to amalgamate European expertise and resources within and across technological sectors. At a micro-level, the sharp increase in inter-firm cooperative agreements in the early 1980s, especially those aimed at 'knowledge' production, revealed that national champions could no longer compete in many sectors without pooling complementary assets with other firms.

The need for policy coherence has led to attempts to link common actions at each level of analysis. The SEA presented collaborative R & D as a 'centrepiece' element in the strategy to create the internal market and stressed the links between the EC's R & D, competition and trade policies. The goal of strengthening Europe's R & D effort was prominently featured in nearly every treatise on the internal market issued by the Commission after 1987.[72] Similarly, the Commission's original White Paper on the Internal Market, which laid the groundwork for the SEA, presented its separate legislative proposals as entirely *interdependent*. Accepting the principles of the internal market meant accepting the entire package of legislation to create it. The Commission was largely successful in its effort to persuade EC Member States of the holistic nature of the 1992 project and the need to spend more on collaborative R & D in the process. The creation of the internal market at a macro-level has proceeded – although in fits and starts – in a largely unilinear direction. The integration of innovation policies at the meso-level clearly has not.

As more collaborative arrangements between states and firms emerge, transnational interests naturally develop to sustain them. But the degree to which collaboration is a logical commercial or policy choice will obviously vary between different industrial sectors and policy settings. This is reflected in the substantial variations in decisionmaking structures and types of interest which dominate collaborative arrangements within Eureka and the Framework programme. Both have integrated structures far removed from national political direction for promoting collaboration between oligopolistic firms in microelectronics and tele-communications. Yet, activities in other sectors are loosely organized, many actors compete for subsidies, and national interests are decisive in determining policy choices.

A flexible typology is needed which can accommodate these differ-ences in decisionmaking arrangements, patterns of interest formation, and the tug of war between supranational and national goals. Such a typology must account for unique power dependence relationships between public and private actors in sector-specific arenas of innovation policy. It must also 'capture' varying patterns of interaction within collaborative initiatives between states whose national interests and technological capabilities vary widely. The rise and evolution of meso-level innovation policies such as Eureka need to be understood against the backdrop of the macro-level development of the internal market. What is needed is a model of government–industry relations which has explanatory power at multiple levels of analysis.

IV. POLICY NETWORKS AND NEW FORMS OF GOVERNMENT

Theories of government–industry relations at a macro-level[73] have prompted meso-level empirical studies which seek to fill in the essential characteristics of industrial policies in specific national settings[74] and more recently, specific industrial sectors.[75] Meso-level analytical tools are still being refined. But the value of this scholarship is in its insistence that the process of interest formation both shapes and is shaped by the organization of state structures. Put simply, relationships between states and private industrial interests are symbiotic.

Much research now is geared to testing Grant *et al.*'s claim 'that in many industries, sectoral variations do at least *modify* national char-acteristics and that, in some cases, they produce a more convergent outcome than a simple reading off of national characteristics would suggest'.[76] At one extreme, private actors in certain sectors 'capture' the state, and 'public policy and the public interest become identical with the private interests of the non-state organisation'.[77] At the other, state actors essentially impose state-defined objectives on private actors.

As focus has shifted from states to sectors, typologies have been applied to industrial policymaking which borrow from models of US government–industry relations and British intergovernmental relations.[78] These typologies emphasize the importance of specialist information, technical rationality, the privileged position of selected groups and interdependencies between government and industry. In

Western Europe, the completion of the internal market, the trend toward transnational corporate mergers and the expanded role of the EC in industry support and regulation all reinforce the preoccupation with sector-specific as opposed to state-specific studies. In technology-intensive sectors including telecommunications and consumer electronics, the primacy of the Commission's policy role means that national industries can no longer be viewed as the key units for analysis.[79] Yet, national influences are still powerful in policy terms. The primary task of policy analysts is to make sense of complex interactions between sectoral influences and national influences.

Theoretical models with clear categories and tighter conceptual definitions have slowly begun to emerge.[80] Rhodes has developed the notion of *policy networks* as a meso-level concept which describes arenas for the intermediation of the interests of government and interest groups. A policy network may be defined as 'a cluster or complex of organisations connected to each other by resource dependencies and distinguished from other clusters or complexes by breaks in the structure of resource dependencies'.[81] Resource dependencies – the extent to which different actors depend on each other for resources – are the key variable. They set the 'chessboard' where private and public interests manoeuvre for advantage.

The policy network concept is more a metaphor than a proper theory. But it is flexible enough to be used at different levels of analysis and to gauge which interests dominate policymaking and why. It is not coincidental that the concept of networks has begun to be deployed in a variety of academic contexts as an explanatory tool for determining who gets what and why. Different versions of network analysis share similar assumptions about how interests are intermediated in settings where decisions are neither negotiated in an open 'market' of transactions between independent entities nor imposed through an authoritative hierarchy.[82] Network analysis is deployed by economists interested in the merger of previously distinct areas of knowledge into multi-technological innovations,[83] business studies scholars studying the ways in which non-market factors affect the behaviour of firms,[84] sociologists researching interpersonal relationships within organizations,[85] and, not least, analysts of the EC.[86]

The Rhodes model of policy networks – after having undergone necessary refinements[87] – conceptualizes different types of networks based on the relative stability of relationships between actors, the degree to which outside influences are excluded, and especially varying patterns of dependency between different actors. A continuum thus emerges (see Figure 1.1). At one end are tightly integrated *policy communities* in

Policy communities	Issue networks
Stable membership	Fluid membership
Highly insular	Highly permeable
Strong dependencies	Weak dependencies

Figure 1.1 Conceptualizing policy networks

which membership is constant, outside influence is minimal and resource dependencies are considerable. At the other are loosely integrated *issue networks*, in which membership is fluid, wider influences are brought to bear on policymaking, and resource dependencies are either weak or changeable. Thus, industrial policymaking networks may exist at any point on the continuum, and may be rigidly constructed and strongly insular or loosely organized and easily permeable by outside influences.

Past meso-level models of the EC as a regime or series of networks have usually failed to isolate specific policy sectors or adequately specify power-dependence relationships at different levels of policymaking.[88] By contrast, the policy network approach makes it possible to gauge power-dependence relations between public and private actors in specific policy sectors and at different levels of analysis. It provides a framework for understanding the diverse patterns of government–industry relations which are visible within Eureka. *This is hardly developed. Hunt in it*

In line with new competition state strategies, Eureka is designed to *body of* promote favoured private sector activities. It allows private interests *the work* wide discretion to dictate the priorities and goals of Eureka's activities. Individual Member States do bring their own innovation policy agendas to the initiative and they often clash. However, many of Eureka's activities are far removed from effective political control. Since it is designed to promote favoured private sector activities, the interests of public and private actors naturally blur. Moreover, Eureka encourages intensive interaction between national actors working in distinct industrial and policy sectors. Thus interests, and the policy networks which intermediate between them, are often transnational. New forms of government require new theoretical models. The model of policy networks outlined in this section thus is deployed throughout the study to guide its analysis of who gets what from Eureka.

Understanding Eureka first requires making clear its rules of operation, the extent to which its various Member States participate and the nature of its projects. Because Eureka is marked by substantial controversy about what it is designed to achieve, its 'project mix' subsumes a wide range of R & D activities in a diverse array of technological sectors. Chapter 2 thus analyses Eureka's process and partners, with special focus on its projects.

Previous attempts to promote pan-European collaborative R & D informed the definition of Eureka's goals and structures. The 'making of Eureka' occurred against a backdrop of intense competition for political and industrial support between it, the American Strategic Defense Initiative (SDI), and the EC's Framework programme. Chapter 3 assesses the impact on Eureka of pre-1985 collaborative ventures and examines the highly politicized negotiations which yielded its structure and principles.

Eureka's loose, flexible administrative structure contrasts sharply with many of its intergovernmental precursors as well as many EC programmes. Eureka cannot be understood without evaluating the initiative's 'fit' with national innovation policies as well as its national and intergovernmental institutions, its procedures for the selection, support and monitoring of individual projects. Above all, an effective policy study of Eureka must consider to what extent the initiative represents continuity or change in European innovation policies. Chapter 4 evaluates how Eureka operates.

The Commission's own political agenda – which includes expanding the EC's innovation policy powers and resources – permeates the 1992 project. This agenda has affected the organization of its own technology initiatives as well as its approach to Eureka. Eureka's Declaration of Principles explicitly acknowledges the role of the EC in creating 'an environment conducive to technological co-operation [which] is a prerequisite for the success of the Eureka initiative'.[89] Chapter 5 assesses relations between the Community and Eureka.

Eureka is industry-led as no European collaborative programme ever has been. Industrial perceptions of Eureka are critical because any programme which depends so heavily on private initiative will fail if firms do not believe that participating in the initiative brings them tangible benefits. Chapter 6 analyses the results of two recent surveys of Eureka's industrial participants. Its primary goal is to assess what the survey results say about Eureka's additionality, or the extent to which it has made possible projects which would not exist without Eureka, or provided 'added value' to those that would.

Because it encompasses so many different types of R & D, Eureka must be assessed on the ground at the level of its individual projects. 'Micro-level' analysis is needed to evaluate how selected Eureka projects are managed by industry and supported by governments. Chapter 7 presents a series of case studies of individual projects.

Eureka is in some ways indicative of the wider tensions and contradictions which have characterized the creation of the internal market. Free market principles lie at the heart of the 1992 project, but

Eureka and other collaborative programmes channel large subsidies to industry. More generally, Eureka's very existence shows that it is increasingly difficult to understand the process of European integration merely by studying the institutions and policies of the EC. Chapter 8 explores these themes and synthesizes the main findings of the study about how well Eureka works and how it might be altered to work more effectively.

As a final step in defining the parameters of the study, the reader may find it useful to know what falls *outside* its purview. This book does not seek to explore or critique theories of interfirm collaboration in any systematic way.[90] Nor does it seek to referee debates about the extent to which collaboration between firms and nations is a 'good' thing for technological development or competitive advantage. A diligent student of modern industrial policies will no doubt be aware of the divergent views of Porter, who sees 'widespread collaboration [as] a sign of decline, or of government intervention preserving uncompetitive rivals',[91] and Reich, who argues that innovations are increasingly a product of 'new organizational webs of high-value enterprise . . . reaching around the globe'.[92] The analysis in the present study is sensitive to the potential costs of collaborative R & D, particularly for competition between market rivals which collaborate in R & D. But it is left to other policy analysts to judge whether collaboration *per se* is an appropriate response to the problem of European technological competitiveness.[93] European governments have created Eureka as a method for increasing the amount of 'near-market' R & D that takes place across borders and between firms. This study is primarily concerned with assessing how effectively Eureka performs the policy task which has been set for it. It is not, as such, concerned with second-guessing the wisdom of the policy task.

The study's approach is justified on the grounds that, while European innovation policies have changed in response to accelerated rates of technological change, the globalization of markets and the 1992 project, policy analysts have not adequately explained the rise nor assessed the effectiveness of new policy tools such as Eureka. It is not enough merely to explain why Eureka was created and describe how it works, and then to conclude that Eureka may succeed if the wider policy environment within which it works evolves favourably. To do so is to take what Katzenstein has termed a 'Peter Pan' approach to public policy: one assumes that policies as they now exist are the best of all possible worlds, one sets out the variables that will determine policy success or failure, and then 'one closes one's eyes and wishes really hard'.[94] This study rejects the Peter Pan approach and aspires to be a better informed and more critical policy analysis of Eureka than previously has been on offer.

2 Partners, process and projects

This chapter provides an overview of Eureka and a foundation for understanding how it works. The nature and extent of each Member State's participation are spelled out in Section I. Section II reviews Eureka's institutions and administrative process. Most of the chapter is preoccupied with analysing Eureka's projects: Section III provides a general survey and Section IV presents a more detailed treatment of Eureka's activities in specific technological sectors.

I. THE MEMBER STATES

The participation of individual Member States in Eureka may be gauged according to three criteria: the amount of public funding each commits to Eureka, the number of projects in which indigenous organizations participate, and the number of projects 'led' by organizations from each Member State. Public funding policies are distinctly 'nationalized': the total amount committed to Eureka by each Member State and the circumstances under which indigenous firms qualify for public funds vary widely. Information on the total amount of public funding spent on Eureka is closely guarded by some Member States. A survey of national funding policies was compiled and circulated to all Member States in 1990 but its contents were kept 'internal' to Eureka.[1]

A set of 'Procedures for Eureka Projects' accepted by all Member States in 1986 requires that projects have at least one partner to act as the 'contact point for Eureka purposes'.[2] In practice, these participants commonly are referred to as 'project leaders', since they typically take on primary responsibility for a project's management, legal arrangements and communications. Project leaders often receive a large portion of the total public funding devoted to any single project and perform a large share of its R & D work. By contrast, project partners who are not 'leaders' may be involved only minimally as subcontractors.[3] Thus,

Table 2.1 Project participation by Member States[a]

States	Projects[b]		Project leaders[c]	
	no.	%	no.	%[d]
France	206	41	73	23
Germany	184	36	30	9
Italy	168	33	35	11
Spain	140	28	27	8
UK	131	26	25	8
Netherlands	130	26	38	12
Sweden	92	18	11	3
Denmark	74	15	12	4
Norway	73	14	10	3
Austria	69	14	19	6
Finland	61	12	9	3
Switzerland	60	12	10	3
Belgium	57	11	11	3
Portugal	33	7	7	2
Greece	29	6	1	<1
Ireland	15	3	0	–
CEC	14	3	2	1
Iceland	7	1	1	<1
Turkey	6	1	0	–
Luxembourg	5	1	2	1

Sources: Eureka secretariat, *Annual Progress Report 1991*, Brussels, 1992; Eureka project database, January 1990.
Notes: [a]Hungary is not included since it joined Eureka in June 1992. [b]Based on 505 projects approved as of June 1991. [c]Based on 273 projects listed in Eureka data as of January 1990; some projects have more than one 'leader'. [d]Column does not add to 100% due to rounding.

simply comparing sum totals of projects in which each Member State participates can give an inaccurate picture of the true intensity of each Member State's involvement in Eureka.

Eureka was created after an initiative by the French President François Mitterrand in 1985 (see Chapter 3). In many respects, it remains a French-led initiative. France leads all other Member States in the number of projects in which its organizations participate and by far in the number of projects led by its national participants (see Table 2.1). France also has committed far more public funding to Eureka – upwards of 150 million ECU per year since Eureka's origins – than any other Member State.[4]

In explaining the motives which lay behind the original French proposal to create Eureka, it must be noted that French state aid to industry generally increased by nearly 150 per cent between 1981 and 1985.[5] By the time of Eureka's creation, France accounted for nearly 30 per cent of total national public spending on R & D in the EC and its spending rate was 70 per cent higher than the EC average.[6] Many of those involved in the creation of Eureka seconded the view of a Scandinavian official who argued:

> Well, the French needed Eureka in order to give state support to a lot of projects and not go against Community rules on state support . . . So they were creating this European surrounding for projects which were predominantly French projects.[7]

Early French intentions were reflected in statements in 1986 by Yves Sillard, the director of the French Eureka office. Sillard estimated that 60 per cent of all Eureka projects would include French participants and 40 per cent of their cost would be met through French public funds, which eventually would total close to 450 million ECU per year.[8] France never has dominated Eureka to the extent such figures would imply. But this outcome is due more to the ardent embracing of the initiative by other Member States than to a lack of French commitment to it. Whatever their motives, the French clearly viewed Eureka from the outset as a centrepiece of their national innovation policy and an initiative which would be strongly French-led.

By most indices, Germany has been the second most active participant in Eureka since 1989. The Federal Ministry for Research and Technology, the BMFT,[9] is primarily responsible for German participation in Eureka. However, many German project participants are funded through programmes run by the individual German states, or *Länder*, which accounted for nearly 40 per cent of total public spending on R & D in Germany by the late 1980s.[10] Unlike France, Germany has committed no special funds to Eureka. In principle, nearly any source of German public funding for R & D can be used to finance Eureka projects. There is no accurate method of estimating the amount of public funding spent on Eureka projects in Germany, but the figure is probably between 80 and 100 million ECU per year.[11]

The Germans have championed and now lead most of Eureka's 'infrastructure' projects, or those which seek to develop some form of technological infrastructure as opposed to a tangible product. By 1992 more than 41 per cent of German Eureka participants were universities, public research laboratories or public administrations. France had the second highest number of 'non-industrial' participants, but they accounted for less than 29 per cent of all French participants.[12] Most German public funding for Eureka is allocated to non-industrial organizations and the BMFT claims that nearly 45 per cent of all German participants receive no public funding at all.[13]

British firms and research organizations initially approached Eureka with much enthusiasm. By 1988 the UK was second only to France in the number of projects involving its 'home' organizations. However, the rate of increase in British participation tailed off markedly after 1989 and the UK ranks low among Eureka's larger states in the share of all projects that its organizations lead (see Table 2.1). No new funding was ever committed by the British government to Eureka. Projects compete with purely national collaborative projects for R & D funds which are not earmarked specifically for Eureka. By the end of 1989, only about 45 million ECU in British public funds had been committed to Eureka projects since the initiative's launch in 1985, and only one-third of that figure had actually been allocated.[14]

The rate of Italian participation in Eureka has increased more rapidly than that of any other Member State since 1989. Its firms now lead more projects than those of Germany or the UK. Italy has devoted 10 per cent of its general Fund for Innovation to the support of Eureka projects since 1987. Its annual spending on Eureka has averaged about 75 million ECU and one-fifth of this total has been reserved for SMEs.[15]

The Netherlands was one of few Member States which created a special funding mechanism for Eureka in 1985. Although this budget was and remains relatively small, the Dutch appeared to be spending more on Eureka than any other Member State besides France by the early 1990s.[16] The comparatively large amount of public support on offer was reflected in the number of projects led by Dutch organizations, who ranked second only to the French by this measure.

Spain is certainly the Member State which has most increased its involvement in European collaborative R & D over 'pre-Eureka' levels. Although it has committed no specific funds to Eureka, Spanish public spending on R & D generally increased by almost 30 per cent between 1988 and 1991.[17] The number of Eureka projects with Spanish participants rose steadily through this period.

The participation rates of Eureka's other fourteen Member States is sharply lower than those of the 'Big Six'. This disparity is reflected in sum totals of 'participations', or the total number of times organizations from the 'Big Six' participate in any Eureka project: 958 compared with 595 for all others (see Table 2.1). It is even more striking that around 80 per cent of all Eureka project leaders are French, Dutch, German, Italian, British or Spanish.

Compared with other Eureka 'small states', the rate of participation by Swedish organizations is quite high. Sweden is one of only seven Member States which has 'dedicated' a fund specifically to fund Eureka projects, although its total value is only 3 million ECU. Denmark more than doubled its funding for Eureka between 1989 and 1992, and its relatively large dedicated budget of 7.5 million ECU helped ensure that the Danish rate of participation increased substantially through this period. Neither Norway nor Finland has specific budgets for Eureka, but Norwegian participation has increased substantially in recent years and Finland spends more than 9 million ECU on support for its participants, which helps explain its high rate of participation given the size of its economy.[18]

Austria spends relatively little (less than 4 million ECU per year) on Eureka, but Austrian organizations tend to lead Eureka projects more often than those from other 'smaller' Eureka Member States.[19] Austrian participants led thirteen projects which were launched in 1989, thus reflecting the higher national profile Eureka received in 1988–89 when Austria held the initiative's rotating chairmanship. Switzerland gives no public funding to private firms but spends about 7 million ECU per year supporting the participation of its public research institutions. It has had a relatively high rate of participation by indigenous SMEs.[20] Belgium has provided more funding to Eureka than most other Member States (about 16 million ECU in 1987) but money has been spread thinly across a range of projects to ensure proportionately equal distribution in the three Belgian regions of Flanders, Wallonia and Brussels.[21]

Greece has had considerable success in encouraging Greek SMEs to participate and it is involved in a number of expensive projects in the laser sector. Portugal and Ireland both participate most often through their universities and public research laboratories. Iceland, Turkey and Luxembourg were each involved in fewer than ten projects by 1992, the year that Hungary was admitted to Eureka as its twentieth Member State.

The European Commission is a nominal extra 'Member State' in Eureka. It participates in projects either by providing funds or through the involvement of its Joint Research Centre (JRC) or both. The Commission is represented in all of Eureka's intergovernmental fora.

Two key observations emerge from this sketch of patterns of national participation. First, Eureka is very much dominated by its six largest Member States. Officials from these countries tend to view this as a natural reflection of varying levels of technological development across Europe. Those from smaller states frequently express disillusionment with the tendency of firms from larger countries – often supported by their governments – to 'snap up' the most interesting and viable projects while denying participation to firms from smaller states on the grounds that they are potential competitors.[22]

Tensions between large and small Eureka Member States occasionally are exposed. Officials involved in the original negotiations on Eureka's structure admitted that Greece, Portugal and Turkey among others lobbied unsuccessfully for the creation of a powerful central secretariat which could actually propose or manage Eureka projects.[23] A Norwegian research minister complained that her request for discussions about creating a more centralized Eureka secretariat had been 'buried' by the larger Member States in 1988.[24] The 'participation gap' between large and small states thus has produced debate at the political level about Eureka's methodology and institutional framework.

Second, promises made by several governments at the time of Eureka's launch to create new tranches of public funding for the scheme have never materialized. Most Member States give some type of priority to Eureka projects in allocating general public funds for R & D, but only France, Italy, the Netherlands, Belgium, Sweden, Denmark and Switzerland have earmarked money specifically for Eureka.[25] In many cases, officials appear not to know how much public funding their government actually provides to Eureka since it originates from so many different (usually pre-existing) schemes administered by different departments or levels of government. Only a few countries have a single office responsible for all national funding of Eureka projects.[26]

While estimates vary widely, it appears that between 25 and 35 per cent of Eureka's total financing comes from public sources.[27] But even this estimate represents a complex mixture of soft loans, direct grants and other forms of public aid. It is impossible to calculate accurately how much public money has been committed to Eureka.

II. EUREKA'S INSTITUTIONS AND PROCESSES

The first official French pronouncements on Eureka in spring 1985 stressed that its institutions and rules of operation would be marked by '*flexibilité*' and '*souplesse*'. Despite early ideas about creating a more centralized and *dirigiste* programme, the French were forced to adopt minimum bureaucracy as a selling point to generate political support for Eureka, since other potential Member States – particularly Germany and the UK – were sceptical about the need for Eureka in the first place. Moreover, the French wished to ensure that the Eureka proposal would not be 'hijacked' by the Commission, whose initial response was that Eureka should be subsumed within its own proposals to create the Framework programme.

As the UK took on Eureka's rotating 'chairmanship' in late 1985, the British clearly took the lead in defining the initiative's administrative structures. British negotiators produced proposals for an extremely small bureaucracy and a guarantee that members could determine their own criteria for public funding. The British view was that Eureka should perform a simple 'marriage broker' function for firms and research institutions with as little governmental involvement as possible. A UK official involved in negotiations on Eureka's structure later commented:

> There was nothing anti-Commission in the British attitude. But we were not happy with idea that this should be a another block of state-funded research . . . we had enormous debates about the secretariat: how big it should be, whether there should be one. We were concerned to keep the secretariat as small as possible. A permanent, inflated bureaucracy was to be avoided.[28]

The UK secured agreement that the secretariat would be staffed by only seven civil servants seconded from national ministries for two to three years, and six clerical assistants. It now acts as a 'contact point for Eureka purposes' by collecting and circulating information on proposed and ongoing projects.[29] The secretariat is purely functional with no policy responsibilities.

To sustain political interest in Eureka, national research or industry ministers were granted the power to formally approve projects for Eureka status at ministerial conferences. Conferences were held every six months in 1985–86, but now are held once annually. A 'High Level Group' (HLG) of senior national civil servants meets regularly between ministerial conferences. It provides medium-term policy guidance and 'notifies' projects for Eureka status so that they can be launched before being officially approved at ministerial conferences.

Most of the real administration of Eureka is conducted at the Member State level by national Eureka offices, which are usually special agencies responsible to a ministry or group of ministries. However, national administrative arrangements are eclectic: the British Eureka office is located within the Department of Trade and Industry (DTI), the Germans have a special '*referat*' within the BMFT, and the Eureka office in Belgium is part of a science policy unit attached to the Prime Minister's office. National Eureka offices are quite minimally staffed, with an average of four full-time employees, many of whom also work on national or EC R & D schemes.[30] Each country designates a National Project Coordinator (NPC) to oversee projects and proposals which involve indigenous organizations.

Political leadership is rotated between Member States who take on Eureka's chairmanship for one year. Each national chairmanship has pursued a distinctive 'action plan' during its tenure. For example, the

Spanish chairmanship of 1986–87 worked on attracting private venture capital to Eureka, Denmark (1987–88) focused on encouraging SME participation, and Italy (1989–90) explored methods of increasing the rate of technology transfer to less-developed countries through Eureka.

Eureka has few strict rules or procedures related to its projects. All must include participation by organizations in at least two Member States. Proposals first are submitted to relevant NPCs, who are responsible for technology assessment on a national and international basis. Proposals approved at this level then must be circulated to the Eureka offices of all other Member States for at least 45 days before they may be officially granted Eureka status by ministers or 'notified' by the HLG. The intent of the '45-day period' is to ensure that as many potential partners as possible may learn of a proposal's existence. However, organizations which prepare proposals are entirely free to accept or reject the overtures of other organizations which may wish to join a project. Project participants are also responsible for negotiating their own agreements on work-sharing and intellectual property rights (IPRs). In short, Eureka is highly decentralized, administratively thin and industry-led.

III. THE PROJECTS: AN OVERVIEW

After Eureka's structure and rules were established, the 1986 Swedish chairmanship culminated with the approval of thirty-seven projects worth 730 million ECU.[31] At this point, Eureka was acting more to reinforce established patterns of collaborative R & D in Europe than to encourage new ones. Nearly three-quarters of its projects were in information technology, communications or robotics – areas where collaboration was already relatively widespread – with biotechnology, health, energy and new materials notably underrepresented. About half were led by either large information technology firms or manufacturers such as ICI, Peugeot, Aérospatiale, Porsche, Volvo and Rhône-Poulenc. Projects led by large European multinational corporations (MNCs) accounted for close to 70 per cent of Eureka's total value. Ministers admitted that 'projects at all levels of high technology have been approved, but there has been an uneven distribution'.[32]

Successive ministerial conferences at Madrid in 1987 and Copenhagen in 1988 approved fifty-nine and fifty-four new projects each. During this period, the share of smaller, short-term projects featuring substantial participation by SMEs reflected in Eureka's project list increased significantly.[33] The 'spread' of projects across technology sectors also broadened, as the number of biotechnology projects tripled, several

Table 2.2 Evolution of Eureka's project list (1986–88)

Sector	Projects approved			Project costs (MECU)		
	To 1986	1987-88	Total	To 1986	1987-88	Total
IT	26	16	41	1294	107	962
Robotics	19	35	51	344	361	659
Communications	8	5	13	416	74	490
Environment	9	3	11	290	132	421
Transport	8	10	18	299	89	371
Biotechnology	14	27	41	161	185	345
Lasers	4	7	11	98	148	231
New materials	13	6	18	201	13	189
Energy	6	4	10	132	34	137
Total	107	113	214	3234	1142	3805

Sources: Eureka secretariat, *The Eureka Projects: An Overview*, Brussels, October, 1987; Danish chairmanship, 'Some statistical data about Eureka projects', Copenhagen, 16 June 1988.
Notes: Totals do not equal sum of previous columns due to cancellation of previously announced projects. IT, information technology.

Table 2.3 Eureka's project list (1989)

	Added in 1989	*Total list in 1989*	*Value (MECU)*
IT	15	50	1512
Communications	4	19	1194
Robotics	21	70	1078
Environment	21	32	607
Transport	3	21	591
Biotechnology	14	55	542
Energy	4	14	526
Lasers	2	13	271
New materials	5	23	153
Total	89	297	6474

Sources: *Eureka News*, 19 October 1989 and other official Eureka documents
Note: Includes all projects approved as of sixth ministerial conference at Vienna, June 1989.

large environmental projects were added, and substantially more projects and funding were approved in lasers and transport (Table 2.2).

In 1989, Eureka's project total surged upward when eighty-nine new projects worth 1.6 billion ECU were approved at the seventh Ministerial Conference in Vienna. Nearly one-quarter of the total ECU value of these projects was accounted for by two large transport projects, but otherwise the trend toward smaller, less expensive projects continued,

Table 2.4 Eureka's project list (1992)

Sector	Number of projects	Total value (MECU)
IT	69	1823
Communications	32	1545
Robotics	97	1266
Biotechnology	93	871
Environment	108	867
Transport	23	764
Energy	20	586
Lasers	15	344
New materials	48	318
Total	505	8384

Source: Eureka secretariat, *Annual Progress Report 1991*, Brussels, 1992.
Note: Includes all projects approved as of eighth ministerial conference at The Hague, June 1991.

with about fifty new projects carrying estimated values of less than 5 million ECU.[34] The technological thrust of Eureka's projects continued to diversify, as a large number of biotechnology and (especially) environmental projects were approved (see Table 2.3).

A number of trends were firmly established in the evolution of Eureka's project list by 1989. A majority of projects combined some aspect of information technology with new production technologies[35] – an encouraging trend considering the overhaul of components, software and systems integration needed to modernize most European production-oriented industries. Progressively more SMEs were brought into Eureka: about 28 per cent of all industrial participants were SMEs by 1992.[36] The initiative's early bias towards large, expensive, long-term projects in just a few technological sectors diminished. By 1991 the average project duration was three years and a large number of projects – about 30 per cent – were valued at between 2 and 5 million ECU.[37]

Eureka sustained its increased momentum by adding increasingly larger numbers of new projects at successive ministerial conferences in Rome in 1990 (91 projects) and The Hague in 1991 (121 projects). The total estimated value of all Eureka projects was 8.38 billion ECU by 1992 (see Table 2.4).

The general overview of the kind presented here is about as far as most academic or press analyses of Eureka have been taken. But Eureka cannot be evaluated properly without detailed analysis of its projects. The section which follows provides a 'snapshot' of Eureka's projects in the nine technological sectors which are the focus for its activities.

IV. THE PROJECTS: BY SECTORS

Information technology

Projects in information technology have dominated Eureka's activities since its origins. It had become clear by the time of Eureka's launch that global markets for information technology were exploding and European competitiveness in the sector was eroding. From mid-1970s until 1985, domestic demand for information technology products in countries belonging to the Organization for Economic Cooperation and Development (OECD) grew nearly 6 per cent per annum in real terms, or nearly twice the growth rate for all industrial output. Among OECD countries, only Japan and the USA increased their production fast enough to keep up with demand. All Eureka Member States except Finland grew increasingly reliant on information technology imports.[38] The growth rate of world markets for information technology products continued to accelerate, and the total market was expected to be worth over 1000 billion ECU by 1995.[39]

The information technology sector is broad, ranging from microelectronic components to software development to integrated computer systems. Innovations within it account for a steadily increasing percentage of added value in nearly every manufacturing industry for which there is an international market.[40] However, except for telecommunications switching equipment and software, Europe's competitive position in global markets is weak. Eureka always has been viewed by many Member States primarily as a forum for strategic information technology projects. Four of twenty major projects contained in the original French Eureka proposal in 1985 were in microelectronics, with heavy French participation envisioned in collaboration with European information technology leaders such as Philips, Siemens and Plessey.[41] Eureka's creation reflected the perceived need to push basic, 'upstream' or 'pre-competitive' R & D already underway in the EC's European Strategic Programme for Information Technology (Esprit) programme and several national information programmes 'closer to the market'.[42]

Eureka's information technology projects can be grouped into three broad categories: hardware components, software components and applications. This section focuses on the hardware components sector, because of its strategic importance and its inclusion of many of Eureka's most ambitious, expensive, and high-profile projects involving European MNCs.

European competitiveness in information technology hardware declined steadily after the 1970s, especially in microelectronic components and particularly in semiconductor devices.[43] Semiconductors became widely viewed as the most critical product sector in the electronics components industry. R & D efforts began to focus on the integrated circuit (IC) market, where product innovation was proceeding most rapidly and the implications for end users were most profound.

The two most critical IC product areas are microprocessors, or single chips which perform the processing functions of a computer, and memories devices, which store information. These are basic 'building block' technologies which feed into so many final markets – military, industrial, commercial and consumer – that they are widely viewed as the 'crude oil' of the 1990s. Technological backwardness in this sector implies severe consequences for a host of end-use sectors.

Only Philips among all European firms was competitive in global markets for semiconductors at the time of Eureka's launch. Japanese and US firms controlled nearly 90 per cent of the world market and the European market alone was predicted to quadruple between 1986 and 1996. European firms such as Siemens, Thomson, SGS, Plessey and Ferranti had strong domestic market shares, but were weak in export markets. Heretofore, these firms had concentrated on 'low volume, domestic niche markets', and their strategies had been 'cautious, inward-looking and nationalistic'.[44]

National microelectronics policies in Europe traditionally concentrated on providing a broadly based, independent technological 'backbone' for domestically based telecommunications, computer and defence industries, rather than improving European specialization.[45] The sort of product specialization that a common EC market should offer never materialized, and European firms were forced to develop extensive ties with US and Japanese producers to have access to new technology and widened product bases. A truly 'locally based' European industry was retarded by a lack of European interfirm cooperation.

In the 1980s, the microelectronics manufacturing industry became radically more R & D and capital-intensive and barriers to entry rose steadily. Large firms became the only competitors in many product sectors, as overcapacity and extreme swings in demand drove out most SMEs. The high costs and importance of R & D made mergers or collaboration a logical strategy for nearly all surviving firms. In 1987–88, Plessey took over Ferranti's semiconductor manufacturing arm, GEC and Siemens joined forces in a hostile takeover of Plessey, and Thomson merged its semiconductor operations with those of Italy's SGS and then acquired the UK's Inmos.[46]

While semiconductor production requires large, integrated oligopolies, 'upstream' producers of production equipment and materials in the USA have often been highly innovative and dynamic SMEs. Equipment production recently has become more capital-intensive and the technological lead of US small producers has been eroded severely by Japanese firms, many of whom benefited from the very large scale integration (VLSI) programme supported by the Japanese Ministry of International Trade and Industry (MITI), which spurred development of the Japanese equipment industry in the 1980s. European firms have been generally unsuccessful in penetrating this market, and fears have arisen that European chip manufacturers may lack access to semiconductor manufacturing equipment in the future.[47]

Markets for customized and semicustomized ICs are growing faster than those for any other semiconductor products. Particularly in application-specific integrated circuits (ASICs) development, the role of start-up firms downstream at the stage where ICs are designed has become critical. Design technology (customizing the chips) has become decoupled from process technology (making the chips) in much the same way as computer software design became decoupled from hardware manufacture in the late 1960s and 1970s.[48] Yet, the European semiconductor industry has traditionally lacked dynamism at both the 'top' and 'bottom' ends of the industry.

Many of Eureka's largest projects bring together large national champions in high-risk R & D on specialized microelectronic products. For example, the Megaproject II project links Thomson and SGS in a formal shareholding arrangement to run a jointly owned microchip company. Their combined sales of semiconductors reached 720 million ECU in 1987, second only to Philips among all European producers.[49] Megaproject II seeks to develop reprogrammable standard memory chips and carries a total value of 227 million ECU.

The Joint European Silicon Structures Initiative (Jessi) involving Siemens, Philips, Thomson–SGS and Plessey seeks to radically modernize Europe's microelectronics production capability, and eventually to commercialize a 64 megabit dynamic random access memory (DRAM) chip, which would equal a radical technological leap on current DRAMs. DRAMs are general purpose ICs which can be used to store very large quantities of information. Jessi is Eureka's single largest project, and is set to cost 3.8 billion ECU over ten years. By 1989, about 550 million ECU had been committed to Jessi by Eureka Member States, with the EC contributing its own funds to the project's basic research through Esprit.[50]

One of the earliest Eureka projects, European Silicon Structures (ES2), is a joint venture involving Philips, Olivetti, British Aerospace, Saab and others with a total value of nearly 82 million ECU. It aims to design ASICs using direct impression on silicon, a process which allows custom-designed production in much shorter cycles than previously possible. ES2 has headquarters in Munich, R & D facilities in the UK, and Europe's first plant for the production of ASICs in France. The consortium had generated a turnover of 18 million ECU by late 1988.[51] ES2 is a truly pan-European venture which aims to capture the economies of scale crucial to long-term growth in the industry. It has been hailed as one of Eureka's biggest successes although it was approved as a Eureka project at a very late stage in its development.

Both public and private protagonists involved in Jessi and ES2 argue that these projects are encouraging the development of innovative SMEs and start-ups at the 'bottom end' of the semiconductor industry. Jessi's activities are split into four separate technological sectors: memory and logic technology, applications, long-term research, and equipment technology.[52] The intent is to establish links with innovative outside firms in each area of technology and 'completely overhaul the entire European micro-electronics production line'.[53]

Chip production within ES2 is carried out by Thomson–SGS, while customers are offered a computer-assisted design service which allows them to customize chips to meet their needs. ES2 aims to develop a network of 'partner firms', many of them SMEs, with manufacturing teams which can provide customers with assistance and follow-up services in chip definition and design.[54] ES2 is the largest and most significant start-up firm to enter the European microelectronics industry in many years, but its decentralized structure is intended to give it the sort of flexibility needed to provide small volumes of design-intensive products to many different users. ES2's potential technology transfer effects are substantial since it offers chip producers and consumers a permanent forum for exchange. This point was illustrated by the entry of Aérospatiale, a major microelectronics customer, into ES2's shareholder portfolio in 1989.[55]

Three broad factors will determine whether Eureka's information technology flagship projects are successful. First, they must avoid centralized, bureaucratic organizational structures so decisionmaking can respond quickly to competitive and technological developments. They also must genuinely support the development of dynamic SMEs in the specific subsectors where they provide dynamism or help to diffuse innovations. Decisionmaking within these projects is still dominated by large MNCs, whatever attempts are being made to include SMEs through contracting links. Jessi has separate managing boards for each of its four subprogrammes. Each develops 'blueprint proposals' for specific R & D subprojects which are then approved by the Jessi Council, a sort of 'Board of Directors' comprised of the chief executive managers of the large chip-makers. More than 40 per cent of Jessi's total finance is being directed toward its memory and logic technology subprogramme, which is mostly the domain of large MNCs. The equipment sector, where SMEs have been a driving force in the USA and Japan, is receiving only 13 per cent of the total investment.[56] Jessi's structure has criticised by Eureka officials as 'unwieldy' and 'top-heavy'. One offered the sound-bite: 'Jessi is very, very messy'.[57]

Second, for these projects to succeed, a broad range of changes in European innovation policies must occur which extend well beyond the confines of Eureka. These changes include liberalization of public procurement markets, the development of larger pools of venture capital to support start-up firms, encouragement of the diffusion of new innovations across industrial sectors, the redirection of public subsidies toward new market entrants in sectors such as manufacturing equipment and ASICs design and, above all, the development of a truly internal market for microelectronic components. Large national champions are loathe to give up cozy national niches, especially when many have survived only because of them. For example, the telecommunications industry, where highly nationalistic procurement patterns are entrenched, emerged in the mid-1980s as the largest European end-user sector for ICs, surpassing the consumer electronics and computer industries.[58]

Finally, developing a European microelectronics industry which can reconquer the domestic market must not obscure the critical need for European firms to pursue more outward-looking export strategies. In several semiconductor product sectors, market shares in Japan and the USA will be required if European firms are to have the production volumes necessary to exploit economies of scale and achieve price competitiveness. Exports to the USA and Japan, where markets are more technologically advanced, will provide a 'technology-push' dynamic which will force European producers to innovate. In short, 'if European firms fail to achieve export market success, they will serve a market which lags behind the technology frontier'.[59] Alliances with Japanese or US firms may be needed for European firms to gain access to foreign markets or technology, such as advanced semiconductor manufacturing equipment. The decision in 1990 to allow IBM Europe to participate in Jessi is indicative of the sort of flexible approach to strategic alliances which European firms and governments must adopt, while the decision to expel ICL from a number of Jessi subprojects after the purchase of 80 per cent of the company's shares by Fitjitsu in 1991 shows that old attitudes die hard.[60]

If nothing else, Eureka's information technology projects have promoted new thinking about European strategies in information technology. Approximately 35–40 per cent of all industrial participants in Eureka's information technology projects are SMEs. Most projects in this sector are small, relatively inexpensive and pitched 'close to the market'.[61] Yet, the success of collaborative R & D in this sector is dependent on a wide range of market-opening measures and policy changes. In particular, this points to the symbiotic relationship between Eureka, national innovation policies, the EC's own R & D programmes, and the internal market programme.

Communications

Compared with the information technology sector, a much smaller number of communications projects are underway in Eureka (see table 2.4). However, total project values are roughly similar in these two sectors, which highlights the large size and ambitious aims of many of Eureka's communications projects. Several seek to contribute to a general overhaul of Europe's communications infrastructure by developing 'front-end' specialized products which are based on new technical standards and can be marketed to specific groups of customers.

Eureka's High Definition Television (HDTV) Project is, along with Jessi, the largest and best-known of all Eureka projects. Launched in 1986, it aims to develop both production and broadcasting standards for the next generation of television. Another longstanding and large-scale communications project is Cosine (Cooperation for Open Systems Interconnection Networking in Europe). It seeks to establish a pan-European computer communications infrastructure by 'federating' research networks and databases using common Open Systems Interconnection (OSI) standards. Cosine is the only Eureka project for which the European Commission itself acts as project leader. Because of their distinctiveness and strategic importance, both the Cosine and HDTV projects are singled out for case studies in Chapter 7.

Most other communications projects deal with specialized systems improvement, such as computer image synthesis or the development of the 'smart telephone'. A common theme of nearly all of Eureka's communications projects is the development or preparation of new standards. Eureka's promise to contribute to the development of Europe-wide standards will be tested in this sector as much as any other.

Robotics and production automation

Eureka's activities in robotics and production automation link many diverse types of partners in a wide range of projects. Until 1991, there were more Eureka projects in this sector than in any other. As many as one-quarter of all SMEs participating in Eureka projects do so via robotics projects, compared with less than 20 per cent in the information technology sector, despite the much higher value of the latter project portfolio.[62]

Global markets for flexible manufacturing systems (FMS) are expanding exponentially. Annual investment in factory automation in the USA more than tripled in the 1980s and global markets for industrial automation are set to quadruple in the 1990s.[63] Automation usually is geared to one of three goals: to reduce quality control costs (which equal 25–35 per cent of total production costs in many industries), to enable 'just-in-time' and other techniques to reduce inventory costs and lead times, or to make customized 'microproduction' techniques commercially viable. While parts manufacturing is typically highly automated in all industrialized countries, the application of automation to assembly is still in its infancy. Perhaps 10 per cent of all industrial robots in the EC are used in assembly and most have been installed since 1985. Assembly is a key area for the application of advanced robotics since it often accounts for as much as 40 per cent of manufacturing expense.[64]

The FMS sector in Europe is ripe for collaborative R & D. First, the information technology component of automation, particularly software, is usually critical to successful application. The computing side of FMS typically accounts for up to 30 per cent of total costs, with software alone accounting for about 20 per cent.[65] Innovation thus requires extensive collaboration between manufacturers and information technology firms.

Second, non-commercial actors (i.e. university laboratories and research institutes) provide opportunities for 'learning-by-doing' that commercial firms guided by 'return-on-investment' management criteria often lack. Software of the level of sophistication needed for many FMS systems can require three years to write, while the mechanical equipment involved can often be installed and commissioned in fifteen months.[66] This disparity helps explain the heavy participation of non-commercial actors, which account for one of every five partners in all Eureka FMS projects.[67]

Third, European countries generally trail the USA and especially Japan in the application of robots and flexible assembly to the shopfloor. Nearly 40 per cent of all Japanese industrial robots are used in assembly, compared with only 10 per cent in Europe. While Japan had seventy-eight industrial robots per 10,000 workers in 1987, the leading Eureka country, Sweden, had thirty-nine, followed by Germany with fourteen.[68] Meanwhile, US firms dominated markets for the computer hardware used most often in FMS.

Finally, different Eureka Member States have clear complementary national assets. Germany has more installed assembly-oriented robots than any country in Europe. France has developed a software systems industry which is world-class. Due largely to its very high labour costs, Sweden produces about 30 per cent of all European robots and offers front runners in FMS such as Volvo and Electrolux. The UK offers a wide coterie of manufacturing firms which are strong competitors in niche markets in the automotive, textiles and mechanical and electrical engineering sectors. In short, a clear rationale exists for combining Europe's R & D efforts.

A centralized, 'top-down' approach to organising R & D in this sector is undesirable due to the specificity of technological solutions in particular automation settings. Europe's robotics and software industries both are characterized by many innovative SMEs. Successful collaboration often must bring together robotics firms, software houses, university or public research laboratories and the eventual industrial user of FMS systems.

About half of all Eureka projects in robotics and production are organized under an 'umbrella' framework called Famos (Flexible Automated Assembly Systems). It is a 'mini-Eureka' within Eureka designed to catalyse individual FMS projects through workshops, publicity and links to venture capital. Famos was announced as a separate Eureka project in 1986 and underwent a two-year definition phase to identify where FMS could be most profitably applied in European manufacturing. The Famos framework now includes teams of government officials and FMS industrialists from most Eureka Member States working to develop projects in areas identified by the study. The Commission has full membership to establish links between Famos projects and the EC's own FMS efforts through its Basic Research in Industrial Technology for Europe (Brite) programme.

The Famos methodology is unique within Eureka. The strategic planning which preceded the launch of Famos and the rigorous technology assessment that occurs before FMS projects are approved are unduplicated in other technological sectors. For example, the Famos definition study estimated that only four of ten project proposals would move successfully through a rigorous assessment process and receive Eureka status.[69]

At the top of the Famos structure is a steering committee responsible for setting overall policy guidelines. It is assisted by a secretariat which is staffed by different Member States in rotation. Member State criteria for public funding of FMS projects are more similar than those for most other sorts of Eureka projects. The role of industry in actually managing Famos is strong, but public sector support, especially related to the development of FMS standards, is institutionalized.

Famos projects are more 'true' to Eureka's original goals than those in many other sectors. They are 'industrial-led, real projects' with 'time scales to be kept short, with a maximum of 5 years'.[70] More generally, nearly all robotics and production automation projects involve the eventual user of the product being developed in the actual R & D.[71] In many ways, Eureka's activities in this sector are a yardstick against which its projects in other sectors might be measured.

Biotechnology

As in the robotics and FMS sector, Eureka claims a large number of small projects in biotechnology which feature heavy participation by SMEs and non-commercial partners. The total ECU value of Eureka's biotechnology projects is only about two-thirds that of all robotics/FMS projects, which points to the small size of most biotechnology projects. Biotechnology projects accounted for 17 per cent of all Eureka projects in 1991, but only 7 per cent by value.[72]

Biotechnology groups together related techniques in the application of biological organisms, systems and processes to a wide variety of industries. Most techniques involve process, not product technologies: creating new methods of making products, rather than creating new products *per se*. The science as a whole is entering a 'take-off' phase. To date, its impact has been largely confined to health care and medicine, and over half of Eureka's biotechnology projects focus on medical technologies.[73] But biotechnology is beginning to invite comparisons with microelectronics in its potential impact on a diverse array of industries.[74] Many commercial applications of basic research in biotechnology are just now beginning to become clear in pharmaceuticals, fine chemicals, food processing, waste treatment and agriculture. The world market for applications in agriculture and food processing alone could reach 100 billion ECU by the end of the century.[75]

Biotechnology is a relatively young science. Barriers to entry in many subsectors of the industry are low, capital costs of R & D are relatively small and links are often direct between basic research, much of which occurs in university or public research laboratories, and commercial development. Links between commercial and non-commercial actors are critical and a strong coterie of SMEs is key to the rapid diffusion of innovations. As with robotics and FMS, market demand is an important 'cue-giver' for biotechnological R & D despite the 'science-push' dynamic which springs from the close link between laboratory discovery and product innovation.[76]

Europe's R & D effort in biotechnology is small and fragmented compared with those of the USA or Japan.[77] The relatively narrow focus of Eureka's projects in biotechnology on medical applications is disappointing, especially considering the recent emergence of new growth areas such as agro-food technologies. Arguably, Eureka has generated an unacceptably small number of biotechnology projects given the virtues of collaboration in a sector where frontiers are being pushed back so rapidly. However, coordination of national European biotechnology research efforts is a relatively recent phenomenon. The EC in particular has been late to appreciate the importance of biotechnology as a growth industry. Technological trajectories are still uncertain, and these are early days in the development of a European 'collaborative culture' in biotechnology. The effectiveness of near-market R & D in biotechnology is highly dependent on background factors, such as raw materials supplies and prices, harmonization of national regulatory regimes and patent systems, and EC protection of farmers threatened by biotechnological substitutes. As in the information technology sector, a setting which is desirable from the point of view of commercial exploitation of biotechnological R & D depends on institutional and regulatory changes well beyond the scope of Eureka's activities. Here again, the ability of public actors to promote and implement changes which extend far beyond Eureka's mandate is critical to the success of its projects.

Environmental technology

The role of environmental R & D in Eureka's project portfolio has grown extremely rapidly both in terms of project numbers and ECU value since 1989. Only twelve projects in environmental technology were approved at five ministerial conferences between 1985 and 1988, but nearly 100 were added to the project list in the following three years (see Tables 2.2 and 2.4). The fact that the environmental area is the fastest-growing cluster within the Eureka portfolio is not surprising given the increasing political salience of environmental issues in Europe and the way in which stricter anti-pollution legislation stokes markets for environmental technologies.

Nearly three-quarters of Eureka's environmental R & D is conducted within umbrella projects which resemble Famos. However, many of Eureka's environmental projects have objectives which are not clearly product or market oriented. For example, Eureka's largest, oldest and most expensive environmental project is Eurotrac, whose *raison d'être* is to conduct R & D which is quite clearly 'pre-competitive' into the tracking of environmental pollution (see Chapter 7).[78] Another umbrella project, Eurocare, deals with the conservation and restoration of public monuments. Well over half of all participants in Eureka's environmental projects are non-industrial organizations such as universities or research institutes.

Eureka's environmental umbrellas have had much success in generating large numbers of new projects since 1988. However, concerns have been voiced within the Eureka network about the 'complexity of the structures and the overhead(s)' associated with environmental umbrellas, as well as their relatively low level of industrial participation.[79] Eureka has evolved in ways which were unforeseen when it was created in 1985 and this point is illustrated most clearly by Eureka's environmental project portfolio.

New materials

The total value of Eureka's projects in new materials is the smallest of any cluster. New materials are an increasingly critical source of competitive advantage in a widening range of manufacturing and process industries. By its very nature, this area of technology is difficult to assess because it ranges so widely across plastics, composites, ceramics, metal alloys, surface treatment techniques and even semiconductors. But what is clear is that the overwhelming lead the USA enjoyed in this sector until the mid-1970s has been steadily eroded by Japan, while European innovation generally has stagnated. By 1985, nearly three-quarters of European patents in new materials were being granted for innovations developed in the USA or Japan. The importance of new materials applications to traditional industries, such as automotives, mining, and metal manufacture, and the loss of European market shares in these industries to Asian competitors is not unrelated.

Perhaps Eureka has generated so few projects in new materials because of the closed character of the sector, which is dominated by large chemical companies which tend to keep close links to national schemes. Another possibility – which is acknowledged by many Eureka officials –

is that Eureka compares unfavourably with national or especially EC programmes which offer far more public funding for materials R & D.[80] Whatever the explanation, Eureka's impact on Europe's position in new materials has been minimal.

Infrastructure projects: energy, transport and lasers

Many Eureka projects in the energy, transport and laser sectors are engaged in R & D which is clearly pre-competitive. It is within these sectors (as well as environmental technology) that a large number of projects – about 15 per cent of Eureka's total – seek to develop Europe's 'technological infrastructure'. Eureka's laser projects are organized under an umbrella framework similar to Famos called Eurolaser. Here, project work is mostly focused on basic or pre-competitive research, with a standing group of civil servants and representatives of the Commission developing new frameworks for health and safety standards which are appropriate for new innovations.

Eureka's activities in the transport sector have a similar emphasis. The umbrella project 'Prometheus' brings together thirteen of Europe's largest automotive manufacturers to develop the enabling infrastructure for a 'clever car' which would respond to weather and traffic conditions automatically.[81] The Eureka Road Transport Monitoring Group is similar to the boards set up for Eurolaser and Famos to work on standards development.

Again, these sectors make it clear that Eureka's activities are in no way confined to downstream R & D. Indeed, the extent of Eureka's activities geared to developing technological 'infrastructures' has increased over time. The idea that Eureka should primarily be a framework for 'near-market' R & D has not been applied strictly in practice.

V. SYNTHESIS: NEAR-MARKET OR 'CATCH-ALL' R & D?

While Europe's record in producing scientific and technological innovations has always been world-class, a basic competitive weakness has been the inability of her industries to turn innovations into marketable products and global market shares. This weakness helps explain why Eureka was launched as an initiative to promote down-stream collaborative projects. Yet, Eureka's industry-led, 'bottom-up' methodology grants wide discretion to industry and the European research community to design and propose their own projects. The logical results are that Eureka's activities are spread across a very wide range of technologies and its projects have very diverse aims. Close to 40 per cent of Eureka's projects aim to develop marketable products or processes in less than three years, but a majority have longer lead times. Logically, the longer a project's scheduled R & D time, the less certain participants will be about its eventual outcome and the market for its output.

While Eureka clearly is not an initiative strictly for 'near-market' R & D, this does not necessarily mean that even long-term projects designed to develop Europe's technological infrastructure are not market-oriented. For example, the annual global market for goods and services in the 'environmental protection industry' is about 75 million ECU and growing, with Western Europe accounting for nearly 40 per cent of the total.[82] For many of Eureka's infrastructure projects, the eventual user of outputs will often be governments. Coordination of the actions of public and private actors in these Eureka projects can actually help 'create' markets and consumers. As the head of the Eureka secretariat, Olaf Meyer, argues:

> Eureka projects are market oriented. This means they aim at or even try to create consumers who desire solutions and are prepared to pay for them, which in the case of environmental problems more often than not, calls for international political actions and rules.[83]

However, Eureka has become less an initiative with a clear purpose than a sort of 'catch-all' framework for R & D. The official 'line' on precisely what Eureka is trying to accomplish has evolved accordingly. Even British officials, who in 1985 had insisted that Eureka projects should be industrial, near-market projects, admit that the initiative incorporates a far more eclectic range of R & D activities than originally was envisioned:

> I think we're coming around more to the view that Eureka is a framework for collaborative projects that don't fit easily into other European collaborative activities . . . Where we have some doubts is concerning the earlier environmental projects where it seemed to us existing frameworks within Europe or wider than Europe could carry out some of that R & D. It didn't seem to us that Eureka provided these projects with anything special. The Germans . . . tend to be keener on upstream projects generally and projects where there's a large research institute involvement. We've nothing against university or research institute involvement, but we normally expect to see industry in the lead on Eureka projects.[84]

Potential costs may be involved if Eureka turns out to be too many different initiatives to too many different people. First, with the exception of France, most Member States generally devote quite modest amounts of public funding specifically to Eureka projects. These resources may be spread too thinly to have much impact if large infrastructure projects, which are hard to fund without public subsidy and promise commercial returns only in the long run, make large claims on what funds are on offer.

A second and related concern stems from Eureka's modest administrative structure. Eureka's Member States have devoted very limited administrative resources to supporting their national efforts in Eureka. A primary task of Eureka's public actors is meant to be 'supportive measures' to help industry to turn R & D into commercial returns quickly. Obviously, the effectiveness of supportive measures may be diminished if Eureka's public actors are preoccupied with measures to support projects aimed toward markets that are not yet clearly defined.

A third problem is that Eureka, because it clearly encompasses R & D that is 'pre-competitive', may in some cases end up duplicating R & D already underway within the EC's Framework programmes. One of the justifications for creating Eureka in the first place was that it would make it possible for pre-competitive EC-sponsored projects to continue 'nearer to the market' under Eureka.

Finally, there is the simple problem of promoting Eureka to industry as an initiative with a clear goal and purpose. As a British official admits, that the 'plaid' nature of Eureka's project list has made it difficult to explain to industrialists why they should be involved with the initiative:

> There's no escaping that. The fact that it can include such a wide spectrum of projects is a strength in one sense, but is also a weakness because it's difficult to see any coherence to what Eureka is trying to achieve. From UK point of view, we see it as primarily for competitive R & D which is eventually is going to find its way into marketable products, processes and services. But the nature of the projects varies quite considerably, even among the projects we participate in.[85]

Given the different national priorities which came into play in the original negotiations to launch Eureka in 1985, it is not surprising that Eureka has evolved into an initiative with rather vague central objectives. Explaining how and why national attitudes to the original French proposal varied is necessary to understand why Eureka now works as it does. This task is the focus for Chapter 3.

3   The weight of history and origins of Eureka

Eureka cannot be understood without considering its origins, and its
origins cannot be understood in a historical vacuum. Previous attempts
to promote collaborative R & D in Europe conditioned the strategies of
those who put Eureka in train. Eureka also was shaped by *sui generis*
political developments within the EC and the Western Alliance in 1985.
Section I of this chapter sketches the post-war history of pan-European
R & D and illustrates how and why lessons learned influenced decisions
about Eureka's design and purpose. Section II examines the development of political momentum to launch both Eureka and the EC's
Framework programme. The critical role of industry in the making of
Eureka is analysed in Section III. The chapter concludes by placing
Eureka in the context of broad structural and attitudinal changes in
Europe in the 1980s which help explain why it exists.

I. THE PRECURSORS AND THEIR IMPLICATIONS

From 1957 until the early 1980s, efforts to promote European collaboration in science and technology mostly focused on energy research.
The European Atomic Energy Community (Euratom) was launched in
1957 amid high hopes that the pooling of national nuclear programmes
would lead to the development of a 'Euroreactor', which could provide a
cheap, secure source of energy in the face of fuel shortages anticipated
for the early 1960s. France possessed the most advanced nuclear
programme of any Member State by far. Under President Charles
DeGaulle, the French used anxieties about German participation to
ensure that there would be no obligation to share R & D results which
impinged on 'national security'.[1] The result was that little actual
collaboration took place and Euratom ended up subsidizing competing
national programmes.[2] Its disappointing record hampered efforts to
bring innovation policy within the EC's remit.

Similar troubles plagued the European Launcher Development Organization (ELDO), which was created in 1962 to challenge the US monopoly in space launchers. The collective goals outlined in ELDO's convention never were matched by sufficient political consensus on the part of its Member States, who were prohibited from withdrawing from ELDO even after it became clear that the intiative was a failure. ELDO suffered from acute cost control problems and produced little of commercial value.[3]

Attitudes shifted in 1967 when Jean-Jacques Servan-Schreiber's *The American Challenge* popularized the notion that a 'technology gap' had developed between Europe and the USA and that direct investment by US MNCs in Europe would lead to economic subservience.[4] The EC's Council of Science Ministers was convened for the first time and the Commission developed a twin-pronged strategy to pool R & D efforts and national purchasing policies for technology-based products. Yet, progress was first delayed by disagreements about the participation of non-EC members and then halted altogether by DeGaulle's second veto of the UK's application to join the EC.

Eventually, a watered-down set of proposals approved by the intergovernmental Medium-Term Economic Committee yielded the Cooperation in Scientific and Technology (COST) mechanism.[5] Eventually, COST was expanded to include all OECD Member States plus the Commission in a structure similar to that of Eureka, although governments themselves retained primary responsibility for proposing and organizing projects. COST remains a 'useful, if low-key, framework for . . . pan-European projects of applied science research'.[6] But its goals have never been clearly defined and its political profile has been low. By 1989, COST had attracted only about 150 million ECU in public funding in its eighteen-year history.[7]

When it became clear that COST would be strictly intergovernmental, the Commission issued the Colonna Report in 1970 which proposed the creation of a European R & D Committee (CERD) and a European R & D Agency (ERDA).[8] The intent was that CERD would design collaborative programmes and ERDA would implement them with partial funding from the EC. The Commission argued that companies which collaborated transnationally or actually merged with other firms across borders should receive first priority when EC funds were allocated. The Colonna Report thus struck at the heart of national champion-centred innovation policies and brought to light severe clashes of philosophy between Member States, particularly West Germany and France.[9] They eventually were dropped as the EC became distracted by negotiations on the entry of new members in 1971.

The period also yielded two notable intergovernmental schemes linking European computer firms. ICL, CII, Philips, AEG-Telefunken, Saab and Olivetti formed Eurodata in 1969 to cooperatively produce a high-speed computer for the European Space Research Organization (ESRO). Acceptance of Eurodata's tender by the ESRO offer ultimately was vetoed by West Germany under pressure from Siemens, the only major European computer firm left out of the consortium. The venture collapsed in the ensuing acrimony.[10]

The French and German governments engineered a second consortium, Unidata, in 1973. However, when Siemens, Bull and CII submitted plans to consolidate the project under a single management, the French government instead sought to merge CII with Honeywell–Bull after negotiating a market and product-sharing arrangement with Honeywell USA.[11] German fury at the failure of the French to consult them on the merger poisoned relations within Unidata and contributed to its demise.

In 1974, the EC's own R & D activities were expanded after Member States endorsed the principle of EC involvement in most fields of science and technology. From 1974 to 1982, EC annual spending on R & D increased nearly seven-fold in real terms, but over 60 per cent was earmarked for large energy research projects such as Joint European Torus (JET), Euratom's nuclear fusion programme. EC spending on R & D stood at 2.5 per cent of total national public expenditure in 1968, but had fallen to 2.2 per cent by 1982.[12]

Thus, the primary effect of European alarm at the 'technology gap' was to reinforce existing patterns of national support for R & D which remained jealously guarded after twenty-five years of attempts to promote collaboration through EC programmes. In the event, initiatives launched intergovernmentally did far more to lay the groundwork for Eureka than 'stop–go' experiments at the EC level. For example, ESRO developed from the bottom up on the initiative of scientists at the international particle physics laboratory, the *Centre Européen pour la Récherche Nucleaire* (CERN). ESRO provided good value-for-money in space R & D and acted as a effective 'marriage broker' between commercial aerospace firms.[13] It contributed much to the development of a European space community of policy makers, researchers, engineers and industrialists.

Both the success of ESRO and failure of ELDO informed the launch of the European Space Agency (ESA) in 1973. The ESA was designed to coordinate existing national, bilateral and multilateral programmes. It became a clear manifestation of variable geometry and managed to accommodate the different priorities of its Member States. The ESA maintains close institutional links with Arianespace, which is multi-nationally funded but allows France near total control of production. Arianespace has become the world's leading commercial space launcher, and both the Ariane rocket and the ESA's Spacelab now compete with US equivalents. With virtually no link to the EC, the ESA includes Sweden and Switzerland and its annual budget is set to top 2.5 billion ECU by the mid-1990s.[14] In short, 'ESA has thus become something of a model framework for technological collaboration'.[15]

The European effort to maintain an independent capability in space technology paralleled similar developments in civil aviation. Public policy studies usually characterize Concorde as a wasteful and ill-conceived 'great planning disaster'.[16] Concorde suffered, as did ELDO, from extraordinary cost escalations, inadequate government–industry contracts and a lack of legal control over finance.[17] It also highlighted the ruin which can ensue when collaborative R & D programmes become tools of wider political agendas. Commercial considerations carried little weight in the calculations of the UK Foreign Office, which hoped to use Concorde as leverage to gain entry to the EC.[18] Concorde was supported consistently in both France and the UK by the political left for its employment effects and the right for its prestige value.[19] The project yielded a technological masterpiece, but required $4.28 billion to build two prototypes and fourteen planes, which were then sold to reluctant national airlines at a loss of $187 million each.[20]

Yet, Sharp and Shearman insist that Concorde's 'psychological legacy' made it 'an important ice-breaker for reluctant French and British aviation companies'.[21] Concorde's impact on the Airbus project, begun in 1967, was critical. After difficult early years, Airbus gave Europe a strong presence in global markets for civil airliners, where the USA maintained an 83 per cent market share from 1958 to 1983.[22] The EC as a whole now maintains a balance of payments surplus in the sector. The launch of new Airbus projects has required massive government subsidies, but 'Airbus has steadily become a more industrially-driven programme, and routine official involvement in the programme is far less intensive than in many past collaborative programmes'.[23]

The continuity of more than forty years of European collaboration in civil aviation has helped the Airbus consortium to advance on learning curves and act increasingly as a single firm.[24] Collaboration has become routine for Europe's major aerospace firms, and they have become progressively larger, more diversified and involved with one another. For example, in 1987 the major Airbus partners launched a major Eureka project to develop a civilian helicopter.[25]

Several of the Airbus partners have also collaborated in developing military aircraft and weapons systems, although with more modest and mixed results. The first major defence project in post-war Europe involving more than two countries, the Multi-Role Combat Aircraft (MRCA, later called the Tornado), paralleled Concorde in its cost overruns, emphasis on technological sophistication over value-for-money and political division of labour. Most cost savings were eroded by conflicting national standards in procurement and high development costs.[26]

Clashing national priorities also plagued the European Fighter Aircraft (EFA), launched in 1988. France's Dassault, which opted out of the MRCA and instead developed its own loss-making Variable Geometry aircraft, refused to join the EFA project and instead elected to develop its own Rafale advanced fighter. Germany first clashed with the UK over the participation of US firms in EFA, and then effectively pulled out of the project under the budgetary strains of German unification in 1992.

The latter part of the 1980s witnessed rising political interest in joint weapons and equipment development as a response to tightened national defence budgets. The joint development of a combat helicopter was perhaps the most important in a host of Franco-German collaborative military projects announced during the period.[27] France even attempted to launch a 'military Eureka' within the North Atlantic Treaty Organization's (NATO) Independent European Programme Group (IEPG) in 1989.[28] The assignment of Sillard, the French Eureka NPC, to head France's IEPG delegation pointed both to the high political profile the French had given to military cooperation and their insistence that Eureka's methodology was working.

However, French efforts to transplant the 'industry-led' model of collaboration from Eureka to the IEPG made little headway. Member States remained reluctant to alter national defence procurement patterns and IEPG was constrained by the lack of any effective joint European defence planning.[29] The UK, France and Germany each continued to spend less than 10 per cent of their total military equipment budgets on imports by the late 1980s.[30] European governments continue to approach collaborative R & D in the military sphere cautiously and incrementally.

One of the central lessons learned from collaborative experiments between 1958 and 1985 was that politics can ruin projects despite their economic, policy or strategic logic. Euratom failed primarily due to DeGaulle's *realpolitick*. Joint computer schemes collapsed more due to bickering between governments than between industrial partners.

Political criteria mandated a collaborative structure which ensured Concorde's commercial failure. COST showed that schemes which do not enjoy a high political profile tend to produce only modest results. Military cooperation has been complicated by the exigencies of 'high politics'. In short, governments rarely entered into collaborative agreements with identical objectives. The separate priorities of national champion-centred innovation policies usually overrode any notion of a general 'European interest' in collaboration. 'Industrial patriotism,' to borrow Hayward's term,[31] usually prevailed.

The period also illustrated the danger of constructing schemes based on speculative assumptions about the future. When the anticipated fuel shortage of the 1960s failed to materialize, the political will surrounding the launch of Euratom evaporated. The same problem dogged the JET project, which sought to develop three new fast-breeder reactors on the erroneous assumption that uranium supplies would become scarce in the 1980s.[32] The UK and France made no attempt to estimate the future market for supersonic transport, but signed a treaty which prevented either party from withdrawing from the Concorde project, even though each wished to at least three times.[33] Another lesson of past collaborative experiments appears to be that provisions for review, reappraisal or even withdrawal by Member States should be built-in.

Commission proposals for new collaborative programmes quickly became bound up in wider political disputes. Particularly between 1967 and 1972, technology policy initiatives were often included in plans for transforming the EC into a political union which were consistently resisted by Member States.[34] Commenting on the period, Williams argued that 'in the science, technology and industry field the EEC Commission has been excessively preoccupied with the pursuit of an executive power which itself really presupposes a political unity'.[35] If anything, the Commission's tactics backfired and mistrust of its motives meant that few important EC projects outside of energy R & D existed until the 1980s.

Uneven national technological capabilities meant that sector-specific projects accommodated the principle of *juste retour* only with great difficulty, or at a high cost to efficiency. Effective compromise within Euratom was impossible because bargaining was confined to a single technological sector, with no scope for the aggregation of issues into complex 'package deals' of the kind that are routine at the EC level generally.[36] Airbus accommodated varying national capabilities with some success, but also with substantial efficiency costs.[37]

The importance of continuity in collaboration became clear. The European aerospace, electronics and computers sectors were all characterized by extensive collaboration in the twenty years prior to 1985. If the results of these efforts were often disappointing, they at least brought advances on learning curves for both governments and firms about how collaborative projects could best be designed. The development of 'collaborative communities', particularly in information technology and aerospace, had powerful implications for the development of Eureka.

The emergence of these communities and the sorry record of government-directed projects such as Concorde and Unidata led governments to seek collaborative arrangements that were 'industry-led' by the 1980s. European governments and the Commission itself appeared to accept Williams' maxim that once governments provided an environment which left firms to choose avenues of collaboration themselves:

> good balance between efficiency and equity later will be facilitated by initiative-phase commercial and industrial bargaining, thereby minimizing commitment-phase political negotiation. This is also likely to be the simplest route to permanent European industrial and commercial links.[38]

Finally, recalling the experiences of Euratom and Unidata, European governments suspected French motives and methods when they proposed Eureka, but they could not deny France's crucial role in the successes of Airbus and Ariane. On a political level, a Franco-German axis was firmly established after a decade of extensive collaboration in aviation, space technology and microelectronics. In the event, the strong French commitment to Eureka and the gradual evolution of German political support were decisive in 1985.

II. SDI, FRAMEWORK AND EUREKA

A sea change in European perceptions about technological competitiveness occurred in the mid-1980s as a new 'technology gap' debate emerged.[39] The European share of world semiconductor markets fell steadily and US firms controlled over 80 per cent of the European computer market.[40] The Reagan administration's defence build-up spurred a 30 per cent increase in US government spending on R & D between 1980 and 1985.[41] The Commission, along with some EC governments, noted with alarm that only about one-quarter of collaborative agreements entered into by European firms in technology-intensive industries during this period were with other EC firms, while over half were concluded with US partners.[42] Export embargoes imposed by the USA on European firms participating in the con-

Telecom Devel'n in the US?

struction of the Soviet gas pipeline raised serious worries about restrictions on technology transfer in US–European collaboration.[43] Deregulation in the USA brought the repeal of anti-trust provisions which had prohibited American Telephone and Telegraph (AT & T) from foreign operations and kept IBM out of telecommunications, and focused attention on European vulnerabilities in information technology.

A new feature of the technology gap of the mid-1980s was acute European anxiety about the rise of Japan as a technological power. MITI's programmes in ICs and computers – particularly the fifth generation computer project – appeared on the brink of technological leaps undreamt of by European producers.[44] Japanese penetration of the European market contributed mightily to the rapid deterioration of the EC's balance of payments in information technology, which went from surplus in 1975 to a sharp deficit by 1982. EC firms were supplying only 40 per cent of their own market and 10 per cent of the global market.[45]

Meanwhile, the recession of the early 1980s hit West European economies hard. All suffered substantial capital flight due to persistently high US interest rates and an overvalued dollar. Urgent pleas by European leaders for lower US interest rates were ignored by the Reagan administration.[46] Fears that Western Europe was in a rapid state of deindustrialization were nowhere more acute than in France. The Socialist government's ill-timed reflation had induced severe economic crisis by 1982 as France's budget deficit soared, her balance of payments deteriorated rapidly, and intense pressure on the franc forced multiple devaluations.[47] France's technological dependence on US and Japanese know-how in key industrial sectors was highlighted in negotiations to nationalize CII-Honeywell-Bull in 1982. A 20 per cent stake had to be conceded to US concerns during the capital restructuring of the group after the Americans used technological expertise as a leverage device.[48]

The French government repeatedly issued calls for new collaborative R & D programmes throughout this period. Mitterrand's plan for a cooperative effort 'to analyse prospects offered by new technologies' was accepted at the 1982 Versailles summit of the Group of Seven industrialized nations. A working group led by the new French technology assessment organ, *Centre d'Etudes des Systèmes et des Technologies Avancées* (CESTA), produced proposals in eighteen research areas that were approved at the Williamsburg summit in May 1983.[49] However, little came of the proposals, which France's partners appeared to accept 'almost as if to humour the French government'.[50]

After this point, the French shifted their focus to the EC itself. André Chandernagor, the French Minister for European Affairs, presented a multi-pronged strategy for increased European technological collaboration to the EC's Council of Ministers in September 1983. French concern for her severe balance-of-payments problem was reflected in Chandernagor's proposal for a 'significant, but temporary increase' in EC tariffs on imports of high-tech goods.[51] Mitterrand urged acceptance of the plan in an address to the British Parliament a month later, and again in speeches in The Hague, Strasbourg and Paris in 1984.[52]

If French urgings went essentially unheeded by most EC governments, they were taken seriously by the Commission. It already had unveiled plans for Esprit's 11.5 million ECU pilot phase in June 1982. Industry Commissioner Etienne Davignon had sought to create a Japanese-style strategic consortium by taking the unprecedented step of bringing together the top executives of Europe's twelve information technology firms to define priorities and collectively endorse the initiative. Yet, despite Esprit's industry-led approach, Commission plans in 1983 for a substantially expanded ten–year 1.5 billion ECU programme soon became caught up in wider EC budgetary disputes. The Commission's proposals reawakened suspicions – especially in the UK and Germany – about the linking of R & D to broader political goals.[53]

A key development in the technology gap debate was the Reagan administration's launch in March 1983 of its SDI proposal to construct a space-based nuclear defence system.[54] The US initiative was preceded by virtually no consultation of European governments, for whom an immediate concern was the negative impact SDI might have on arms control talks with the Soviet Union. However, SDI's economic implications clearly caused as much alarm in European capitals, particularly Paris, as did its military implications. A primary concern was the effect of 26 billion ECU in new public funding on the already powerful US technology community.[55]

In the spring of 1985, the European debate about SDI suddenly took on added urgency when the US Secretary of Defense Caspar Weinberger sent letters to all NATO defence ministers inviting collaborative bids for SDI contracts. European governments were given sixty days to decide whether they wished to participate. The UK's response was generally favourable, although 'hesitant and even disjointed . . . slow to emerge and not particularly well coordinated when it did appear'.[56] The Germans demurred at first, but eventually endorsed the idea of participation in SDI research, if not the fundamental objectives of the system itself.[57] The French government immediately and vigorously rejected the offer.

Sensing doubts about SDI in many European capitals, the Americans rescinded the deadline, but meanwhile began approaching European firms and even individual researchers in April 1985. Within weeks, about seventy industrial groups or European financial firms had been privately solicited. Several of the EC's toprank technology firms, including Messerschmidt Bölkow Blohm (MBB), British Aerospace and Selenia, announced their intention to take part.[58] European leaders began to wonder why the Pentagon chose to extend the offer through official channels if their European firms were being solicited with or without governmental sanction. SDI's director, Lieutenant General James Abrahamson, hinted publicly that since the US approach was bilateral and targeted individual European firms, it made little difference whether or not European governments endorsed the project.[59]

The Commission seized the moment to reveal its own plans for a new European Technology Community. The Commissioner for Science and Research, Karl-Heinz Narjes, called for a tripling of current EC funding for R & D. The Commission's manoeuvering along with the Reagan administration's announcement that it would seek a collective endorsement of SDI at the Bonn Group of Seven summit in May 1985, convinced the French to act. Preliminary ideas were circulated by French embassies in European capitals in early April. On 17 April, Mitterrand formally proposed Eureka after the weekly meeting of his cabinet in Paris.[60]

The ensuing French diplomatic effort to secure partners for Eureka was remarkably intense and fundamentally shaped by the domestic political agenda of the French Socialists. The Eureka initiative came at a time when the popularity of both Mitterrand and his party was in serious decline. Mitterrand's repeated assertions that Eureka would be industry-led yet supported by substantial French public funding were consistent with his government's effort to ingratiate itself with business as the Socialist party drifted rightwards and adopted slogans such as '*c'est l'enterprise qui crée la richesse*'.[61] Moreover, the SDI–Eureka debate allowed Mitterrand to cast his neo-Gaullist political opponents – many of whom supported SDI – as short-sighted, anti-European and by association, promoters of the nuclear arms race and Reagan's America.[62]

The French opposition's response was inauspicious. For example, Simone Veil of the centre-right *Union pour la Démocratie Française* accused the Socialists of 'short-circuiting' the Commission, attempting to pull a 'national coup' on other potential Eureka Member States, and rejecting SDI without 'a clear look at the dossier'.[63] By contrast, Mitterrand presented himself as taking bold action to hasten the 'technological renaissance of Europe' at a time when the SDI proposal was reminding Europeans of their relative weakness in science and research. Mitterrand drew much attention to a study by the French Ministry of Foreign Affairs which argued that SDI would aggravate European technological backwardness while enhancing US 'technological maturity and industrial competitiveness'.[64] The report also contrasted the 'divide and rule' strategy of the SDI initiative and its military aims with the opportunity provided by Eureka for European unity in the development of civilian technologies.

Mitterrand took care to nurture political support for Eureka in France and in Europe. The President convinced Edmond Maire, Secretary-General of the Socialist-aligned trade union *Confédération Française Démocratique du Travail* to publicly endorse Eureka and suggest that 'the degradation of the economic and employment situation calls for European solutions'.[65] Mitterrand also sought and secured a ringing endorsement of Eureka from a May 1985 meeting of European socialist parties.[66]

More generally, Eureka was a response to trends in public opinion which suggested that the French were becoming strongly pro-European and keener than any other European people on the idea of increased spending for R & D on a Europe-wide scale.[67] Sociological research confirmed that the French generally viewed themselves as well served by state-led technological modernization of their telecommunications, transport and energy systems. The rise of leisure and consumerism as social values in France meant that new technologies were increasingly viewed as 'vehicle[s] for positive changes in values and lifestyles'.[68] Eureka promised to expedite European technological modernization with France in the lead. Its appeal to French public opinion was distinct and not coincidental.

Mitterrand's use of Eureka to score domestic political points acted to reopen the SDI–Eureka debate in France after the Socialists were defeated in National Assembly elections in March 1986. André Giraud, the new conservative government's Defence Minister, was on record as a strong supporter of SDI, and the Prime Minister Jacques Chirac appeared unenthusiastic about Eureka.[69] Yet, by 1986 other Member States had invested far too much in the effort to launch Eureka for it to be quietly abandoned. Chirac knew he would incur much wrath from Mitterrand if France's commitment to Eureka was weakened at a time when both the President and Prime Minister had incentives to demonstrate that *cohabitation* could effectively govern France. Most importantly, Eureka was popular among French industrialists and Chirac had little to gain from tampering with a pro-business initiative.

In the event, Eureka was little affected by *cohabitation*. A French Eureka official later recalled:

> There was no significant change. During the first months we were wondering, but in November 1986 there was a meeting chaired by the Prime Minister, which took the decision that we had proposed and everything was approved: 900 million francs per year for support of Eureka projects . . . We had more difficulties with the Ministry of Industry and Ministry of Research during this period. But at the level of the Prime Minister, the attitude was as positive as before.[70]

However, Eureka re-emerged as a domestic political issue as Chirac challenged Mitterrand for the presidency in 1988. Mitterrand repeatedly reminded voters that he personally had launched Eureka and charged that Chirac had slashed French public funding for R & D. Chirac called the accusations 'woolly' and 'misinformed', but the French quality press gave them substantial play and helped Mitterrand to take the moral high ground on the technology issue.[71]

Despite its partisan political associations, Eureka is indicative of how France's technological prowess has remained a symbol of national pride throughout the Fifth Republic. The point was illustrated by Mitterrand's spurious claim that the Concorde's technology was 'entirely French' during a visit to the USA in 1982.[72] Eureka was sold in public statements throughout 1985 as an initiative which would resemble Airbus or Ariane, both of which were widely perceived as 'French projects' in France.[73] Yet, Eureka's viability depended crucially on West German support. Before Mitterrand formally proposed the initiative, Dumas had exchanged letters and had several contacts with the German Foreign Minister, Hans-Dietrich Genscher. In public statements, CESTA stressed, 'It's above all between Paris and Bonn that the Eureka pilot projects will be defined'.[74]

The Germans had not yet formally responded to the invitation to participate in SDI when Mitterrand proposed Eureka. The US offer, on its surface, held much appeal for West Germany. Industrially, SDI promised to open US markets to export-minded German technology firms. Strategically, despite grave misgivings about replacing nuclear deterrence with ballistic missile defences, SDI gave the west leverage in arms control negotiations with the Soviet Union. Politically, it provided the German Chancellor Helmut Kohl with a chance to reaffirm his government's close ties to the Reagan administration. Kohl initially welcomed the French proposal but implied that Eureka was a counter-weight permitting West Germany to negotiate a stronger position with the USA on SDI. The Chancellor described SDI as 'justified, politically necessary and in the security interests of the West as a whole'.[75]

The SDI–Eureka debate was complicated in early May when the French delegation engaged in negotiations with West Germany suggested that Eureka could lead to a network of surveillance satellites as part of a truly European defence system. Although an apparent violation of Eureka's civilian emphasis, the French argued that the idea would fit strategically and technologically with a European orbital space station having both military and civilian uses.[76] The idea was received with much interest in Bonn. It highlighted the fact that the French would neglect virtually no possible argument in their bid for German support.

The debate in West Germany brought to light a complex mosaic of attitudes within the Federal Republic's centre-right coalition government. Kohl had to take account of the faction within his own Christian Democratic Union (CDU) party, which seemed intent on SDI participation exclusively. Meanwhile, Franz-Josef Strauss, the leader of the CDU's Bavarian sister party, the Christian Social Union, favoured participation in both Eureka and SDI. The Finance Minister, Gerhard Stoltenberg, spoke of the need to avoid squandering state finances on either programme.[77] Meanwhile, Genscher and his strongly pro-European Free Democratic Party, a minority partner in the Bonn coalition, cast Eureka as a litmus test for Franco-German relations.

Genscher fought his corner by seizing on domestic concerns about the general deterioration of Franco-German relations in 1985. Earlier in the year, the Kohl government had declared its preference for developing Columbus, a module to be attached to future US orbital space stations, instead of the French-built *Hermes*. Another rift centred on treatment of the ECU: the French favoured its increased use and development while the Germans seemed hesitant for fear of importing inflation from other EC economies. Within the EC, French-backed proposals to reduce cereal support prices were vetoed repeatedly by West Germany.[78] Within the General Agreement on Trade and Tariffs (GATT), the USA pushed for a new round of talks to focus on agriculture and services. The French fiercely resisted the US agenda on the grounds that it would threaten the EC's Common Agricultural Policy and European information technology industries. The German position seemed agnostic.[79]

The Group of Seven economic summit in Bonn in early May 1985 brought both the Franco-German diplomatic rift and the SDI–Eureka debate to the forefront of international attention. In a pre-summit interview with the French newspaper, *Libération*, President Reagan implied that Eureka was simply a European response to SDI, but said that he felt no hostility towards the initiative and expected to hear more about it in Bonn. An obviously irritated Mitterrand appeared on French television the following day to state that Eureka had 'nothing to do' with SDI. He added that 'Eureka does not require US benediction and therefore does not need to be discussed in Bonn'.[80]

Predictably, the Bonn summit ended in acrimony, with France vetoing both the setting of a date for new GATT talks and a collective endorsement of SDI. Mitterrand later recalled a conversation he had had with Reagan at the summit: 'Subcontractors. That's the word I heard. The word was said in English. It confirmed my intuitions'.[81] In classic Gaullist style, the President termed SDI a 'pigeon shoot – an imprecise sport'. In a worst case scenario, Mitterrand claimed that 'France would launch itself alone in Eureka', but he also expressed hope that the 'play' in Franco-German relations could be reduced and that other European states would join the 'reformed couple' in Eureka.[82]

In a speech to the NATO Assembly on 20 May, Kohl declared that Europe needed to forge ahead with SDI, but he also spoke enthusiastically about Eureka and confirmed that 'we accept and support the principle of regrouping European capacities in high technologies'.[83] However subtle, Kohl's change of position was noted in the UK. The day after Kohl's speech, the British Foreign Minister, Geoffrey Howe, confirmed British interest in Eureka for the first time after a meeting with Dumas in Paris. Much diplomatic gamesmanship was involved at this point, with one Downing Street aide admitting that to avoid offending Mitterrand, 'We can't flat out say Eureka is no good'.[84]

In Bonn, the SDI–Eureka debate heated up considerably. On 23 May, the Chancellor's predecessor, Helmut Schmidt, wrote to Kohl and the presidents of all major German political parties urging that West Germany should not scatter its technological resources between Eureka and SDI. Schmidt firmly endorsed Eureka and termed the crisis in Franco-German relations 'an event without precedent'.[85] Despite Schmidt's self-imposed retirement after being marginalized by his Social Democratic party (SPD), he remained by far the most popular politician in West Germany. His position – in accord with those of Genscher and the SPD – could not be ignored by Kohl.

For their part, the Americans announced that the Vice-President, George Bush, would begin a tour of Europe to dissipate the 'confusion [of] European leaders regarding the volume, cost and consequences of SDI'.[86] Kohl's subsequent statements on Eureka were evasive and lukewarm at a bilateral Franco-German summit in Constance on 30 May. Yet, when asked in Constance about the idea of combining Eureka and SDI, the German Research Minister, Heinz Riesenhuber, made a point which had become obvious to all involved in the debate: Europe's human and financial resources were limited. The British Minister of State for Information Technology, Geoffrey Pattie, earlier had expressed similar concerns: 'We have finite resources of manpower and money, and the technologies involved appear to be rather similar'.[87]

Kohl returned to Bonn after the Constance summit to find the German press scathingly critical of his indecisiveness and strongly supportive of Eureka.[88] At this point, Kohl was approaching a watershed in his political career. In the previous month, the chancellor had strained US–German relations by insisting on Reagan's visit to the Bitburg cemetery, witnessed the defeat of the CDU in the North Rhine-Westphalia *Länder* election, and presided over the deterioration of Franco-German relations. His government had been shaken in the previous legislative term by a series of scandals including the Flick/Barzel affair. Throughout the period, Kohl appeared increasingly incapable of fixing priorities to guide both domestic and foreign policies.[89]

A complex mixture of motives thus led Kohl to declare that West Germany was 'beyond diplomacy' and 'ready to participate in the Eureka programme' on 31 May.[90] A day later, Mitterrand responded:

Eureka is a Franco-German idea. For the Federal Republic, it is a vital necessity . . . In terms of objectives, these two projects are not competitors, but Eureka has civil objectives for mastering space. Where could one find competition between the two projects? On the budgetary level, on the level of researchers, who might be exported under the US project, but who with Eureka could stay on our continent. In my view, Germany must do one or the other.[91]

The German endorsement was a watershed in Eureka's evolution. On 1 June, Howe confirmed the UK's intention to participate and Denmark announced it would create a special government commission on Eureka. On 3 June, Norway declared itself ready to participate in Eureka projects of a 'civil and pacific' nature.[92]

The French effort to secure German support for Eureka seized upon ambiguous lines of authority in German foreign policy-making. The clash of views between Genscher and Kohl pointed to the general heterogeneity of cabinet government in the Federal Republic. Article 65 of the West German Basic Law gives the chancellor primary responsibility for determining general policy, but explicitly grants other ministers powers to conduct the affairs of their own departments autonomously. Individual ministries in Bonn have always operated far more independently than those in Paris or London.[93] German ministerial autonomy is particularly visible on matters of EC policy and is reinforced by the Franco-German relationship. As Bulmer and Paterson observe.

> extensive bilateral discussions held at various levels between the two governments are essentially conducted on a specialist basis . . . there is no agency in Bonn with the task of checking whether views expressed by one federal minister to his French counterpart are compatible with those expressed by another German minister to *his* opposite number.[94]

Thus, the French engaged Genscher and German foreign office in defining Eureka even before the Chancellor's office had officially responded to the Eureka or SDI proposals. Kohl was forced to walk a tightrope between Atlanticists within the CDU, who saw SDI as a way to reinforce the US nuclear guarantee to Europe, and Europeanists such as Genscher and Schmidt, who provoked alarm about Franco-German relations and led German public opinion. Domestic criticism of the Chancellor's inability to develop clear policies had been building up long before the SDI–Eureka debate came to a head. The French skillfully exploited Kohl's vulnerabilities.

The weight of the official German endorsement made it virtually certain that Eureka would become a reality. Yet, political endorsements meant little without support from European industry. After German support was secured, French diplomacy was directed toward industry itself.

III. THE INDUSTRIAL PHASE

Long before collaborative R & D reached the top of political agendas in 1985, a core of leading European information technology firms had begun to cooperate extensively. Siemens, Philips, Companie Générale d'Electricité (CGE), and to a lesser extent STET, CII-Honeywell Bull and Thomson, had all become involved heavily in joint pre-competitive research in the early 1980s.[95] Davignon's efforts to engineer an industrial consensus for new collaborative schemes began to have an impact in 1979, when leading representatives of these firms plus AEG, Nixdorf, GEC, ICL, Plessey and Olivetti were brought together to form the 'Big 12 Roundtable'. An executive committee resolved that the group would lobby for new collaborative schemes, cooperatively develop basic technologies and seek to develop common European standards.[96]

Representatives from the Big 12 were intimately involved in the design of Esprit's pilot phase and its subsequent management by the EC's information technology Task Force, which consists of industrialists, academics and Commission officials. Between 70 and 80 per cent of all Esprit contracts were awarded to Big 12 firms from 1981 to 1983.[97]

During this period, a separate group of twenty leading representatives of large manufacturers such as Volvo and Pilkington was convened under the chairmanship of Per Gyllenhamer. The Gyllenhammer group issued a programme in 1983 calling for an end to national subsidies, barriers between European national markets and divided R & D efforts. It actively pushed national governments to launch the 1992 project and new collaborative R & D programmes.[98] The combined weight of the Big 12 and Gyllenhammer group was evident in the distribution of projects for Esprit's phase II. The percentage involving Big 12 firms had fallen to 62 per cent by 1985, but more than half of all projects brought one of the Big 12 firms together with large European manufacturers such as Renault, Peugeot, BMW, Volkswagen, British Aerospace, Aeritalia or MBB.[99]

In early June 1985, the Big 12 and Gyllenhammer group became key actors in the Eureka–SDI debate. Edward Teller, the White House science adviser, was dispatched to London to announce that nearly 2 billion ECU out of SDI's projected total budget would be earmarked for 'unclassified, innovative' research to be conducted by non-US firms and research teams.[100] The French Research Minister, Hubert Curien, immediately responded that Eureka had entered its 'industrial phase'. European companies were rapidly brought into discussions to help draw up lists of projects to be supported. While unable to estimate Eureka's eventual budget, Curien predicted that the programme could 'mobilize' up to 1.4 billion ECU out of France's civil R & D budget.[101] Curien reiterated that France would contribute no public funds to SDI and insisted on the necessity of making 'a distinction between political attitudes and industrial attitudes'.[102] However, he conceded that there was little governments could do to prevent European firms from participating in SDI and even acknowledged that some form of coordination of SDI and Eureka might have to be considered to avoid duplicated efforts.

On 14 June, representatives of French and German Big 12 firms met in Munich to discuss Eureka with Riesenhuber and Curien. Riesenhuber revealed that the Germans were ready to devote more public funding to the project than originally thought.[103] In London, Pattie chaired an meeting on 18 June with representatives from Plessey, Ferranti, ICL, Racal, GEC and Thorn EMI to map out possible projects in electronics.[104] Then, amid much fanfare on 20 June, Siemens, Philips, GEC and Thomson signed a 'declaration of common intent' to cooperate within Eureka on the development of strategic components. A group statement urged that, 'Eureka should be product and market-oriented . . . Projects undertaken in the framework of Eureka should lead to finalized and saleable products and systems'.[105] The agreement brought together Europe's four largest information technology firms with home bases in four different countries. Their collective weight gave Eureka – which had to this point been very much a political initiative – a critical endorsement from European industry.

A flurry of announcements of new Eureka projects followed in subsequent weeks. On 21 June, the Norwegian computer and electronics firm, Norsk Data, announced that it would work with Matra on the development of a high-performance desktop calculator for laboratories and research centres. In attendance at the accord's signing, Curien insisted, 'Each alliance must lead to the development of a program which corresponds to a market, as opposed to the European Community's Esprit program, whose goal is to develop basic technologies'.[106]

Curien's statement was a clear attempt to distance Eureka from the EC itself. The idea that Eureka would fund near-market projects automatically made the EC's involvement problematical, as Treaty restrictions required that the EC limit itself to funding pre-competitive research. Moreover, if Norway was to participate, any notion of incorporating Eureka into the Framework programme became a dead letter. The Commission faced the problem of applying the principle of *juste retour* to a programme which included non-contributors to the EC's budget.[107]

Part of the French strategy in launching Eureka was to exploit even stronger EC Member State suspicions about the wider agenda which lay behind the Commission's own proposals for increased spending on R & D. In Brussels, the Eureka proposal was viewed as a French attempt to 'pirate' the Commission's Framework initiative. Unveiled just a week before Eureka was proposed, the Framework proposal sought to triple funding for EC R & D schemes after a call for Esprit proposals had been heavily oversubscribed in March 1984.

EC Commission President Jacques Delors' immediate reaction was to urge that Eureka be brought within the Framework programme. In mid-June, Delors announced to the European Parliament that the Commission was preparing a memorandum for the forthcoming Milan summit which would include ideas on Eureka's organization and goals.[108] Taking account of British and German concerns about the Framework programme's budgetary implications and with an eye toward the progress of SDI, the French appeared to hasten the pace of events surrounding Eureka at this point.

At the Milan EC summit in late June, Mitterrand bluntly stated that Eureka would be launched outside the EC. A member of the French delegation admitted, 'We don't want the Commission to get its hands on this and create a bureaucracy which will frighten everyone away'.[109] The summit closed with a unanimous endorsement of Eureka and an agreement to convene a ministerial level meeting on 17 July in Paris to further define the programme. While Ministers also pledged support for the Framework proposals, Eureka was considered as an entirely separate proposal.

Even before the official launch of Eureka in Paris, three more Eureka projects were announced, involving Aérospatiale, MBB and Matra, among others.[110] Remarkably, projects were being announced before any clear guidelines had been agreed at a political level on Eureka's methods of finance, national membership, rules of participation, or precisely what made a Eureka project different from any other collaborative project. Yet, politically sophisticated firms realized the wisdom of signing on at this early stage. MBB, British Aerospace and Matra were all seeking SDI contracts, and thus were able to use their association with Eureka as leverage in negotiations with the Pentagon. European MNCs logically calculated that governments would provide some sort of incentives, although yet unknown, to hasten industrial involvement in Eureka. Philips, Thomson, Siemens, Norsk Data and others wished to be first in line for whatever was on offer.

In July, Mitterrand announced that France would commit 160 million ECU in new public funds to the scheme at the first Eureka ministerial conference in Paris. Riesenhuber said West Germany might provide as much as 145 million ECU for Eureka in 1986, although German officials were vague about how much would come from a reorganization of existing R & D subsidies and how much would be 'new' money.[111] The most important point of debate in Paris was the relationship between Eureka and the EC. France, the UK and Switzerland wished to exclude the EC as much as possible. Other states, including Italy and the Benelux countries, favoured integrating a Eureka secretariat with the Commission. In the event, pre-conference lobbying by Delors along with perceptible Anglo-German suspicion of French intentions produced the compromise that the Commission would be an extra 'Member State' of Eureka.[112]

Another point of controversy was a French proposal to create a centralized secretariat which would coordinate 'technical steering committees' to analyse current European activities and weaknesses and suggest specific topics for collaborative R & D. A CESTA paper argued that this was necessary to give the initiative overall policy direction and coherence in the face of the autonomous management of individual projects by industry.[113] Several delegations staunchly resisted the idea, suggesting that the proposal was a 'Trojan horse' to allow France to retain organizational control of the initiative.[114] A British official later commented, 'Eureka stands for European Research Co-ordinating Agency and that's what Mitterrand wanted: a top-down bureaucracy to determine where money should be going in Europe'.[115] But the French were by now bound by earlier commitments to compromise on Eureka's structures in consultation with its partners. The Paris conference thus produced an extremely brief and vague communiqué, whose only clear provision was that Eureka would have no central funds.

Not since the Fouchet Plan had any collaborative European scheme been the subject of so much publicity and diplomatic effort and so little consensus on goals, methodology and structure. Eighteen Member States agreed to join Eureka at the Paris conference, but divergent views on funding, administrative arrangements and what sort of projects Eureka should pursue were still to be reconciled. After the conference, the French issued statements insisting that Eureka would need a total of 8 billion ECU in finance over the next five to six years, with half coming from public sources.[116] The German cabinet reportedly considered proposals to commit upwards of 500 million ECU to Eureka, then announced that only funds from existing national R & D schemes would be available.[117] A similar line was taken by the UK as Pattie warned, 'There won't be a pot of money to which people will form up and ask for funds'.[118]

As the second Eureka ministerial conference in Hanover approached in November 1985, industrialists began to grumble about Eureka's lack of clear objectives or funding provisions. Otto Wolff von Amerongen, the president of the German industry association, the *Bundesverband der Deutsche Industrie*, criticized Eureka as 'still far too imprecise and unexplained, particularly the financial aspect'.[119] One British official recalled, 'There was a lot of criticism and questioning from business circles. They wanted to know what was in it for them and we couldn't tell them'.[120]

To underline its political commitment to Eureka, West Germany had assumed its chairmanship after the Paris conference. A German official intimately involved in negotiating Eureka's Declaration of Principles explained:

After the Paris conference when Germany took over the chairmanship, we used the August holidays in France to work hard to put proposals on the table which were more to the German ideas ... So we arrived at a bottom-up approach and not a top-down approach which was perhaps at first supported by the French partners. The result was the basic declaration. But we had support also from the Netherlands, Sweden, the UK, the Swiss.[121]

The Declaration approved by ministers at Hanover clearly reflected German thinking on how Eureka should work. Environmental and transport technologies were added to the six technological sectors chosen by the French for Eureka. The Declaration confirmed Eureka's near-market emphasis, but stated that it would 'also embrace important . . . projects aimed at the creation of the technical prerequisites for a modern infrastructure and the solution of transboundary problems'. It insisted that all Eureka projects should be backed by an 'adequate financial commitment by participating enterprises'.[122]

The divisive issue of creating a Eureka secretariat again was put off for further study. Smaller Member States reportedly pushed for a strong secretariat to protect their interests against what an Italian source described as the 'rich, big-nation club'.[123] By contrast, the UK objected even to the use of the word 'secretariat' and suggested that 'task force' would be more appropriate.[124] In the event, the Declaration stipulated that the secretariat would be 'small and flexible', and simply act as a clearing house for project information.

Ministers in Hanover gave formal approval to ten Eureka projects with a value of approximately 440 million ECU. The most expensive project brought together Acorn, Olivetti and Thomson to develop a standard microcomputer for educational and domestic use. The UK presented it as a flagship project, with Pattie stating, 'The need for the product is there, it doesn't cost the taxpayer any money, and it can be in the marketplace by 1987'.[125] The second largest approved project, involving MBB and France's Solems/CFP in semiconductor research, claimed 50 per cent funding from the German and French governments.[126] Eurotrac and Cosine – both clearly pre-competitive projects – also were approved.[127] Eureka's variable geometry was already accommodating differing national priorities and funding policies.

The Eureka chairmanship next passed to the UK. In early 1986, the HLG announced that sixteen new projects worth up to 560 million ECU would be approved at the next ministerial conference, and that the secretariat would be kept remarkably small.[128] By this time, responsibility for developing Eureka clearly had shifted from ministers to the HLG itself.

In June 1986, the London ministerial conference formally approved sixty-two new Eureka projects worth an estimated 2 billion ECU, thus increasing the total value of all Eureka projects almost sevenfold.[129] Repeated expressions of ministerial support were made for using Eureka to speed up the creation of the internal market.[130] The British Prime Minister, Margaret Thatcher, opened the conference by declaring that, 'Eureka is a key element in Europe's industrial strategy . . . Through Eureka, European firms can help us to identify the steps to open markets which will most help them'.[131]

Ministers announced that Eureka's secretariat would operate from Brussels. The French had lobbied for Strasbourg, but the choice appeared to be a response to the industry view that Eureka should be based near the EC's main offices.[132] An Italian proposal to require governments to circulate full details on their public funding of individual projects was rejected.[133] Ministers also decided that Eureka participants, instead of public authorities, would determine the conditions of patent protection and IPRs resulting from Eureka projects. A British representative later observed, 'By the time Thatcher made that speech, Eureka was going very much the way we wanted it to'.[134]

IV. THE LOGIC OF INDUSTRY-LED INTERGOVERNMENTALISM

In many respects, Eureka was a product of structural and attitudinal changes in both the public and private spheres of the European science and technology community which had become clear by 1985. The initiative was timely, in that it became viewed as an alternative to SDI or the Framework programme, both of which had trappings that European governments found politically distasteful. Eureka also served the political agenda of the French Socialists under Mitterrand, as well as that of their allies in the German political class. However, the distinction between public and private support for collaborative R & D became blurred in the mid-1980s, and proposals emanating from one sphere began to reinforce those from the other.

In political terms, Davignon and the Commission, as well as the French proponents of Eureka, all required support from European industry to place collaborative R & D on the agenda of European governments, and to channel the political momentum for new schemes to the support of wider political agendas. The Commission's agenda included overcoming the EC's history of failure in collaborative R & D, increasing its own *acquis* in innovation policy and, ultimately, linking support for collaborative R & D to the relaunch of the EC itself via the 1992 project. For the French Socialists, industrial backing for Eureka lent credibility to their efforts to discourage European participation in SDI, cast France as the leader of a new 'technological Europe', and to seize on the symbolic potency of technological modernity and pro-Europeanism in French domestic politics.

The French and German officials who were charged with the task of fleshing out the original Eureka initiative allowed Big 12 and Gyllenhammer group representatives a powerful voice in determining how Eureka would be organized. Eureka's industry-led ethos was more a matter of necessity than choice. European MNCs logically wished decision making to be based on commercial, not political, criteria. For their part, the French could not push for a centralized, *dirigiste* programme because both industrialists and political leaders were sceptical of their intentions and mindful of past French efforts to dictate the terms of collaborative R & D.

The original Eureka proposal sought to promote collaborative R & D in virtually the same technological sectors as SDI and the Commission's Framework proposal. Yet, several factors conspired to ensure that Eureka would be launched as a non-EC initiative. First, the Commission tacitly linked technological collaboration with its wider aims of amending the Treaty of Rome. Article 24 of the SEA gave firm legal sanction to the EC's role in promoting industrial R & D, endorsed the notion of variable geometry in EC R & D schemes, and mandated that non-EC Member States could participate in appropriate circumstances. But suspicions about the Commission's agenda produced the caveat that the Framework programme's total budget would require unanimous approval by the Council of Ministers. Narjes was forced to scale back by almost one-quarter his original proposal to spend 10 billion ECU on EC R & D. Even then, the Framework programme became embroiled in acrimonious EC budgetary disputes, with German and particularly British opposition severely delaying the launch of several new sub-programmes after 1987.[135]

By contrast, the French Eureka proposal required no formal treaty and funding was left an open question. Essentially, it asked for a commitment to an idea – enhanced European technological competitiveness – not a clear-cut programme. Early French statements on Eureka often contradicted one another, as when Curien said, 'The six [technological] areas cited constitute the keys to the future . . . but this list is only an example, it could undergo refinements, notably following meetings which we will have with our partners'.[136] The vagueness of the original French proposal was calculated, not accidental. As one commentator suggested, 'They can't say no to reinforcing European technological cooperation . . . It's hard to be against something when you don't know what it means'.[137]

Eureka's near-market emphasis made the initiative attractive to industry, but it also served a separate political goal: it ensured that Eureka could not be hijacked by the Commission. EC funding of downstream, product-oriented R & D would leave the Commission open to charges of distortion of competition under EC law. Moreover, Eureka's overtly commercial emphasis was presented by the French as complementary to the Framework programme's preoccupation with pre-competitive R & D. In theory, Eureka would allow for the sort of continuity in collaboration seen as critical to the successes of Airbus or the ESA.

Finally, Eureka's strict intergovernmentalism made the principle of *juste retour* a non-issue for its Member States. No public funding commitments were required and industry was left to define project proposals on an *ad hoc* basis. Thus, Eureka was not built on speculative assumptions about the future, as were Euratom and JET. Provisions were even made to allow any Member State to leave Eureka on three months' notice so that no Member State could become locked into collaboration which went awry *á la* Concorde.[138]

The making of Eureka was a highly politicized and contentious process. In the event, its minimal public administration, intergovernmental structure, industry-led ethos and civilian emphasis were designed to depoliticize the initiative. Eureka was created to generate collaborative R & D projects which deserve public support because they are underpinned by economic, strategic or policy logic, not because they fit political criteria. Yet, the chapter which follows reveals that the intergovernmental politics of Eureka remain spirited and contentious.

4 How Eureka operates

unique

Yet Peterson thin, done previously and masterfully.

It is difficult to imagine how any international organization could be harder to evaluate than Eureka. Its structures are decentralized, multiple national and intergovernmental institutions share responsibility for information collection, and it bears close resemblance to no other past or present collaborative R & D scheme. A British official acknowledged:

> To a large extent information on Eureka comes entirely from people like myself . . . Eureka will always be bedeviled, for those who want to analyse its impact or evolution, by a lack of information. And you won't be alone in that. Eureka is one of the initiatives that we have trouble evaluating ourselves.[1]

An appraisal of how Eureka operates must proceed on several distinct levels of analysis. Section I considers how Eureka complements national innovation policies, many of which have undergone significant changes in the past ten years. Section II analyses how Eureka's intergovernmental institutions work. Eureka's projects are the focus for Section III, which assesses the effects of the initiative's methodology for the selection, support and monitoring of Eureka projects. The chapter concludes in Section IV by synthesizing the evidence presented thus far about Eureka's 'added-value' for collaborative projects and national R & D policies.

I. EUREKA'S 'FIT' WITH NATIONAL POLICIES

The period immediately preceding the launch of Eureka was marked by general stagnation in national R & D spending in Western Europe. The global recession of the early 1980s placed severe strains on European welfare states. Public spending on short-term palliatives such as unemployment compensation and income support cut into public R & D budgets. Private spending on R & D also fell as European firms focused

Table 4.1 R & D spending in OECD countries

	Government-financed				Business-financed			
	1969 %	1975 %	1981 %	1983 %	1969 %	1975 %	1981 %	1983 %
EC	26.3	31.2	30.9	30.8	30.2	30.2	28.3	27.1
Japan	5.2	8.0	9.7	9.5	13.2	17.0	19.9	22.1
USA	61.6	52.4	50.9	51.1	49.0	44.9	44.6	43.7
Other	6.9	8.3	8.5	8.6	7.7	7.9	7.2	7.1

Source: OECD, *Science and Technology Indicators No. 2: R & D, Invention and Competitiveness*, Paris, 1986
Notes: OECD total equals 100. EC represents 10 Member States in all years listed.

Table 4.2 Business-financed R & D in OECD countries

	Total spending (million US $)		Compound real growth rates (%)			
	1981	1983	1969–75	1975–81	1979–81	1981–83
Germany	8,919	10,541	3.8	7.0	4.1	2.9
France	4,368	5,511	5.5	5.4	3.4	6.2
UK	4,695	5,283	−0.4	4.4	2.1	0.3
Italy	2,277	2,508	5.6	4.3.	6.7	−0.5
Japan	15,929	21,822	7.8	9.3	14.4	10.7
USA	35,944	43,246	1.8	6.4	7.4	4.0

Source: OECD, *Science and Technology Indicators No. 2: R & D, Invention and Competitiveness*, Paris, 1986.

on lowering costs and maintaining short-term profitability. Only in France, Denmark, Finland and Sweden did total R & D spending increase between 1980 and 1985. Spending levels in all other Eureka Member States remained static or increased less than inflation.[2]

European R & D spending patterns contrasted sharply with those of its main competitors. Table 4.1 reveals rapid increase in Japan's share of total OECD spending in the 1970s and continued growth in the early 1980s. It also highlights the very large share of the total OECD private R & D effort funded by Japanese industry.

While business-financed R & D in Japan grew steadily in the early 1980s, growth rates declined in all of the large EC Member States except France (see Table 4.2). The EC's overall rate of growth during this period was less than half the US rate and less than 25 per cent of Japan's. Compared to European countries, Japan's R & D spending remained low as a percentage of its gross national produce (GNP), but the fact that nearly two-thirds was performed by Japanese industry appeared to make its national R & D effort far more productive.[3]

European interest in the Japanese 'national system of innovation'[4] grew substantially in the early 1980s. European policies began to imitate Japanese strategies of fusing industrial policy with science and technology policy. The mandates of ministries of economics or industry in the Netherlands, Ireland, Finland and France were widened to encompass science and technology policy tasks previously assigned to research, science or education ministries.[5]

Innovation policies also began to reflect 'growing awareness of limits to growth in [public] research and development budgets and increasing pressure from finance ministries to get value for money from limited resources'.[6] European governments sought to reverse alarming declines in levels of private R & D spending by providing incentives for firms to devote more of their own resources to R & D in the style of Japanese firms. Interest in collaborative R & D was stimulated by the success of collaborative Japanese initiatives such as the VLSI microchip projects. Eventually, Eureka emerged as a tool which governments could use to stretch limited public R & D budgets by sharing subsidy costs while providing private firms with incentives to spend more of their own resources on R & D.

But the story is incomplete without placing Eureka in the context of changes in national innovation policies prompted by the 1992 project and the emergence of new competition state strategies in Europe. The sections which follow explain how Eureka serves new innovation policy agendas; particularly those of the states which wielded the greatest influence on the making of Eureka: France, Germany and the UK.

France – the European solution

Nowhere in Western Europe was the integration of all instruments of innovation policy pursued more enthusiastically in the early 1980s than in France. After coming to power in 1981, the Socialist government nationalized five major firms in key technology-intensive industries: CGE, Pechiney, Rhône-Poulenc, Saint-Gobain and Thomson, and the state became a majority shareholder in Dassault and Matra. The Socialists created a new Ministry for Research and Technology (MRT) and merged it with a substantially expanded Ministry for Industry, which took responsibility for nearly half of the country's industrial capacity and virtually all public civil R & D capacities.[7] The new 'super-ministry' was charged with organizing the French national R & D effort into '*filières*', or integrated strategies extending from raw materials to finished products in industries such as electronics, chemicals and new materials.

The electronics sector was made the number one industrial development priority. Major French electronics producers were nationalized and rationalized to create clear national champions in computers (Bull), office automation (CGE), telecommunications (CIT-Alcatel), semiconductors (Thomson-CSF and Matra-Harris) and consumer goods (Thomson). The *Filière Electronique* programme, with total planned funding of 23 billion ECU over five years, took on extremely broad objectives, with public funding focused both on areas of national strength such as telecommunications and software, and weakness, such as microcomputers, computer-aided design (CAD) and robotics.[8]

By the time Laurent Fabius succeeded Pierre Mauroy as Prime Minister in 1984, the limits of the *filières* strategy had become clear. 'Technology-push' strategies failed to improve export performance, as French global market shares in high technology markets slumped from 9 to 7.7 per cent between 1980 and 1984.[9] High global interest rates and heavy corporate debt led French MNCs to abandon much high-risk R & D.

The *filière* programme was hampered by acute shortages of qualified technologists and private funding, and overwhelmed by far superior investments in the USA and especially in Japan. By 1985, the Japanese were spending twice as much as the French on electronics R & D.[10] Moreover, the *filière* programme made no attempt to achieve complementarity between French efforts and those of other EC Member States. Since it aimed primarily to 'reconquer' the domestic French market, the programme required protectionism of a sort that had traditionally been the 'hallmark of French policy in support of its electronics industry'.[11] For example, imports of video cassette recorders (VCRs) were blocked by routing them through a customs post in the provincial town of Poitiers. The tactic was a bald attempt to pressure JVC-Matsushita to produce VCRs jointly with Thomson in France.

After 1984, the French Socialists began to search for alternatives to past, state-led, *dirigiste* innovation policies. French policy shifted markedly toward more 'environmental' methods of support for innovation, such as worker retraining, the creation of centres for regional technology transfer and modernization of the French banking sector.[12] The Socialists' second three-year plan for research and technology for 1985–88 urged that French policies had to be developed against the backdrop of public and private actions elsewhere in Europe.[13] The MRT, now autonomous from the Ministry of Industry, was charged with coordinating French initiatives with those of the EC and other European states. By the time Eureka was proposed in spring 1985, the

Quote – Seminar book

Socialists clearly had decided that the only solution to the problem of French technological competitiveness was a European one.[14]

Eureka fitted the new French innovation policy agenda on several levels. The *filière* experiments had shown that even a massive infusion of national public funding was inadequate to hasten French international competitiveness in key sectors, particularly that of information technology. Moreover, nationalization had cut the international ties of several of France's largest technology firms as the state bought out foreign shareholders. A key policy goal of French innovation policy after 1984 became inducing French industry to commit more of its own resources to funding R & D. Eureka's emphasis on market-led R & D and links to European markets and technology made it a logical policy foil in the shift toward more outward-looking strategies which embraced commercial criteria as a central organizing principle for public R & D support.

The emergence of the 1992 project reinforced the need for change in French innovation policy. Traditional French protectionism, such as the virtual exclusion of foreign bidders for public contracts in telecommunications or professional electronics, sat uneasily with French leadership in negotiations on the SEA. Many French firms in technology-intensive industries were competitive only by virtue of patron–client relations with the Ministry of Defence or national Post, Telephone and Telecommunications (PTT) authority. In consumer-led sectors such as personal computers or consumer electronics, France ran chronic balance-of-payments deficits. More generally, post-war France had been marked by less competition or collaboration in technology-intensive industries than any other OECD country.[15] 'Big Science' projects such as *Plan Cacul*, *Force de Frappe* and Concorde had all served Gaullist foreign policy agendas and produced impressive technological innovations and French independence in the manufacture of computers, nuclear weapons and aircraft, but none yielded competitive advantage in global markets.[16] The 1992 project generally, and Eureka specifically, thus provided a new set of policy incentives designed to encourage long-overdue changes in the behaviour of French firms.

The Socialist government also began to tackle the problem of inadequate technology transfer between private and public research organizations. France's 'producer-biased' style of innovation policy traditionally had devoted far more funding to the development of innovations than to their diffusion.[17] The French Socialists inherited a science and research community with considerable know-how, but also one marked by rigidly vertical and compartmentalized research structures and few channels for horizontal technology transfer across industrial sectors or between national public research institutes and industry. The creation of CESTA in 1981 and a major 'mobilization programme' in biotechnology in 1982 were aimed at aggregating the French R & D potential and encouraging more exchange between public and private R & D efforts.[18]

French innovation policy also took on a distinctively regional flavour never before seen in the Fifth Republic. A series of regional technology transfer and consultancy centres were launched to narrow wide disparities in technological modernity between France's urban and provincial economies. The Socialists created the highly successful *Agence Nationale de Valorisation de la Recherche* (ANVAR) in 1982 to provide R & D funding and consulting services to French SMEs.[19] By 1990, ANVAR had been directed to assist SMEs in finding foreign partners and coordinating the delivery of multinational funding commitments to Eureka projects.[20] A substantial portion of French public support of Eureka projects was taken from MRT funds earmarked for regional technological development. Thus, Eureka fitted with new efforts to hasten technology transfer and the modernization of provincial economies through collaboration with other European firms.

Finally, the shift from direct subsidy of national champions to more environmental support for innovation in the mid-1980s sprang from the assumption that entrepreneurialism, particularly among SMEs, badly needed to be nurtured in France. The 'national-champion' emphasis of French innovation policy had provided MNCs with few incentives to pursue anything but risk-averse strategies, as economies of scale possible in production for the French domestic market dulled incentives to seek new export markets. Meanwhile, SMEs provided up to 60 per cent of industrial employment, but conducted little of their own R & D and remained technologically backward and isolated from innovations developed by large firms or national research laboratories.[21] Collaboration with other firms in Europe was extremely rare among French SMEs. Asked in 1987 if French SMEs were reluctant to seek partners elsewhere in Europe, a delegate of the MRT replied, 'We can't get them to collaborate with firms across the street'.[22] Eureka, with its industry-led ethos, emerged as a tool for encouraging entrepreneurialism of a sort that rarely had existed in France.

Summarizing the implications for innovation policy of the French Socialists' failed Keynesian experiments of 1981–83, Hall observes:

> Since it was no longer possible to stimulate French industry through the expansion of demand, supply-side measures would have to be used . . . Moreover, once France's commitment to the EC was confirmed, the emphasis would have to be on measures designed to

improve the competitiveness of French firms *vis-à-vis* their European rivals.[23]

In short, France began to transform itself into a 'competition state' in a clear and decisive manner after 1984. The sea-change in French innovation policy was readily accommodated in the Eureka initiative. The French Socialists were motivated to propose Eureka as much by pragmatic policy considerations as by the overtly political imperatives detailed in Chapter 3.

Germany – playing a strong hand

Post-war innovation policy in West Germany has contrasted sharply with that in France. Of all European states, Germany has the longest and most powerful tradition of indirect environmental support for innovation and export competitiveness. Innovation policy has been based more on general incentives to encourage investment, the development of SMEs, and technology transfer than on direct support for particular firms or sectors.[24]

In many ways, the French sought to 'Germanize' their innovation policy after 1984. The private share of total West German national R & D expenditure was higher than that of any other EC country.[25] German SMEs received nearly a quarter of all federal R & D subsidies by 1983.[26] A network of public research institutes, the *Fraunhofer Gesellschaft*, focused far more on commercial technology than on basic research.[27] West Germany led all European states in promoting the general diffusion of innovations such as installed robots, numerically controlled machine tools and information technology in the 1980s.[28]

The BMFT is the key national ministry for the development of German innovation policy. Its creation in the early 1970s marked a shift away from 'Big Science' aircraft and nuclear power programmes to more project-oriented interventionism. Esprit in many ways mimics BMFT-funded initiatives in its definition of broad technological areas for support, scrutiny of project proposals by both public and private experts, and provisions for public funding of generally less than 50 per cent of total project costs.[29]

Especially compared with their French counterparts, German technology-intensive firms emerged relatively unscathed from the economic recession of the early 1980s. The loss of German export shares was much lower than for most other EC countries and industrial R & D remained relatively steady through the period. German innovation policy successfully induced firms 'not to cut back innovative activities in recession and to stick to longer-term technological strategies'.[30]

At first glance, it is not difficult to see why the Germans were more reluctant to support Eureka, or new collaborative R & D programmes generally, than were the French in 1985. Initially, Eureka was viewed in Bonn as a French attempt to appropriate some of the benefits of Germany's generally successful innovation policy. Eureka was a dead letter without enthusiastic West German support.

The Germans thus brought substantial leverage to the 1985 negotiations on Eureka and pushed to ensure that the initiative served the Kohl government's political agenda. For example, environmental degradation had become a highly salient political issue in West Germany by the mid-1980s as research revealed that much of the Black Forest was 'dying' and support for the Green Party grew.[31] The Germans insisted that Eureka should incorporate pre-competitive environmental projects in part because this demonstrated to voters that the government was seeking new solutions to environmental problems.

Yet, as for the French, practical policy considerations also motivated German support for Eureka. The German record in a number of strategic technologies, particularly microelectronics and telecommunications, was mixed and certainly not up to Japan's. Germany's trade balance in electronics fell from a 400 million ECU surplus in 1979 to a 82 million ECU deficit by 1984.[32] In telecommunications, only a highly favourable public procurement relationship with the German Bundespost kept Siemens in the first rank of global producers.

Led by the BMFT, innovation policy became decidedly more strategic and activist at the meso- and micro-levels. A German cabinet report on information technology in 1984 resulted in an ambitious 440 million ECU programme to develop the entire sector over four years, and a follow-on commitment of 293 million ECU for 1990–93.[33] The new activism also extended to expensive, high-risk ventures such as the first Mega-Project which linked Siemens and Philips in the development of advanced semiconductors, and featured a BMFT contribution of more than 140 million ECU.[34]

Eureka was broadly compatible with new priorities in German innovation policy. In the words of one BMFT official, 'each initiative which brings together scientists and engineers and enterprises is in itself worthwhile, if it's not overruled by bureaucracy and red tape . . . [Thus] projects of a Eureka type get a certain sort of bonus compared to purely German projects'.[35] While Germany lacks a 'dedicated' budget for Eureka, applications are handled more quickly than those for funding under other schemes.

Mega-Project II eventually was launched as a Eureka project and German firms actively participate in most of Eureka's largest information technology projects. The rate of participation in Eureka by German SMEs was generally low until 1989, when a special fund was created as part of the BMFT's new 'overall concept' for promoting the R & D activities of SMEs.[36] Germany now leads all Member States in the number of SMEs which participate in Eureka.[37] Moreover, the decentralized nature of German innovation policy is accommodated as a substantial portion of German public funding for Eureka projects is granted autonomously by the *Länder*.

In short, French and German innovation policies began to converge in the mid-1980s: the French sought to emulate German measures designed to promote technology transfer, privately funded R & D and regional technological development; while West Germany engaged in French-style, supply-side interventionism. The Germans got most of what they wanted out of the initial negotiations with the French on Eureka. The scheme became a useful tool for bolstering German weaknesses in strategic technologies and generating environmental R & D projects. At the same time, it forced no compulsory changes on a national innovation policy which had been more successful than any other in the EC.

United Kingdom – Thatcherism and innovation policy

Of all large European states, none has had greater difficulty turning laboratory innovations into commercial successes than the UK. The British share of total world exports of technology-intensive products fell from 12 to 9.6 per cent between 1965 and 1975, and to 8.5 per cent by 1984.[38] Post-war British innovation policy was diffuse and compartmentalized with decisions on support for innovation made autonomously by different government departments. The free market ethos of the 1971 Rothschild Report – that overarching national priorities do not and should not exist – remained strong under the Thatcher governments.[39] No serious attempt was made in the UK to fuse science and technology policy with industrial policy as occurred in France and Germany in the 1980s.

The Thatcher governments' innovation policies were fiercely criticized by both policy analysts and scientists. 'Brain drain', or the emigration of scientists and engineers to better posts abroad, became a domestic political issue.[40] Yet, the general transition to more strategic, selective supply-side interventionism was evident in the UK as elsewhere in Europe. For example, while central government funding for regional development was slashed in the 1980s, funding for R & D fell only marginally.[41] Profound concern for declining British competitiveness in information technology led to the launch of the Alvey project in 1983, which earmarked more than 285 million ECU in public funding over five years for the development and manufacture of strategic information technologies. In many respects, the Alvey project was a response to the Japanese fifth generation computer project and thus represented a radical departure from the principles associated with the Rothschild report. It took a programmatic approach to R & D, implicated three different government ministries, brought industry into actual programme management, and promoted collaboration between industry, research laboratories and government.[42]

A comprehensive evaluation of the Alvey project in 1991 concluded that it had generally failed to improve the global competitiveness of the UK in information technology.[43] Critics viewed it as an attempt to emulate Japanese innovation policy without the parallel industrial policy measures which induced the widespread exploitation and diffusion of innovations in Japan.[44] Yet, the Alvey project clearly yielded a new 'collaborative culture' in the British information technology industry. The subsequent participation rate of UK firms in Esprit and Eureka information technology projects matched or exceeded that of French or German firms.[45]

Significantly, the 1985 French Eureka proposal coincided with the convening of the Bide Committee, set up both to evaluate the Alvey project and advise ministers on British participation in collaborative R & D schemes more generally. The report noted the 'very large assistance given by foreign governments to their own industry' and urged that a comprehensive, 'near-market' programme of British R & D in information technology be integrated with European-level programmes.[46] The initial response of the Thatcher government to the Bide Report was to ignore it. Yet, as Freeman observed, 'the discussion on the European dimension in the Bide Report indicate[d] a growing recognition that some of the structural and scale problems of British industry can only be solved on a European scale'.[47]

This realization was reflected in British attitudes toward Eureka. After the 1986 British chairmanship had secured most of its goals in defining Eureka's structure and objectives, the initiative was embraced enthusiastically by the DTI. In 1988, the British Secretary of State for Industry Kenneth Clarke declared:

> We place quite a high value on Eureka. We decided to give priority to this particular route to encourage industry to get into collaborative research with partners in the rest of the Community . . . We like it

because it's bottom-up, it's industry-led, and it's our own industry which really determines the areas in which we get most involved.[48]

Perhaps the primary source of Eureka's appeal for the Thatcher government was that it emerged as an alternative to the EC's Framework programme. Thatcher almost single-handedly held up the start of the first Framework funding cycle for nine months by demanding that its budget be reduced. Meanwhile, Eureka provided incentives for British firms to establish links with continental firms and markets without the ideological distasteful involvement of the European Commission.[49]

More generally, Eureka placed no demands for change on British innovation policy and was viewed in Whitehall as a way to make limited public funds for R & D go further. Two initiatives launched during the 1980s by the DTI, the Support for Innovation and Link programmes, respectively sought to promote R & D among SMEs and strengthen ties between industry and academic research. The two programmes received relatively low funding – a combined total of approximately 400 million ECU annually.[50] Funds already allocated to these schemes were used to support Eureka projects, although only a very small portion of the total (perhaps 10 per cent) ended up being committed to Eureka projects.

Eureka was embraced enthusiastically by Conservative governments in the UK because it provided a tool for selective, supply-side intervention to support R & D which is industry-led and largely industry-financed. It made no compulsory demands on the public purse and encouraged British firms to develop links with continental firms and markets. British support was also attributable to what Eureka was not: an EC programme viewed as the thin edge of a wedge in the Commission's efforts to expand its industrial policy *acquis*. Finally, Eureka was cheap and the British commitment to the initiative was based far more on verbal than financial support. In this respect, as in the others noted above, Eureka was consistent with modern British innovation policy more generally.

The others – an overview

France, West Germany and the UK each had more influence over the making of Eureka in 1985 and 1986 than the other Member States combined. Other states had clear incentives to join Eureka once it was clear that it would be successfully launched. However, the Netherlands and Italy deserve special attention because their national innovation policies were altered considerably in the 1980s and both now participate heavily in Eureka.

Innovation policy in the Netherlands resembles the German more than the French model. The Dutch were a key German ally in support of the Declaration of Principles which gave outline to the initiative's loose, decentralized structure in 1986.[51] Yet, innovation policy in the Netherlands after 1980 had undergone a 'tremendous shift in the priorities of nationally funded research' away from academic R & D to more spending on 'industrial productivity'.[52] The Netherlands was the first Member State after France to pledge public funds to Eureka.

The Dutch commitment to international collaboration is long-established due to the small size of its domestic market and strong economic links to the UK, USA and former Dutch colonies. Yet, the Dutch find Eureka useful primarily because it encourages their domestic firms to operate in a 'home market' which extends beyond northern Europe, where the Dutch presence has traditionally been strong, to southern Europe and particularly to France. Eureka also is compatible with efforts in the Netherlands to forge tighter links between private and academic research. The renowned Organization for Applied Research, known by the Dutch acronym TNO, was transformed in the early 1980s from a traditional, state-funded, academic research institute to an autonomous organization with substantial funding from the private sector.[53] TNO now participates in several Eureka projects including several in transport technologies, where the Netherlands is generally more involved than any other Member State.

Finally, Philips is an MNC in the purest sense of the term, but it remains the Netherlands' largest exporter and private employer. The Dutch government has used Eureka to maximize the impact of its relatively small public R & D budget by encouraging Philips to collaborate with Siemens, Thomson and others in expensive, strategic Eureka projects. In short, Dutch enthusiasm for Eureka has remained steady since its origins.

Much the same could be said for Italy. While the popular impression of dynamic SMEs and stagnant large firms in Italy is overdrawn, 'industrial development is certainly more dependent on dynamic small business in Italy than anywhere else'.[54] Eureka encourages Italian SMEs to bolster their technological acumen and become aware of new market opportunities by developing pan-European links. Eureka also accommodates the strong regional bias on Italian innovation policy, with higher levels of funding available to projects of 'national importance',[55] such as those involving firms from the underdeveloped southern regions.

Substantial privatization and liberalization of the Italian stock market in the mid-1980s led to a stock market 'boom' and the development of integrated capital markets and outward-looking financial institutions.[56] The freeing of private investment helped to mute a long-running innovation policy controversy in Italy which pitted large technology-intensive firms, primarily Fiat and Olivetti, against SMEs. Eureka emerged as a policy foil for matching private finance with collaborative R & D projects. While 20 per cent of Italian public spending on Eureka is reserved for SMEs, its bottom-up approach allows it to be agnostic in debates about whether SMEs or large firms should be favoured.

Smaller European countries tend to have a larger than average proportion of SMEs. Eureka's other Member States thus tend to participate most often in sectors where barriers to entry are low or where SMEs or research institutes play a significant role. For example, about than half of all projects involving Spain are in robotics or biotechnology. Participation by Sweden, Norway and Finland is most often in robotics projects, and Denmark's project list is dominated by biotechnology and environmental projects.[57] Half of all Austrian participants are SMEs or non-industrial organizations.

For Eureka's non-EC states, participation is viewed as a method of developing the international links needed to exploit the internal market. Before a EC–EFTA agreement on collaborative R & D was signed in 1989, EFTA firms were excluded from participation in most industrial EC R & D programmes.[58] More generally, all EFTA countries have domestic markets of 8 million consumers or less, and EFTA's total market is about 32 million, while the EC's is over 340 million.

Eureka's Member States differ in significant respects in the manner and degree to which the initiative complements their national innovation policies. Yet, most have developed new tools for supply-side interventionism in line with new 'competition state' strategies. Most see Eureka as a method for 'weaning' firms away from dependence on public support for commercially oriented R & D. All want their domestic firms to develop transnational links within Europe to hasten technology transfer and become aware of new export opportunities as the internal market is completed. A central goal for most Member States is to strengthen links between academic and private R & D, which have been weak since reforms designed to ensure 'academic freedom' were passed throughout Europe after 1968. Eureka allows government to use subsidies strategically and selectively, provides incentives for firms to commit their own funds to R & D, encourages foreign market awareness, and helps amalgamate private and public research efforts. Perhaps most importantly, Eureka requires little or no alteration of national innovation policies.

II. INTERGOVERNMENTALISM AND UNINTENDED CONSEQUENCES

In many respects, the early negotiations on creating Eureka yielded a 'lowest common denominator' result. The need to forge consensus among such a diverse collection of Member States meant that an absolute minimum number of compulsory rules of process could be agreed in 1985–86. Eureka's new intergovernmental institutions were vested with virtually no power to challenge or alter national policies.

The Stockholm ministerial conference of 1986 revealed how much political momentum to launch Eureka had run ahead of the organization-building to manage it. Ministers admitted that they lacked precise figures on how much of Eureka's finance was coming from public sources. It was revealed that no system existed to monitor the progress of projects and that relatively few projects had advanced past the drawing board or 'definition phase'.[59]

Two years passed before ministers at tne 1988 Copenhagen conference called on the HLG to review Eureka's goals and procedures, and to develop a 'medium-term plan' which could ensure continuity between the objectives of successive chairmanships. To this point, the rotating chairmanship system had yielded a diverse set of policy initiatives launched by countries which held the chair. A basic problem with these initiatives was that they either were abandoned by subsequent chairs, who brought different national priorities to their terms, or Eureka's structure precluded much meaningful, concerted action at an intergovernmental level. For example, little was done to follow up an initiative by the Spanish chairmanship of 1986–87 to attract private finance to Eureka. The subsequent Danish chairmanship instead focused on the 'Eureka Management Research Initiative' (EMRI), which proposed to bring together management researchers from fifteen European business schools to study the problems of managing collaborative R & D projects, 'especially with regard to SMEs'.[60] But the EMRI secured no public funding until 1989 and only then from the Danish Eureka office to study projects with Danish participation.[61] An EC official lamented, 'unfortunately this initiative has not produced any results up to now. It's been passed from one chairmanship to another and there's been a lot of talk, but with no conclusion . . . the results were disappointing'.[62] Meanwhile, a Danish report on increasing SME participation haplessly concluded, 'individual governments participating in Eureka are free to develop solutions building on their national experiences and policies'.[63]

The HLG approached the medium-term plan with the intention of ensuring that the 'work programmes of succeeding Chairmanships . . . be placed within such a framework'.[64] Any outside observer attending meetings held to draft the plan might have thought they were a continuation of those held in 1985 before Eureka's Declaration of Principles were agreed.[65] An Italian delegate stressed the need for more near-market and fewer pre-competitive projects. A Swiss representative agreed that the 'destruction of the market orientation of Eureka destroys the argument that there should be different European R & D initiatives and that there should be synergy'. The German spokesman complained that a recent Eureka document which stated that all projects should have a 'market orientation' had 'been used as a weapon against certain projects', presumably some of the German-led infrastructure projects. The Danish delegation bemoaned the low level of participation by SMEs and public research laboratories. A Commission official tried to intervene, but was ignored by the Austrian chair. A British delegate reminded his colleagues that the HLG had no mandate to implement the sort of broad changes being advocated since, 'Eureka by nature debars us from doing all sorts of things normally associated with an international organization'.

The same delegate later commented on the need for a medium-term plan:

> Eureka can't solve everyone's problems. We should only be dealing with issues that are unique to Eureka. Because it's an international organization everyone tries to throw everything into it, even the kitchen sink. It's to try and bring an element of discipline into the activities of the officials and make sure they deliver their part of the bargain.[66]

Yet, it is difficult to determine precisely what are the issues that are 'unique to Eureka'. The inclusion of pre-competitive or infrastructure projects obviously precludes any notion that Eureka is only a framework for near-market R & D. The presence of long-term, expensive projects involving European MNCs alongside infrastructure projects dominated by public research laboratories and small, product-oriented industrial projects led by SMEs means that Eureka is not just an initiative for one sort of organizational actor. The vague division of labour in terms of policy leadership between the HLG, the rotating chair and Ministerial Conference makes unclear the proper role of Eureka's officials, or what should be 'their part of the bargain'.

Eureka's lack of central direction or objectives recalls earlier debates about the role of the secretariat. The secretariat is purely functional, providing operational support to the chairmanship and acting as a central source of information on Eureka's projects. A Danish official explained:

> The idea [is that] you have the chairmanship to carry on the policy of Eureka whereas the project list should be taken care of by the secretariat. Another way of handling of this, of course, would've been to make the permanent secretariat in Brussels also the secretariat for the chair. But quite clearly in London [in 1986] several countries were strictly against that idea, and the idea of giving them responsibility for policy . . . The secretariat probably would like to get more into the policy of Eureka. It would be easier for them because they are at the centre of the whole thing and have a unique perspective on it.[67]

The comment is typical of calls for a more powerful secretariat that have continued to surface, especially from smaller Eureka Member States. As a member of the secretariat put it, 'The small countries have no power within Eureka anyway . . . So it would be in their interests to have more power located at the secretariat, rather than at the level of single large states'.[68] Officials from larger Member States admit:

> There's inevitably a tension between national administrations about what the secretariat should be doing . . . [For] a country like the UK, which has this massive HMG administration, with press offices and information divisions and line divisions, the use we can make of the secretariat is fairly small. We just don't need it. It was born in controversy: large countries couldn't see why we even needed a secretariat, and the small countries did.[69]

The controversy was compounded by Member States' early experience with the secretariat. Eureka's intergovernmental ethos applies very strictly to the secretariat: its officials are seconded from national ministries for four years and the secretariat has no internal administrative hierarchy. With all of its members equal in terms of executive status, charges surfaced that the secretariat was poorly managed between 1986 and 1990. Several of its members openly admitted that they were working to serve the interests of their home country while working for the secretariat, despite clear provisions that each should 'act in the interests of the Eureka membership as a whole'.[70] Others clearly overstepped their authority by accepting invitations without HLG authorization to travel to New York and São Paulo to explain rules for participation in Eureka by non-Member States.[71]

Proposals to link the secretariat and chairmanship more closely occasionally have surfaced. But, as a member of the post-1990 secretariat explained,

Then we are talking about human nature and jealousy . . . If you are after power, you grab every possibility to get it without telling anybody so you cannot be stopped. Maybe the previous crew did so and ran into difficulties, which is why stupid rules were made for the secretariat. If the understanding is not there from the outset, then the states become suspicious and make stronger rules than are really necessary.[72]

While the secretariat is responsible for maintaining a central database on Eureka projects, it may not approach participants directly to seek information on project costs or objectives: any information compiled on projects must come from national Eureka offices. Thus, as a Commission official observed, the secretariat often can make only educated guesses about what stage projects have reached:

The secretariat has said there's a certain percentage of projects which are near their conclusion. But that's only a calculation, because their information is so unreliable . . . The problem is that no one knows when any project really starts. They know when it's been announced, but they don't know when it really starts.[73]

In practice, responsibility for compiling information on Eureka's projects has been shared by the secretariat, rotating chairmanships and national offices. At times, the system has produced the sort of results common to games of 'Chinese whispers'. For example, the secretariat issued figures at the 1988 Ministerial Conference which indicated that 187 of 565 industrial firms involved in Eureka were SMEs. Yet, the conference's communiqué claimed that 'some 50 per cent of the industrial participants [in Eureka] are SMEs'.[74] The total value of 214 confirmed projects in 1988 was estimated by the Danish chairmanship at 3.8 billion ECU.[75] Less than a year later, the secretariat issued figures which inexplicably estimated the total value of 208 projects at 4.9 billion ECU.[76]

Few involved in Eureka would argue that the negotiations of 1985–86 yielded a set of institutional arrangements which provided for effective policy leadership or information-gathering. After 1986, the HLG was placed 'in charge of general policy matters'.[77] But its members typically are senior civil servants who spent 'perhaps five to ten per cent of their time working on Eureka'.[78] National chairmanships have launched initiatives based on their own policy agendas which have tended to yield very little. The secretariat remains, at best, small and purely functional, and, at worst, weak and badly run. Eureka was meant to be flexible and non-bureaucratic. In practice, it often appears to be ill-organized and lacking clear lines of authority. The strict intergovernmental ethos of Eureka clearly has had unintended consequences.

III. THE PROJECTS: THE 'GLORY OF NON-HARMONIZATION'

Eureka's bare minimum of compulsory rules of process is particularly evident at the project level. When a project proposal is officially granted Eureka status at a ministerial conference, it does not mean that R & D necessarily begins at that point. Most Eureka projects go through two designated stages. During a 'definition phase', partners negotiate a collaborative agreement, determine work and finance-sharing arrangements, set up a management system, negotiate rights to exploitation and so on. When agreement on these particulars is secured, the 'implementation' or actual R & D phase begins, and normally work begins on constructing a prototype.

Eureka officials provide conflicting information on how long definition phases typically last. One official suggested that a two-year definition phase was 'not uncommon',[79] while another responded, 'that's far longer than most require'.[80] In late 1989, a British official went as far as to say, 'There are, what, 297 projects? I couldn't tell you how many have actually been started. I should be surprised if it's more than 200'.[81] A Danish official responded 'I don't think we've granted status to any projects that aren't in operation and don't understand how anyone could claim that many project haven't started'.[82] Regardless of who was right, the point is that Eureka status may be granted to partners who merely have agreed to discuss the *possibility* of collaboration on a specific project.

Granting Eureka status means different things for different Member States. For some, it means that partners should pool resources and conduct R & D as if they were one organization. But significantly, the Declaration of Principles states that Eureka's aim is simply to promote 'closer cooperation' between research organizations.[83] A British official commented:

> I would say there's a very strong difference between collaboration and cooperation. In many Eureka projects, the degree of collaboration I think you can say is open to doubt . . . Essentially, it is a national R & D activity taken in tandem with somebody else's. The timescales may be completely different, the objectives may be completely different, but there is some degree of cooperation. It could be expressed in a letter: 'we agree to share results with you' or 'swap experiences every six months'. It's as minimal as that. But from our viewpoint, we want

to see a far clearer degree of collaboration because we are funding only collaborative projects, whereas other countries are funding single-company support or they're funding that R & D activity through national programmes anyway.[84]

The lack of agreed criteria for determining when a proposal deserves Eureka status has led to concerns about the uneven quality of Eureka's projects. NPCs are fully responsible for technology assessment of project proposals. Ensuring that only high-quality proposals are approved logically requires effective communication between NPCs.

As often is the case in evaluating Eureka as a whole, broad generalizations about the assessment of proposals are difficult to make. Technology assessment appears to be quite rigorous within several umbrella projects, particularly Famos.[85] Eight countries use outside experts to evaluate proposals, although only the Dutch Eureka office, which requires that all proposals be independently vetted by Arthur Andersen Consultants, and Switzerland, which requires that proposals be vetted by at least two outside experts, appear to do so systematically.[86] No public funding may be released to British Eureka participants unless their proposal has undergone a notoriously rigorous 'ROAM' evaluation.[87] In several Member States, the perception persists that Eureka provides a more rigorous method than the EC's programmes for ensuring that subsidies for collaborative R & D are spent wisely. The British attitude is particularly strident on this point:

> Eureka's a different kind of mechanism altogether. It's not there just to channel public sector money into industry . . . I get quite a few customers who come to me who have failed with an Esprit proposal and they look at Eureka as an alternative. When I put them through the test and when they try to go through Eureka procedures, their proposal falls apart. And the reason it falls apart is that the motivation was to get some cheap money, whereas the motivation for Eureka has to be something entirely different. In fact, I would say one of the strengths of Eureka is, because it's decentralized and it's not purely a funding mechanism, it means that proposals are put to a real test . . . And that produces a kind of natural sieve that only quality proposals get through. By quality I mean projects that partners are committed to at all the various levels.[88]

Yet, by the author's own count, fifty-six projects approved for Eureka status between 1985 and 1989 eventually were withdrawn from the project list. As this figure represents nearly one out of six Eureka projects that were approved during the period, the claim that Eureka acts as a 'natural sieve' which grants status only to 'quality proposals' must be viewed sceptically.

In response to widespread dissatisfaction throughout the Eureka network about project quality, the HLG convened a group in 1988, chaired by the British delegate, Alistair Keddie, to make recommendations on more effective project assessment and follow-up.[89] The 'Keddie Group' sought to determine what could be done to ensure that more projects succeeded, that existing projects were closely monitored, and that more transparency on national public funding criteria was achieved. A principal member of the Keddie Group commented:

> It was a general recognition that there probably wasn't enough clarity or transparency, to use the jargon, amongst NPCs as to what their policies were and what they were trying to achieve. And in particular in the sort of information being communicated both to and from the secretariat, and between NPCs and sometimes between NPCs and participants. Eureka is very much a federated structure and a very loose one at that. So there's ample scope for a lot of pretty loose information or simply no information. So the job of the Keddie group was essentially to define how the NPCs might go about doing their job better, but done in terms of guidelines on how NPCs should go about doing their jobs. They're not requirements simply because (A) there is no central executive, and (B) each country will put in whatever it feels is appropriate for what it wants out of Eureka. That's a fact of life.[90]

The Keddie Group recommendations did appear to result in informal commitments by NPCs to strive for closer coordination of the timing of public funding decisions. But the idea of jointly conducting technology assessment was not discussed. Eureka's intergovernmental structure meant that acceptance of the Keddie Group's recommendations was purely voluntary. A Commission official commented:

> The problem is the same. There is no common evaluation of the projects and that will not change . . . There have been discussions about harmonization of procedures, but we didn't discuss it very long because for the Greeks and Portuguese hi-tech projects are not the same as for the British or German. They must keep the flexibility of considering what is hi-tech for them.[91]

In short, there are no agreed criteria for project approval, nor any objective reasons to deny a project Eureka status. A Commission official's claim that 'It is impossible to refuse any proposal for a Eureka project'[92] seems only a mild exaggeration.

Moreover, a report by the Finnish chairmanship of 1991–92 pointed soberly to 'an apparent lack of evaluation and follow-up of the projects as a whole'.[93] With such loose provisions for technology assessment, the credibility of the ECU values placed on Eureka's projects is subject to question. Essentially, project partners themselves arrive at these figures. By their very nature, the costs of R & D are always subject to much uncertainty. Engaging in R & D as a collaborative venture makes cost estimates even more speculative. But as projects approved for Eureka status are often merely agreements to share results or discuss collaboration, cost estimates may be wild guesses. A Scandinavian Eureka official cautioned:

> I would be very careful with the figures . . . We have one project, for example, with an estimated cost of 1 billion kronor. But first of all, the manufacturers have not committed themselves for the whole project. Secondly, we don't know if it will be carried through to a conclusion.[94]

One reason why restrictions were placed on the ability of the secretariat to approach project partners directly appeared to be the secretariat's propensity to issue inflated figures on project costs early in Eureka's life span. A Danish official admitted, 'I personally don't place much faith in the numbers because they [the secretariat] have an interest in the budget not being too low'.[95]

As for public funding, Eureka NPC's are prone to providing eloquent and entirely logical explications of their own government's philosophy, then admitting that national policies vary significantly. A Dutch Eureka official's comments are indicative:

> We promise each other as governments to give our companies seed money on the projects. So we finance the first phases of the project . . . But our philosophy is that Eureka projects should be market-led, and once the project has found a market, it has to finance itself. And I think that philosophy is adopted by, well, nearly 60 per cent of the Eureka membership.[96]

A British official claims, 'as for the countries with the most projects, their rates of support, their conditions for support and so on are broadly similar'.[97] But even this degree of uniformity among Eureka's large states seems overstated. Nearly all projects involving French partners receive some sort of public support from France.[98] Exactly half of eighty-six projects involving UK partners in 1989 received public funding.[99] Yet, twenty-seven of thirty-three German projects announced in 1989 were 100 per cent financed by the private sector.[100]

When the German Research Minister Riesenhuber asked the BMFT in 1988 for details on public support given to Eureka projects by each Member State, the inevitable response was that such information simply did not exist. A member of the Keddie Group observed:

> Countries like Germany are interested in getting a bit more clarity about what's going on ... What they were really getting at was, even if it has to be done on a confidential basis bilaterally, is a greater degree of clarity as to if governments are committing money, when they're doing it, under what conditions and how much for how long.[101]

Even after the Keddie Group recommendations were endorsed by the HLG in 1988, several Eureka officials expressed doubts about whether this new commitment to transparency would in practice make much difference. A member of the secretariat predicted, 'On funding, you will never have transparency. We run the central database and Riesenhuber asked me as well and I couldn't tell him'.[102]

The general problem of funding has led to repeated discussions at an intergovernmental level about attracting private finance to Eureka projects. Obviously, the more that Eureka acts as a 'magnet' for private finance and yields projects which are mostly or entirely funded by private sources, the less that differing funding policies and priorities between Member States matter. The Spanish chairmanship of 1986–87 sponsored a study of Eureka's projects by the European Bankers Round Table, a group of executives from leading European financial institutions, to assess the suitability of individual projects for private funding. The Round Table commended Eureka in broad, rhetorical terms, but urged that 'in the selection process as applied to Eureka project proposals, more emphasis [should] be placed on the estimated future economic potential of projects, which have a commercial perspective'.[103] Strikingly, the report concluded that only 11 per cent of all Eureka projects were likely to generate a commercially viable product – and thus attract private funding – in the near future. More than half (55 per cent) were viewed as having long-term commercial prospects, while 34 per cent by their nature were unsuitable for private investment.[104]

The report was a public relations disaster for Eureka. It legitimized the view of critics who suggested that the initiative had generated few high-quality projects and was merely an exercise in symbolic politics. Many Eureka officials claimed that the report simply showed that European banks were ignorant about the opportunities offered by collaborative R & D. A British official's comments were typical:

> The basic idea was that if this bloody thing got Eureka status that would trigger bankers' euphoria to throw money at it. An awful lot of

people got upset. I think it was [particularly] the Deustchebank that looked at these projects and said, 'well, we don't want to fund them.' Basically it was just a judgment that most of these f..ing projects aren't a normal bank's business.[105]

A Dutch official argued that the exercise was useful because:

At the start of this [Spanish] presidency, we were very ambitious to create a mix between public and private financing in projects based close to the market. Well, that was very ambitious, but what we gained is that we at least know where and when the technology and projects are . . . [But] the main problem, I think . . . is that our banks are trade banks, and not industrial or technology financiers.[106]

Sponsoring such an analysis of the commercial potential of Eureka's projects when a majority of projects were still in their definition phases was premature, if not ill-judged. However, it did give an indication of how intractable is the problem of insufficient venture capital formation and investment in Europe as compared to the USA and Japan. Eureka's creators clearly overestimated the initiative's appeal to venture capitalists, who generally invest in companies, not R & D projects. A British official summed up the episode succinctly: 'Public relations disaster? Possibly, given the general ignorance of what Eureka's supposed to be. But I thought it served a useful purpose in that it stopped a lot of b.s. about attracting money to Eureka'.[107]

The problem of securing funding is at the root of one of Eureka's most intractable problems: delays in project schedules after they are approved. A common complaint of industrialists is that the lack of common public funding policies between Member States and the use of so many different national funds and agencies to support Eureka projects inevitably delays the delivery of funding. Generally, the more Member States involved in a project, the greater the scope for delays and the more likely that participants will see their project fall off schedule. A British official observed:

Funding decisions often have different timescales. I've got cases where the Italians have taken a funding decision for five years, whereas we've only taken one for eighteen months, then we're going to review it. The French practice is only to offer funding for the financial year, with a comfort letter, if you like, saying provided the money's there, you'll get it the following year . . . I've got projects where in theory a commitment was made to release funding three years ago. But no money's been forthcoming. For any number of reasons: bureaucratic delays, cock-ups . . . [108]

The relationship between Eureka status and public funding varies between Member States. Some, such as Denmark, will provide funding to a project even before it is considered for Eureka status. Others, including France, make decisions on granting Eureka status and providing funding at the same time. Meanwhile Italy will not even consider an application for public funding until Eureka status has been granted.[109]

After 1990, the HLG was given the ability to 'notify' Eureka projects at four intervals in each year, thus making it possible for projects to be funded even before formal approval by the ministerial conference. Yet, a Commission official commented:

> In some countries, they can give finance after notification at the HLG. In others, they have to wait for the ministers' approval. But in any case, it takes a long time to get finance in general . . . a minimum of six months, according to the participants I've talked to.[110]

These delays and discrepancies clearly make planning a collaborative project difficult for industrial participants. A UK official wearily termed them 'part of the glory of the lack of harmonization within Eureka'.[111]

While policies on public funding remain distinctly nationalized, Eureka is meant to provide scope for collective action on supportive measures: encouraging the definition of new norms and standards, eliminating fragmented markets for the results of Eureka projects, and opening up public procurement markets. Eureka officials admit that 'the concept is unavoidably abstract'.[112] But, as a British official explains:

> The idea is to ensure that participants in projects begin to address standards or regulatory issues early enough in a project's life. The usual thing is, 'until the project's completed, we can't tell you what we need'. By that time, it's too late. It usually takes two or three years to implement the standards and by that time the Japanese have gotten in the door, taken the profits and moved onto the next project. What we're trying to do is to get participants to focus on standards earlier than they normally do.[113]

Declarations emanating from Ministerial Conferences continually urge that top priority be given to supportive measures. At this level, Eureka has contributed to the mobilization of political support for the 'MAC' standard developed within the HDTV Eureka project as a world standard (see Chapter 7). Within Prometheus, the Eureka Road Transport Monitoring Group was formed to develop standards for an enabling infrastructure related to the 'clever car.' The Dutch Eureka office published guidelines on European health and safety regulations related to products which are expected to emerge from the Eurolaser umbrella project.[114] Links have been established between the Eureka network and CEN/CENELEC, the European Normalization Committee, with goal of prioritizing standards which, if established, may open markets for Eureka products.[115]

However, Eureka has produced notably few success stories related to supportive measures. One problem is that most supportive measures, especially those related to different national regulatory regimes or public procurement, are primary concerns for the EC. It is difficult to imagine that many Eureka initiatives in these areas will get very far without the active support of the Commission. The fragile state of EC–Eureka relations, detailed in Chapter 5, has not proved conducive to concerted action on supportive measures.

A separate problem is that even within single Eureka projects, partners often disagree about how standards-setting should proceed. A British official illustrates:

> Participants are often divided about the sort of supportive measures they need. Many projects have a standards element of some sort, and of course each of the participants probably favours his own standard, and probably that standard reflects national practice or custom. Trying to get them to agree on a joint line or interest is extremely difficult.[116]

About 100 projects in Eureka's history have yielded requests for supportive measures, with most related to standardization. But few requests have been taken up at an international level within Eureka, which indicates that national delegations still tend to approach standards issues in a purely national context.[117] Eureka's strict intergovernmental ethos and structure does little to make easier negotiation of conflicts over standards – or any other type of conflict between Member States or project partners – at a political level.

IV. THE QUESTION OF ADDED VALUE

The closer one studies Eureka, the more complex and elusive the initiative becomes. In particular, the question of what added value Eureka status provides to individual projects persists. It may be a method for securing public funding, but national funding provisions are disharmonized and uneven and can cause delays in project schedules. Eureka may provide participants with an intergovernmental commitment to action which can expand markets for project results, but Eureka's provisions for supportive measures have yielded few concrete results. If firms want firm funding commitments or market-opening assistance, participation in EC-funded R & D would seem to be a preferred route on *a priori* grounds.

Moreover, since collaboration across frontiers by nature implies costs in terms of time, travel, communications and so on, industrialists might logically conclude that Eureka is not worth the time and trouble, especially if funding is available for single-firm R & D or collaboration on a purely national basis. As a Commission official put it, 'Eureka is, after all, only a label'.[118] The response of a British official to the persistent question of what Eureka status really gives a collaborative project, is germane:

> In a hard sense, the answer is nothing. It may convey money in the sense that if in fact participants genuinely need money to develop a technological idea, it may be one of the few avenues open in Europe for getting that money ... The other thing is, by having Eureka status, it gives them a voice in Europe, through the network of NPCs, through the High Level Group, and ultimately through the ministers they otherwise may not be able to have. That's primarily on the standards and regulatory side. It may be very tenuous, I'll admit that.[119]

It is difficult to resist the conclusion that Eureka's added value is clearer for its Member State governments than for its industrial participants. Eureka's lack of any overall strategic goal and minimal rules allow Member States to support collaborative R & D which may suit national policy goals, even if the projects do not fit with the EC's innovation policy agenda. A British official argues:

> The real added value of Eureka is freedom to negotiate your own contract, with less constraints that come from some overall EC strategy. In policy terms, that actually means that you should get projects that have added value over EC R & D, since they're not constrained by EC R & D parameters. So you should be seeing bigger projects, or projects that are nearer to the market, or projects which don't fit EC R & D ... From the national viewpoint, there may be Eureka projects that are worth doing in the national interest, but which aren't worth doing in the pan-European interest. Projects between Greece and Portugal with the UK involved may well be of benefit in the view of all three governments, but not necessarily in the view of the Commission.[120]

Eureka holds appeal for its Member States simply because it provides them with a degree of control over collaborative R & D. The multi-faceted logic of collaborative R & D detailed in Chapter 1 does not mean that governments are prepared to cede responsibility for organizing collaborative R & D initiatives entirely to the Commission. Eureka officials are prone to comparing Eureka with EC programmes, with distaste for the Community's methodology a thinly veiled undercurrent:

> Essentially, from a client's viewpoint, he couldn't give a s..t which of these programmes the project goes in as long as he gets his money. It's basically a question of how much he's going to get, and he'll dress up his project to fit the bill. He'll go and find a Greek university or a Portuguese small firm. But we know all those tricks. Which is why I like Eureka so much, and is why I think it's better value for money at the end of the day.[121]

Eureka provides national ministries with decision-making power and a 'piece of the action' in determining how resources are distributed for collaborative R & D. Eureka's added value for its Member State governments may have as much to do with political control and ideology as enhancing the general competitiveness of European technology-intensive industries. This point helps explain why Eureka's structure provides so little scope for collective action. While the ministerial conference as a whole continues to formally approve projects for Eureka status, projects merely represent intergovernmental agreements between national Eureka offices. No project has ever been refused at a ministerial conference, which now appears mainly designed to attract publicity to Eureka. Procedures for project approval agreed at the London ministerial conference in 1986 set strict limits on the degree to which Member States may challenge each others' decisions to grant Eureka status to any project:

> A Eureka government, or the European Commission, may seek discussion of a project or proposal if it considers that questions arise . . . which merit discussion by the High Level Group as a whole. Such discussions will not call into question the attribution of the Eureka status to a project or proposal.[122]

Thus, while any government may query any proposal, several Eureka officials confirmed that such queries are extremely rare.[123] Obviously, if only a few of the more than 500 projects approved after 1985 were questioned in this manner, there is little actual debate about whether a project is legitimate outside of informal bilateral or multilateral discussions between national Eureka offices.

Proposals to increase Eureka's provisions for collective action – such as those from smaller Member States to empower the secretariat – have not got very far. Yet, consensus has developed over time on the need for Eureka to be more selective and yield more 'quality projects' instead of simply approving any proposal which brings together actors in two or more Member States. For example, a private study commissioned by the French government in late 1989 urged that proposals be assessed more rigorously to eliminate those which are 'very vague' and contain 'alibi partners'.[124] The central conclusion of an evaluation of the project list undertaken during the Dutch chairmanship of 1991 was that Member States needed 'to put more emphasis on project quality', particularly by requiring each project proposal to include a business plan which sets out 'concrete objectives and milestones'.[125]

Moreover, the Medium-Term Plan produced commitments to improve information collection and eliminate discontinuity in the activities of successive chairmanships. Mimicking the arrangements used by the EC's European Political Cooperation mechanism, the HLG in 1988 formed a 'troika' of representatives from successive chairmanships to study ideas for developing more effective documentation procedures and more continuity between chairs. In 1990, the Eureka database was 'rationalized', with new validation procedures implemented to ensure that project cost estimates were not wildly inaccurate. The Finnish chairmanship of 1991–92 issued a report on 'finished and withdrawn' projects which poured scorn on the 'very arbitrary and inconsistent' data compiled by Member States about when and why projects were dropped from the project list.[126]

Thus, in the absence of any wholesale restructuring of the way Eureka operates, the initiative will always rely on informal trust and relationships between NPCs where one might expect to find formal rules and procedures. One British official said of the Keddie Group exercise, 'Basically, all we can hope for is that the NPCs work together, trust one another'.[127] The troika system still depends on voluntary, informal agreements between successive chairmanships to ensure that there is continuity between their policy initiatives. Since Eureka is merely an extension of national innovation policies, it is only natural that Member States use the chairmanship as a platform to push for collective pursuit of national policy goals. Asked if the Medium-Term Plan had resulted in more continuity between successive chairmanships' policy initiatives, a member of the secretariat responded, 'Would you be so kind as to ask the chairs? I'll take the fifth amendment'.[128]

At an operational level, Eureka relies heavily on informal communication between NPCs. The ability of this system to ensure that only quality proposals are approved and funding decisions are as synchronized as possible is put into question by the relatively large number of projects which either 'disappear' after announcement or take years to pass from definition to implementation. These problems may be viewed as an inevitable result of the unwillingness of Member States to harmonize or at least synchronize their technology assessment or funding policies.

Eureka was meant to form a departure from the post-war 'chicken game' of seeking to provide minimum public subsidies to domestic firms while still maintaining maximum national competitiveness *vis-à-vis* other European states. It now appears that an entirely new sort of chicken game often occurs within Eureka. Member States have incentives to try to ensure that maximum support is provided by other governments to any project involving their indigenous firms so that national expense can be minimized. Moreover, Eureka officials acknowledge that competition exists between Member States to ensure that, for political reasons, a sufficient number of projects involving their home firms are approved at each ministerial conference. A British official explained:

> In dealing with applicants, you'll be told 'the other government's already done it' or 'there's more money coming from the other governments than from ours' and so forth . . . So I come under pressure, particularly in bilateral projects. It's a game I resist very strongly, but at every ministerial conference there's obviously a temptation to try to maximize your numbers . . . I often get a lot of pressure from other countries involved to agree to give Eureka status to projects that I have reservations about. If I've got no real reason to say no, what the hell do I do?[129]

Another official responded, 'If there's no real reason to say yes, why should you support it? But I can see the pressure. Especially if funding is only realized after a project receives ministerial approval, that pressure is very real'.[130]

Ironically, Eureka's creation was motivated in part by the perceived need for Europe to respond to Japan's centralized, mission-oriented innovation policy initiatives. In theory, Eureka should serve a set of goals upon which wide consensus developed in Europe in the mid-1980s: weaning private firms from dependence on public support, exploiting the internal market, building bridges between Europe's public and private R & D efforts, organizing large, strategic projects which no European state could fund on its own, and so on. Yet, widely divergent innovation policy goals and political objectives make Eureka's 'mission' unclear.

Moreover, Eureka's catch-all nature blurs its image within European industry. Pre-competitive, infrastructure projects contradict the idea that it exists specifically to promote market-led R & D. Eureka's image is a collective good for Member States, especially since the initiative depends so heavily on industry to set its agenda. The Medium-Term Plan stresses the necessity of establishing a 'distinct identity of the Eureka initiative in the European scientific and technological community',[131] and acknowledges that maintaining a positive image of Eureka is critical to generating quality projects.

A favourable image requires that Eureka be selective and only incorporate 'quality projects,' which in turn would logically require rigorous and common technology assessment procedures of a kind that do not presently exist. The meaning of the Eureka label is so vague and procedures so loose that it is understandable that industrialists would propose poor quality projects merely for the publicity or public funding benefits. Conversely, those with high-quality proposals might reckon that participation in Eureka provides no clear added value to their project.

Part of Eureka's image problem is rooted in the propensity for governments to use it as a tool of political symbolism as well as innovation policy. For example, after environmental projects accounted for only 7 per cent of Eureka's total in 1987, the Vienna ministerial conference of 1989 approved more projects in this sector (nearly 25 per cent of the total) than in any other.[132] Eureka officials admitted that the upsurge was not unrelated to the rise of environmental issues to the top of many national European political agendas in 1989, when the British Greens shocked the Thatcher government by polling 15 per cent in EP elections and the Dutch government collapsed amid disputes over a controversial environmental protection plan.[133]

More generally, Eureka reveals quite starkly the gap between political rhetoric on the need for European innovation policies to pursue collective goals and the persistence of purely nationalist aspirations. Eureka seeks to promote collective action on the part of its Member States and industrial participants, but the structures created to manage and administer Eureka provide little scope for such action. The comments of a British official imply that any collective effort to make Eureka operate more effectively is doomed to failure: 'If we tried to decide on an overall collective direction, a blueprint for where we want to be by a certain time, there'd be no central authority to ensure that it would be happen, even if we decided it's what we should do'.[134]

5 Eureka and the European Community

Eureka's success depends on its relationship with the EC as much as on any other single factor. As a member of the Eureka secretariat argues, 'The power of the Commission is so great that if the Commission really decided to kill Eureka, it could do it. The Commission's machinery is a steam locomotive against the little toy of Eureka when it comes to administrative power'.[1]

This chapter considers all sides of the complex relationship between the EC and Eureka. Section I begins by sketching the evolution of EC–Eureka relations after 1985. Section II assesses the Commission's role as a Eureka 'Member State'. The implications of the 1992 project for Eureka are the focus for Section III. Section IV isolates Eureka's role in the 'Europeanization' of national innovation policies, and considers the implications of the parallel development of Eureka and the Framework programme for government-industry relations in Europe.

I. THE POLITICS OF INSTITUTIONAL JEALOUSY

The political agendas of the Commission and the French governments were clearly at odds when Eureka emerged in 1985. The Commission had encouraged European industry to consider its collective interest in new collaborative R & D programmes beginning in the early 1980s and joined them in lobbying EC governments to create them. Ironically, the Davignon initiatives created the preconditions needed for the French to rally industry and national governments to support Eureka. The French proposal not only distracted public and private attention from the Commission's own blueprint for the first Framework programme. Eureka also challenged the Commission's role as a federative agent for a common European innovation policy.

Key EC Member States – including Germany and the UK – agreed with the French that Eureka should exist independently of the EC. At the same time, all realized that Eureka required some type of formal link with the Commission to ensure that it did not duplicate EC-funded R & D or work at cross-purposes to the 1992 project. After Delors' initial urgings that Eureka be launched as an EC programme, the Commission shifted to stressing the importance of synergy between national and pan-European R & D efforts in a memorandum submitted to the Milan European summit in June 1985:

> Just as it is neither possible nor necessary to bring everything under the Community umbrella, so it would be just as inappropriate to confine the Community's efforts to the portion of public R & D expenditure which it finances from its own resources, even though that portion is to be substantially expanded.[2]

The European Parliament (EP) did not give up the fight to bring Eureka within the EC as quickly as the Commission did. For example, the President of the EP's R & D committee – Michel Poniatowski – continued to argue for a Commission-based task force to run Eureka even after the Milan summit.[3] But the idea was rejected narrowly by the EP in 1986.[4] In the event, the Commission encouraged the compromise by which it was attached to Eureka as an extra 'Member State' by agreeing to contribute the same as France, Germany, Italy and the UK toward funding the secretariat's administrative costs.[5]

After a year of generally ambiguous statements on Eureka, the Commission sought to clarify its position in a communication to the EC Council of R & D ministers in November 1986. It proposed a number of paths toward strengthening EC–Eureka links, but stressed that Eureka duplicated much R & D funded through Framework and threatened to violate EC rules on state aids to industry.[6] A follow-up statement in 1988 urged that 'the time is now ripe to go further' in strengthening cooperation between the EC and Eureka. However, the Commission also ruled out the use of EC funds to support Eureka projects 'that require major public financial support'.[7]

Narjes' statements on Eureka throughout the period ranged from lukewarm to decidedly negative. At Eureka's 1987 ministerial conference in Madrid, he warned that, 'the more market-oriented the publicly funded research and technological development . . . the greater the risk of a distorting effect on competition'.[8] A year later in Copenhagen, Narjes told Eureka ministers that 'the Commission is obliged by the Rome Treaty to assure neutrality of competition in research support, not only for national and Community research but also for Eureka, which by its nature is more exposed to this problem'. Narjes' insistence that the Commission had 'supported Eureka actively from the outset' appeared designed to counter widespread criticism that it had not.[9]

Meanwhile, the UK Minister Kenneth Clarke complained:

> I don't think we are totally satisfied with the synergy between Eureka and what the Commission is doing. The Germans are equally worried about all this as much as we are. Riesenhuber made a thing about it this morning. There were repeated requests to Vice-President Narjes to be more forthcoming, to acknowledge the role of Eureka, for example in standards-setting, to take more notice of what's coming out of Eureka projects . . . I hope we're steadily persuading Karl-Heinz Narjes that Eureka's not a threat to re-nationalize R & D, or any threat to his Framework programme, but rather something with which the Commission can reasonably work.[10]

After the Copenhagen conference, the German presidency of the EC, with support from France and Denmark, urged the Commission to more actively support Eureka projects which 'serve[d] the interests of the Community as a whole'.[11] However, the UK, the Netherlands and others insisted that a clear distinction to be maintained between Eureka and the EC's programmes to avoid 'bureaucratizing' Eureka. The Commission itself appeared split on the issue, with Delors supporting stronger EC links to Eureka and Narjes insisting, 'We don't want to get involved in the gray area too near the market'.[12]

Throughout this period, Commission officials were often scathingly critical of Eureka in private. One described Eureka's Declaration of Principles as a 'public show, [with] some generalities like "be kind to dogs and old women", with no more content than that'.[13] In 1987, a Commission delegate to Eureka's HLG reflected:

> Maybe our position on Eureka seems negative, and maybe that's because our programmes are showing results. We know how they're progressing and what their problems are and how we can do better. But they're working. Eureka is working just at the political level . . . So for us, Eureka is not a plus, it's a zero.[14]

Calls for the Commission to contribute more funding to Eureka usually were met with the response that the Framework programme itself was underfunded:

> Within the existing restricted financial ceiling . . . the Commission is unable to participate financially in more then [sic] 15–20 per cent of the proposals made to it. Moreover, the percentage is falling, with the Commission having to reject an increasing number of good proposals. The scope for financing Eureka projects in this way is

therefore not large. The real solution is to increase the budget available for the Community programmes.[15]

In interviews, EC officials commonly expressed the belief that many Eureka projects were 'rejects', or second-rate projects which had been refused by the EC: 'A measure of the success of our programmes, such as Esprit, is that we have to reject seven of eight proposals ... Often, fifty or so rejected proposals then end up going to Eureka. That's fine with us, but what does this say about Eureka?'[16]

An official involved in one of Eureka's early chairmanships suggested, 'The Commission sometimes seems jealous of the political momentum behind Eureka, I guess because it somewhat dilutes political support for their own programmes'.[17] Asked if this was true, one Commission official responded:

> I must say certainly not. It's a crazy assertion. Why would we be jealous? Maybe some people in the EC would like to manage it, but that doesn't mean they're jealous ... At the last meeting [of the HLG in Vienna], it was said several times by several different Member States that the initial objectives of Eureka have not been met up to now. You cannot be jealous of that ... I would say the contrary, that the Eureka coordinators are a bit jealous of the Community programmes.[18]

Another Commission official admitted that jealousy existed:

> But this is at a basic human level. I don't know that that really has a very lasting effect. What was far more severe was the idea that this is no longer necessarily pre-competitive R & D. Although there is in practice a lot of pre-competitive R & D within Eureka, the way it was going to fit with EC competition policy was not very clear.[19]

In 1988, Narjes was replaced as R & D Commissioner by Filippo Maria Pandolfi. Many Eureka officials and industrialists agreed that EC–Eureka relations improved almost immediately.[20] Since its origins, the development of the Framework programme had been directed and overseen personally by Narjes, and his own view of Eureka had been conditioned by the high political profile it achieved at a time when the Framework programme's budget was first blocked and then cut significantly in 1986–87. Complaints by Eureka ministers about the Commission's lack of support for Eureka (such as Clarke's above) often seemed directed at Narjes personally.

However, other factors were at play in the Commission's new attitude. By early 1989, 214 projects had achieved Eureka status, indicating that whatever the Commission's view of Eureka, a wide cross-section of

European industry had embraced the scheme. Eureka and the EC's programmes had co-existed for nearly four years and European industry appeared enthusiastic about both.

Moreover, the Framework programme had evolved considerably over this period. While the Commission stressed that the majority of its appropriations under Framework (1987–91) were designed to 'improve industrial competitiveness', it equally insisted that all the R & D it funded was strictly pre-competitive and subject to 'high technical and financial risks and uncertainties about the eventual practical applications'.[21] However, Commission proposals for the Framework III programme in 1989 clearly implied that the programme would embrace more industrial R & D and apply the principle of funding only pre-competitive R & D less literally. Pandolfi stressed that a 'new and essential feature' of Framework III would be its emphasis on developing 'appropriate cooperation mechanisms with Eureka'.[22]

II. THE COMMISSION AS 'MEMBER STATE'

The impact of the shift in Commission attitudes toward Eureka can be overestimated. One official conceded that the Commission attitude became 'much more positive than it was in '86 . . . But in reality, in terms of concrete things, I don't see any difference . . . There are no new projects in which we are involved, except for those in which cooperation started under Narjes'.[23]

Even before 1989, the Commission provided funding to selected Eureka projects and provided logistical support such as setting up the Eureka central project database. Despite appearances, the Commission's approach to Eureka was in many respects highly pragmatic. It associated itself with particular Eureka projects which appeared to hold the best prospects for success, while distancing itself from charges that Eureka was ill-organized, included many projects of dubious quality, and lacked any strategic goal.

The first Commission statement on Eureka in 1986 suggested that there were three essential ways in which the EC would support Eureka. First, the Commission would promote information exchange between Eureka and Framework project participants, extend supportive measures or fund the pre-competitive stages of selected Eureka projects. Second, the Commission proposed to monitor Eureka projects to ensure that duplication with its own R & D activities was minimized and synergy was maximized. Third, the Commission pledged to promote the development of legal, technical and commercial environments conducive to the successful exploitation of collaborative R & D.[24]

According to Eureka officials, early statements by the Commission indicated that if any Eureka subproject was funded through Brite or Esprit, then it had to be withdrawn from Eureka. The Commission later lifted this proviso, leading a member of the Eureka secretariat to claim, 'That is really a clear change'.[25] Most EC funding for Eureka projects has gone to large-scale, infrastructure projects, such as Cosine or Eurotrac (see Chapter 7). The Commission also has funded long-term, basic R & D into ASICs within Jessi, and three Esprit projects were approved in 1990 for this purpose.[26] At least three projects funded through the EC's 'Research in Advanced Communications for Europe' (Race) programme, with a total value of 16 million ECU, have sought to develop enabling technologies for the HDTV project.[27] Generally, however, the Commission has provided little direct funding to Eureka projects. As one official observed, there is still reticence within the Commission on *a priori* grounds about the idea of funding Eureka projects:

> What the Member States wanted from Narjes was for the Community to give them the money. But there is no point in giving Community money to national policies . . . Some delegations asked only that the Commission finance some projects, and I think that's the only solution, that the Commission finance some projects of Community interest.[28]

Pandolfi's influence may have been a factor in the EC's doubling of the number of projects in which it participates (to fourteen) in 1991. By 1992, the EC was a member of all Eureka umbrella projects except Famos, and even there the Commission claimed that it was closely involved.[29]

Yet, in theory the Commission's role as a 'Member State' of Eureka should be most pronounced in the area of supportive measures. Logically, attempts to create the 'enabling conditions' for a project's success which are 'beyond the capabilities and the influence of the project participants themselves'[30] will almost always necessitate Commission action. In standards-setting, the Commission offers advice and finance to Eureka participants for the development and transmission of 'mandates' (requests for action on standards) to the intergovernmental European standards organizations, CEN/CENELEC. Yet, by late 1990, CEN/CENELEC had not received a single mandate for standards action related to a Eureka project.[31] At that time, a Commission official complained:

> Most of the time, these requests are not precise enough. Up to now there have not been any precise requests because the projects aren't

advanced enough. These are only ideas of requests . . . So DG III in most cases has written letters to participants asking for more details. But partners are usually unable to give details at the beginning of the projects, especially when they're still negotiating what partners will do what work.[32]

Besides work on standards related to the HDTV project (see Chapter 7) and a contribution to the Dutch-led survey on hazards and safety regulations for Eurolaser, the Commission has taken little action on standards related to Eureka projects.

It may be argued that CEN/CENELEC's 'new approach' to European standards-setting, based on the mutual recognition of national standards, makes unnecessary conscious attempts to harmonize standards for technology-intensive products through initiatives such as Eureka. Yet Eureka's 'bottom-up' style may actually encourage partners to take existing 'patchwork' standards based on national custom for granted. In any event, as more projects move towards a conclusion, more Eureka participants can be expected to be able to identify where supportive measures on standards-setting are needed for 'Eureka products' to be marketed across Europe. This area is one where the Commission's more constructive approach to Eureka has real potential to synergize European efforts.

Another enabling condition required for many projects to be successful – the securing of private finance – has come to be seen as another type of supportive measure. Since the mid-1980s, the Commission has made it a general priority to expand, mobilize and 'Europeanize' national venture capital funds. For example, the EC has supported the development of the European Venture Capital Association (EVCA), a pan-European consortium of venture-capital firms. Proposed and approved Eureka projects are now circulated to all EVCA members and EVCA offers selected Eureka participants access to its database to spread awareness of which EVCA members are, for example, seeking to invest in biotechnology in Germany or micro-electronics in France.[33]

The Commission has also funded its own schemes – such as Venture Consort and Eurotech Capital – to 'pump-prime' private investments in SMEs involved in collaborative R & D programmes such as Eureka. However, the total value of such schemes has been modest: about 7 million ECU in 1987–90. The schemes also have been hampered by feuds between the Commission and EVCA, with the latter claiming that they are 'cut out' of decision making on funding.[34]

The European venture-capital industry grew considerably in the 1980s and EVCA predicted that the volume of venture capital in Europe would surpass that in the USA by 1993.[35] However, the amount of European venture capital invested in new technologies actually appeared to be declining by the early 1990s. Moreover, most venture capitalists continued to seek investments in seed capital or equity shares in start-up firms, as opposed to collaborative R & D projects. While the Commission urged that Eurotech Capital funds be invested 'preferably in SMEs undertaking transnational high-technology projects',[36] it admitted that investors 'generally won't invest in research projects'.[37]

The French Eureka office in 1988 proposed that another supportive measure which the Commission could usefully provide was 'risk insurance' to SMEs involved in Eureka. A French Eureka official explained, 'we thought if we could insure firms engaged in technological collaboration, there would be two effects: first, it would encourage firms to engage in more of these projects, and second, it would get banks more easily involved in the funding'.[38] Plans were tabled which called for the Commission to provide 25–30 per cent funding for a pilot risk insurance scheme.

According to one NPC, the French 'got nowhere with it'.[39] The plan attracted only lukewarm support from other Member States and very little interest from European insurance firms. The Commission itself was never enthusiastic about the idea of restricting such a scheme only to Eureka:

> There have been different ideas about what kind of insurance should be implemented, and the French and Commission ideas on this aren't exactly the same. We'd favour a more general scheme not confined to Eureka. The second question is: should there be public funding or not? . . . We think this kind of insurance should be handled by private insurance firms, not public bodies.[40]

The episode was reflective of a wider debate within Eureka about how much public bodies could do to encourage private financial institutions to invest in collaborative R & D. A principal in the Austrian chairmanship of 1990 argued, 'We tried to find ways to bring private finance to Eureka projects and there simply is no private money for R & D'.[41] Such statements may exaggerate the problem, but clearly Eureka itself has done little to compensate for the risk-averse outlook and nationalist orientation of private financiers in Europe. Moreover, the lack of precise information on the progress of Eureka projects does not help matters. As a Commission official grumbled:

> The problem in Eureka is that there is no reliable information about what stage the projects are in, because there's no follow-up. There's a follow-up at the national level when the projects are financed by

public finance, and the NPC in each country gets information on the progress on the part of the project that's realized in his country, but not necessarily the part realized in other countries.[42]

The Commission claimed that it was actively engaged in 'examining how to encourage the flow of private capital from the banking system and venture capital companies'[43] to Eureka. If so, there was little to show for it. More generally, Eureka's strict intergovernmentalism and the fragile state of EC–Eureka relations conspired to make progress on supportive measures minimal.

III. EUREKA AND THE 1992 PROJECT

The 1992 project already has had profound implications for the EC's industrial, innovation and external relations policies. The Commission has convinced Member States that the development of the internal market necessitates new EC rules or policies on competition, public procurement, business law and assistance to SMEs. The expansion of the Commission's role in these areas combined with the growth of the Framework programme means that the EC is developing an innovation policy of its own. Recent pressures from non-EC states to open up EC-funded R & D programmes to participation by firms domiciled outside the EC twelve have complicated the Commission's innovation policy mission.

The relationship between the 1992 project and effective collaborative R & D programmes is symbiotic. Nearly everything the EC does under the banner of the 1992 project has implications for Eureka. This section analyses developments in EC policy which have had direct effects.

Collaborative R & D and EC's industrial policy

The legal basis for an EC industrial policy – contained in articles 92 to 94 of the Treaty of Rome – is tenuous. National interests and ideologies often clash violently when Commission proposals refer to 'industrial policy considerations'. Delors made this point clear when he presented the Commission's programme for 1990 to the European Parliament and argued that the success of the Framework III programme crucially depended on the development of a 'more coherent, and I know many of you will shudder at this phrase, EC industrial policy'.[44] Yet, the implementation of the 1992 project – and its propensity to create economic losers as well as winners – has caused industrial policy considerations to seep into a wide range of EC policies for competition, public procurement, external trade and innovation.

The Commission's early suspicions that Eureka might be used to violate tougher restrictions on state aids to industry must be understood against the backdrop of the evolution of EC competition policy in the 1980s. The Commission clearly lost any effective control over national state aids to industry in the early 1980s, when annual levels for the EC as a whole topped 30 billion ECU.[45] The Commission's view, articulated loudly during debates on the SEA, was that heavy state aids slowed structural adjustment and yielded 'flabby', uncompetitive firms in technology-intensive industries. In setting out its position on state aids for R & D, the Commission argued that it was 'among the most significant distortions of competition' and that 'aid for R & D had become one of the largest, and in many Member States, *the* largest form of government support for industry'.[46]

The EC's new approach to state aids, reflected in the SEA, sought to encourage more collaborative R & D while vetting aids to purely national projects more aggressively. The Treaty of Rome's 'block exemption,' which allowed licensing agreements which restricted competition if they promoted 'technical or economic progress', was given more legal precision so that it could be applied more flexibly to aids for collaborative R & D. Meanwhile, the Commission warned that it would scrutinize state aids granted to exclusively national projects more closely.

The Commission insisted that it would 'exercise a general presumption in favour of . . . aid [to R & D] because of the contribution that R & D aid can make towards achieving Community goals'.[47] Yet, the Commission clearly feared that Eureka would allow Member States to exploit or evade the twin prongs of its new approach to competition policy. Eureka looked suspiciously like a scheme which would allow Member States to take advantage the new block exemption for aid to R & D and thus automatically sidestep the more vigilant EC monitoring system.

The Commission's annual report on competition policy in 1987 was the first specifically to mention Eureka. National R & D schemes in Italy, the Netherlands and West Germany used to fund Eureka projects were reviewed, as were state aids to several individual projects. All were deemed 'compatible with the requirements of the Community framework' and were not challenged by the Commission.[48]

The 1988 report appeared to consciously draw attention to 'a number of favourable decisions concerning Eureka schemes or projects'. The Commission revealed that it no longer required most grants to small

Eureka projects to be reported because it wished 'to simplify the administrative process, and to take account of the transnational nature of the projects'.[49] Similarly, the Commission approved all state grants to Eureka projects which it reviewed in 1989 and 1990.[50] Yet, as a Commission official observed, early fears that Eureka was a creative arrangement for 'hiding' illegal state aids waned over time but never disappeared:

> The ceiling over which the Commission requires notification was raised in late 1989. I thought that everybody agreed with that and was satisfied with that. But the French and Germans would like to be allowed not to notify any Eureka projects . . . Then the risk is that when you have state aid to give to a project, you just give it the Eureka label . . . But these countries would like that. They've already selectively notified Eureka projects, but not all of them.[51]

More generally, officials in the Commission's competition directorate (DG IV) continue to take a dim view of this 'sacred cow' of state aids:

> The idea of public finance for R & D enjoys strong support in the Community from those who believe it is needed to help Europe catch up with a perceived Japanese and US advantage in high technology. Its economic benefit is, however, unproven . . . Not only is there a risk of R & D spending in the richer central states offsetting aid for regional development, but most R & D aid is probably spent on projects that would have gone ahead anyway . . . The main effect of aid is simply to strengthen the treasury of the company, rather than to stimulate extra R & D activity. Finally, R & D tends to be concentrated on a few large recipients in each member state and thus easily serves to promote national industrial policies.[52]

Despite the EC's commitment to closer inspection of state aids, DG IV is still under-resourced, with fewer than three dozen senior officials policing state aids across the whole of the Community.[53] One DG IV representative admitted, 'There are strong political reasons not to challenge aids to Eureka projects. We have very limited resources and need to pick our battles carefully'.[54]

The Commission's competition authorities have had to learn to live with Eureka. But whether Eureka respects the spirit of the EC's new approach to state aids or merely 'hides' them within a framework where the Commission cannot challenge them with impunity is still an open question. Because its project list and national funding policies are so diverse, Eureka almost certainly does both.

The SEA's new provisions for competition policy were mirrored in those for the liberalization of public procurement.[55] National governments long have favoured domestic firms in bids for public contracts even though such favouritism is prohibited by Article 30 of the Treaty of Rome. Public procurement accounts for as much as 15 per cent of EC GDP, but cross-border purchases in 1985 accounted only for about 0.14 per cent of GDP.[56] Public markets for technology-intensive products or services are particularly 'nationalized'. Public authorities tend to favour local firms to promote their technological development and discrimination is difficult to prove when the products in question are technologically complex.[57]

The Declaration of Principles specifically links Eureka to wider efforts to open up public procurement.[58] Potentially, Eureka fits with the Commission's strategy of deploying blunt legal instruments as seldom as possible and instead promoting 'changes in industrial structures which make production more multinational, thus giving more member countries an interest in the success of a given supplier'.[59] Collaborative R & D and procurement liberalization are mutually reinforcing: the former encourages the development of multinational suppliers, the latter helps create new markets for them.

Within Eureka, Cosine is a key element in the Commission's drive to liberalize telecommunications markets. The HDTV project seeks to produce a new generation of audio-visual products for which publicly owned European television broadcasters will be an important market. Public markets obviously will provide most of the demand for Eureka's infrastructure projects, particularly those in environmental technologies.

Liberalization of public procurement is more a political than a technical problem. The political effect of Eureka is that when governments use national funds to help produce 'multinational products', they then have incentives to ensure that public markets exist for them. The Commission has tried to 'flag' projects which have the potential to contribute to common European standards, especially in sectors where nationalistic public procurement patterns are reinforced by differing national standards. EC funding for Cosine, HDTV and selected environmental projects is justified partly by the potential these projects have to bolster the Commission's strategy for liberalizing procurement. Eureka fits here as much as it does with any other element of the Commission's overall industrial policy agenda. It seems logical that for this reason alone, the Commission should wish to strengthen its links to Eureka.

The legal environment for collaborative R & D

Since the passage of the SEA, the Commission has worked with mixed results to harmonize national laws that impact on collaborative R & D. The Commission's original White Paper on the internal market explicitly linked successful collaborative R & D programmes with EC-wide protection of intellectual and industrial property rights.[60] Separate national patent regimes clearly impose unnecessary burdens on European firms. The high cost of applying for patents in each national setting acts as a barrier to trade in many technology-intensive products. Moreover, insufficient transparency between national regimes means that a vast amount of European R & D – as much as one-third of the total – 'is wasted because the expected products of the research are covered by existing patents'.[61]

Yet, Article 222 of the Treaty of Rome specifically excludes property laws from EC competence. Harmonization here, as in other areas where the Commission lacks Treaty-based authority, is laborious, time-consuming and usually has 'proceed[ed] at the pace dictated by the most reluctant member-state'.[62] Intergovernmental conferences were needed to create a European Patent Office in 1973 and pan-European patent protection in 1978. A uniform patent application now exists which is more expensive than single national applications, but provides savings if a product is marketed throughout the EC.[63] However, litigation under the new regime often still needs to be conducted separately in each country and thus is expensive. The Commission strategy has had to be piecemeal and long-term in focus since all patent regimes need to be continually adapted in response to technological change.[64]

A separate but related set of Commission actions has sought to develop the legal provisions for a 'European company', which would allow firms to merge across frontiers or collaborate in R & D without the burdens of conflicting national laws on accounting or double taxation. Despite much Commission effort, there has been little progress toward approval of its 1985 draft statute for a *Societas Europae*. Related directives on workers' rights and reform of national laws that act to make companies 'bid-proof' have met resistance both on the Council and within industry itself.[65]

The Commission has had more success in the development of European Economic Interest Groupings (EEIGs). These are legal entities into which companies of different nationalities may merge specific activities such as R & D or the promotion of new standards. Several Eureka projects actually occur within EEIGs, and the EC has helped to create and fund one called Vision 1250 to demonstrate the Eureka HDTV standard to European film-makers and TV producers using pilot studios and equipment.[66] More European SMEs have taken an interest in EEIGs since a truly advantageous legal instrument was created for them in 1989.[67]

The EC has far to go in creating a legal framework which promotes collaboration between national firms instead of penalizing it. Eureka is particularly affected by patent regimes since it includes so many projects which seek to produce marketable products quickly. Despite the very modest progress made thus far toward a pan-European regime, Eureka officials claim that most project partners eventually will seek pan-European patents.[68] EEIGs may employ a maximum of 500 people, and are a far cry from the sort of 'European companies' that the Commission would like to see taking a lead role in collaborative R & D programmes. But the Commission's backing for an improved EEIG instrument may be seen as a key supportive measure which, in particular, facilitates the participation of more SMEs in Eureka. In reforming the legal environment for collaborative R & D, as elsewhere, the goals of the Commission and Eureka dovetail considerably.

The EC's innovation policy

The Commission's most critical role in Eureka is ensuring that its own R & D programmes complement the scheme. The Commission's task is made difficult by the blurring of boundaries between basic, pre-competitive and 'near-market' research. Eureka includes a substantial number of infrastructure projects which are clearly not 'near market' projects, while Brite and Esprit have funded more applied research over time. For example, after nearly all of the Big 12 European electronics firms sustained huge losses in 1990–91, Pandolfi insisted that Esprit had to fund more 'near-market' R & D and ominously stated, 'Our aim is to avoid the collapse of the European industry'.[69]

In recent years, the Commission has made some progress towards eliminating duplication between Eureka and the Framework programme. Cosine originally mirrored work on network standards already underway within Esprit before the Commission decided to merge its efforts into Cosine. Eurotrac also duplicated some EC-funded R & D until the Commission agreed to fund two Eurotrac subprojects, although coordination was achieved only 'with some difficulties'.[70] Early overlaps between Prometheus and the EC's Drive programme appear to have been ironed out through the participation of almost the same set of European automobile manufacturers in each. Synergy beween Brite and Famos received a 'high score' in an evaluative report by the Dutch chairmanship of 1991, as did interactions between Eureka and EC

R & D into information and environmental technologies. However, the same report could find no synergy whatsoever between Race or EC biotechnology programmes and R & D underway in the same sectors within Eureka.[71]

Eureka contains no system for ensuring that projects are not approved which duplicate EC-funded R & D. Eureka projects are, after all, merely intergovernmental agreements which the Commission has no formal power to block. The warning contained in a 1988 EP report that, 'given the fragile communications system of Eureka, overlap with Community projects is inevitable'[72] retains an essential truth.

The chances for Eureka and the Framework programme to duplicate one another increases as each grows in size. The EC is still far from the goal set at the Milan summit of 1985 to spend 6 per cent of the EC budget on R & D by 1993. But each successive budget for the Framework programme has been increased substantially.

Approval of Framework's budget still requires unanimity on the Council, after which specific subprogrammes may be approved by majority voting. States which have baulked at the Commission's proposed price tags for Framework – at various times Germany, the Netherlands, Spain and (especially) the UK – constantly push for specific details on actual expenditures when general budgets are debated. The Commission has responded by actively encouraging scrutiny of its programmes by outside experts as well as by the Council's own Research Group.[73] Over time, the Commission has enhanced its credibility on the Council through better operational evaluation of its R & D programmes, expansion of its range of supporting policy 'tools' for dissemination and exploitation of results, and the development of generally more coherent innovation policy strategies.

Both the 1988 German presidency and the 1989 French presidencies of the Council of Ministers pressured the Commission to do more to support Eureka. The Commission responded in its proposal for Framework III in 1989 by stressing that future EC-funded R & D would better complement non-EC R & D at the regional and national levels.[74] Pandolfi's commitment to strengthening links between Eureka and the Framework programme was a central element of this pledge.

In part to satisfy smaller Member States which lack large, integrated national champions of their own, the Commission also has accelerated its efforts to enhance the participation of SMEs in EC-funded R & D. The Commission's first 'action programme' for SMEs was launched in 1986 and a new Task Force was charged with coordinating all EC efforts to promote SME development.[75] In 1990, a new DG (XXIII) was created to incorporate and expand the task force. Framework III featured substantially increased funds for biotechnology, environmental technologies and software engineering, where SMEs benefit from relatively low barriers to market entry. The Commission also has taken steps to try to increase the participation of SMEs in public procurement and has committed substantial structural funds to 'improve the business environment' for SMEs.[76]

One Eureka NPC described the flurry of EC actions to assist SMEs in the early 1990s as 'the flavour of the month'.[77] But Eureka's 'bottom-up' methodology means that the general environment for SMEs in Europe must improve before Eureka, by itself, can contribute much to SME development. Particularly as the internal market develops, promoting a vibrant, dynamic coterie of European SMEs is mostly a matter for EC innovation policy. Here again, the ability of Eureka to contribute to the technological development of European industry depends mightily on what happens at the level of the EC.

In this context, the Commission's political strategy for increasing its innovation policy *acquis* has become more sophisticated, if no less combative. In 1991, it dramatically withdrew the only five Framework subprogramme proposals that were close to approval on the grounds that the Council had amended them beyond recognition. The Commission eventually compromised to avoid delaying the start of Framework III research, but its brinkmanship was designed to impress upon Member States that it expected to be given more independent power in innovation policy after the conclusion of the intergovernmental conference of 1991, which culminated with the Maastricht summit.[78] In short, the politics of EC collaborative R & D remain volatile. The Commission's ability to be an effective Eureka 'Member State' depends crucially on the outcome of its ongoing struggle with EC Member States on a range of innovation policy issues. At the same time, because it has allowed EC Member States to promote collaborative R & D outside the EC's auspices, Eureka represents a challenge to the Commission's argument that effective collaborative R & D programmes require increased EC resources and *acquis*.

The politics of a wider Europe

The EC's role as an actor in international relations has undergone rapid re-evaluation in the early 1990s. The implementation of the internal market and the end of the Cold War combined to enhance the magnetism of the EC for outside states. Increasingly, the EC faced calls from EFTA and the former Eastern bloc states for increased co-operation and reinforced bilateral relationships in advance of the actual expansion of the EC's membership. The Commission struggled to sustain the momentum of the 1992 project in the face of these demands, many of which focused on increased technological collaboration.

The most insistent demands came from the EFTA states. The volume of EFTA–EC trade by 1990 was greater than that of US–EC trade and six times greater than that between the EC and Japan. However, EFTA states remained far more dependent on trade with the EC than vice versa.[79] Beginning in the early 1980s, EFTA states began to press the Commission for favoured access to the EC's market and new mechanisms for ensuring consultation on 'internal' EC matters which affected EFTA economies. The EC responded in 1984 with the Luxembourg Accord, which proposed the creation of a 'European Economic Space' to be negotiated in a regular series of EC–EFTA exchanges. The Commission stated that collaboration in the 'technological fields of the future, such as telecommunications, information systems, and the new audio-visual media' would be a critical element in the project.[80]

Early negotiations yielded a series of agreements on the participation of EFTA states in the Framework programme from 1986–89. Full EFTA participation – including EFTA state budget contributions – was mandated for EC programmes with clearly pre-competitive goals, such as those for environmental and medical technologies (Step), scientific exchange (Science), and economic science (SPES). EFTA participation was allowed in individual projects under schemes with more industrial applications such as Esprit and Brite. Most of the agreements contained the proviso that EFTA states could participate only if projects included at least two EC organizations in order to 'protect the Community interest'.[81]

Eureka was launched with a clear statement that 'the implementation of the Luxembourg declaration between the European Communities and EFTA countries will . . . benefit Eureka'.[82] One Commission official retrospectively observed:

> At the time Mitterrand proposed it, the Community was talking about a European technological space and going beyond the Community itself. It's noteworthy that under the Esprit programme, for example, there had been one or two areas where there was quite a lot of pressure to bring in people beyond the Community. And I think ultimately this idea got through that R & D is one area where Europe could have a little more cohesion than purely the Community *vis-à-vis* the rest of the world . . . Mitterrand proposed then a sort of slightly

different European technological space, and I suppose some individuals in the Commission or the Community as whole may have thought, 'he's taking our idea and perverting it'.[83]

In 1990, the EFTA states formally asked the Commission to extend full participation rights to EFTA in the Framework programme, with its Member States offering to contribute to its financing on a equal footing with EC states. The Commission's response was to demur on the grounds that 'this is a political matter which requires further study in the context of overall relations between these countries and the Community'.[84] In the event, the issue of EFTA participation became highly contentious and slowed full adoption of the Framework III programme in 1991.

The successful incorporation of EFTA countries into Eureka undoubtedly emboldened the EFTA states in pressing their demands on the Commission. The participation of non-EC states in Eureka had been extensive, and between one-fifth and one-quarter of all projects included an EFTA partner. The effect of Eureka on the Luxembourg process was to place additional pressure on the Commission to respond favourably to EFTA demands. In this way, as in others noted above, Eureka complicated the Commission's innovation policy strategy.

Eureka also figured prominently in early EC discussions with new democratic governments in Eastern Europe after 1989. In February 1990, the EC's research council acknowledged pressures to increase technological aid to the East and discussed the possibility of opening European collaborative R & D schemes, including Eureka, to participants from Eastern European countries.[85] The Commission noted 'considerable conceptual difficulties' in extending such aid through its own R & D programmes and instead suggested that Eureka and COST should be 'opened up' first since they provided the most easily arranged opportunities for Eastern Europe.[86]

The Bonn meeting of the Conference on Security and Cooperation in Europe (CSCE) in April 1990 yielded proposals for a series of new 'pan-European procedures and institutions' for economic cooperation. Included among them was the idea of extending Eureka membership to all thirty-five CSCE Member States, including the USA, Canada and all Eastern European countries. The idea was backed by the Commission and urged on other Member States by Genscher, the conference chairman.[87]

The proposal caused considerable controversy among Eureka Member States about how much the scheme could be used as a tool to promote technology transfer to the East. A member of the secretariat argued:

> Eureka is not meant to be a tool for that purpose, but it happens to be a tool that's available for political purposes. The pillars of the Eureka approach – its bottom-up organization and federative approach – shouldn't be destroyed by opening it up to other countries. The danger is if single ministers make statements such as this without having the consent of the deciding body, the ministerial conference. Single members should refrain from such statements.[88]

The incoming Dutch chairmanship appeared to seize the initiative by issuing a study prior to the June 1990 Rome ministerial conference which warned that Eureka governments should

> anticipate political pressure to increase the number of member states, the Eastern European countries being a case in point. An increase in the number of Member States would not seem to be an effective method. It would be better to be flexible about restricting the participation of Eastern Europe in individual projects.[89]

In the event, the Dutch appeared to ease pressures to expand Eureka's membership by developing clearer criteria for 'third country' participation and organizing joint congresses on Eureka with the Polish and Hungarian governments in 1991.[90] The 1991 ministerial conference saw the issuance of 'The Hague Statement' which committed Member States to an action programme designed to increase the number of projects with participants from the former Eastern bloc.[91] In 1992, Hungary – which already participated in three projects – was formally admitted as a Eureka Member State.

Put in the context of EC–Eureka relations, the Commission found Eureka convenient as a framework for extending collaborative R & D to non-EC states at a time when it was under severe pressure to open up its activities to outsiders. Eureka's membership was already wider than the EC and, more importantly, its methodology allowed the Commission to avoid difficult decisions about whether and how much EC R & D funding should be used as a tool of the EC's foreign policy toward Eastern and Central Europe. Eureka's lack of centralized funds made the principle of *juste retour* – which greatly complicated the opening of the Framework programme to EFTA states – a non-issue. As a 'near market' and product-oriented initiative, Eureka may have been wholly inappropriate as a method of encouraging technology transfer to Eastern Europe. But the EC's new emphasis on strengthening ties with Eureka was fuelled by its desire to use the initiative to serve its foreign policy agenda.

IV. THE EUROPEANIZATION OF INNOVATION POLICIES?

No one involved in the making of Eureka in 1985–86 could have expected that granting the Commission status as a extra 'Member State' would leave all parties satisfied. Undeniably, the innovation policy agenda of the Commission in 1985–86 was a highly political one, with the expansion of the EC's powers at its core. The Commission insisted before the landmark 1985 Milan summit that new R & D initiatives 'must be made in the Community context' and should feature a 'considerable delegation of executive powers to the Commission'.[92] Eureka acted to bring into the open latent suspicions about the Commission's innovation policy agenda. The Commission's subsequent participation in Eureka was pursued more with a sense of begrudging necessity than enthusiasm.

After 1989, the Commission's attitude evolved markedly, due partly to the change of R & D Commissioners but also for simple reasons of pragmatism. Political support for Eureka remained solid among large EC Member States from 1985 to 1990 while the Commission struggled to get its proposals for increased EC R & D spending approved. The Commission found several Eureka projects – including Cosine, HDTV and Jessi – which suited its general innovation policy agenda. Eureka fitted, at least in theory, with the EC's strategy to liberalize public procurement and promote common standards. Eureka also emerged as an expedient framework for responding to demands emanating from Eastern Europe for technological assistance.

However, the Commission's efforts to strengthen its links to Eureka were motivated primarily by pressure from European industry itself. In the late 1970s and early 1980s, the Commission slowly built a consensus among European industry to support its agenda for freeing the internal market generally and increasing EC spending on collaborative R & D specifically. In many respects, the Commission's relationship with large European MNCs through the Big 12 and Gyllenhammer group became clientelistic. The interests of key industries and the Commission dovetailed, and EC governments were forced to respond.

At the same time, the Commission never has had a 'monolithic' view in its approach to innovation policy. The dispute which arose in 1987 between Delors and Narjes about how much the EC should directly fund Eureka projects is indicative. Competition policy officials in DG IV remain sceptical about the need for more EC funding for R & D subsidies. Officials in DG III, which is responsible for the internal market, tend to take a dim view of Eureka due to its potential to encourage the definition of new technical standards which may clash with those which DG III is 'pushing' in the interest of the internal market.[93] Substantial rivalries exist even between DGs XII and XIII, despite the fact that they share responsibility for the Framework programme and both wish to see its funding increased. DG XII's remit extends across a broad range of science and R & D sectors and its structure resembles an academic research institute. DG XIII is more narrowly concerned with EC policy for telecommunications and information technology and its style and outlook tend to be far more *dirigiste*.[94]

What does unite the Commission is a conviction that the momentum of the 1992 project must be sustained. In this context, the logic of collaborative R & D is that it waters down clientelistic relations between national governments and national champions. Moreover, a general view within the Commission is that it has enhanced its image and credibility through successful and competent management of most of its collaborative R & D programmes.

A crucial tactic has been the involvement of industry in the design, management and strategic development of many Framework sub-programmes. The Information Technology Task Force, which includes representatives of most of the Big 12 firms, has powerful agenda-setting powers within Esprit, as well as substantial influence over detailed, highly technical funding decisions. Changes in the Task Force's recommended 'work programmes' for Esprit usually are made only at the margins. Watkins argues that when political approval is granted, 'as such, sovereignty is not an issue'.[95] Within Brite, the influence of IRDAC – the Industrial R & D Advisory Committee – is substantial. A Commission official involved in Brite commented, 'It's important to have support on the Council for what we propose. But once we have IRDAC's approval, the Council usually follows their lead'.[96]

The institutionalized power of private interests in EC innovation policymaking has given industry substantial leverage to pressure the Commission to provide more support to Eureka and fund more near-market R & D through the Framework programme. In 1987, Jacques Stern, the President of Bull, urged that Esprit and Eureka should be formally linked, or Esprit should become 'more market-oriented'.[97] In February 1990, Fiat's annual report on European industry noted 'unanimous agreement on the fundamental importance of collaborative R & D for competitiveness', but it also claimed that 'industry is having trouble understanding the pre-competitive constraint of EC R & D'. The report pointedly observed that 'the Eureka programme does not impose this constraint and its projects often reach the threshold of industrialization'.[98] Significantly, the report was unveiled by Fiat's external relations representative together with Pandolfi himself, who reiterated that one of the main priorities of Framework III was increased EC support for Eureka.

Three fundamental points emerge from this discussion. First, to some extent, political support for collaborative R & D has been a 'free rider' on support for the 1992 project generally. The Commission has expanded its *acquis* in innovation policy only by linking it explicitly to the goal of developing the internal market. Clearly, Eureka has not fitted neatly into this strategy. On the contrary, it has provided opportunities for EC members to acknowledge the importance of collaborative R & D while maintaining clientelistic relations with national firms in selected projects and refusing to expand the Commission's powers.

Second, the complexity of EC decisionmaking on budgetary issues, marked by intense bargaining between Member States on the Council, means that funding collaborative R & D will always be a highly political exercise. Sovereignty may not be an issue when detailed distributional decisions are made within individual programmes, but the principle of *juste retour* is still a powerful determinant of general budgeting for the Framework programme. The Commission can 'Europeanize' innovation policies only by accommodating quite divergent national priorities on the Council. Thus, for example, it responded to the insistence of several Member States, notably Germany and the Netherlands, that it increase spending on environmental R & D in Framework III. It also developed new tools for assisting SMEs to satisfy smaller EC Member States, such as Denmark, Belgium and Portugal.

Third, the Commission faced little choice but to respond to the urgings of both industry and national governments that it do more to support Eureka. Yet, several innovative proposals developed by the Commission at the HLG level to strengthen EC–Eureka links were resisted by Eureka Member States. One Commission delegate to the HLG recalled:

> I proposed a lot of things, but I think they all ran into political difficulties. One idea was to create a mechanism which was to be utilized by the Commission to give an advance to certain approved projects. The Member States would then reimburse us later . . . But the Member States could not agree on that because they said it would give the power to the Commission to finance the project instead of them. It would be very interesting for the partners because they would make only one financing proposal instead of five or six, and [would have] only one procedure to follow for reporting, etc. . . . It would be easier for us and easier for the partners. But Member States may lose control over the project, so they would not agree on that.[99]

The point is that the Europeanization of national innovation policies has not proceeded in a unilinear direction because there is still much rivalry between the Commission and national governments for operational control. Clearly, a new EC innovation policy network emerged in the early 1980s and the interests of industry and the Commission converged until 1985, but they never became one and the same. The rise of the competing SDI and Eureka proposals acted to 'loosen' the industry–Commission alliance. To some extent, more funding for collaborative R & D programmes was a means to an end for the Commission: expanding its *acquis* in industrial policy generally. It was an end in itself for European industry. Pandolfi's commitment to strengthening EC–Eureka links and the evolution of the Framework programme show that the Commission has realized that it can only achieve its political goals for innovation policy by satisfying both industry and Member States in tandem.

Yet, there are clear limits on the extent to which the EC and Eureka can both practically and politically be linked. Even when the Commission proposes to fund a Eureka project of obvious strategic importance, the *juste retour* principle can limit its scope for action. A Commission delegate to Eureka illustrated the point:

> There's been a lot of discussion about financing Jessi programmes through Esprit, and some countries didn't agree because all Member States are not participating in Jessi. So Jessi is of strategic interest for some Member States, and it's considered a strategic project at the Community level also. But a lot of Member States consider it outside their interest . . . So I think that the percentage of projects which the Community funds will stay at this level. Maybe more every year, but as a percentage of all projects, about the same.[100]

Herein lies a fundamental difficulty for the Commission: Eureka lacks any central governing body which can legislate for its Member States and present a single 'Eureka position' to the EC. Tensions in EC–EFTA relations suggest parallels with EC–Eureka relations. After successful early negotiations between the Commission and EFTA states on trade and technological collaboration, discussions after 1988 became bogged down because 'in reality the EC was negotiating with six countries, not EFTA as such, which was not constituted for such negotiations'.[101] Delors expressed the Commission's frustration succinctly:

> . . . the ideal formula as far as I am concerned . . . comprised a strengthening of EFTA structures so that we have only one person in front of us. If we had six of them, we would reach a mutual

information and advisory system which would be extremely bureaucratic and very awkward.[102]

The point is that the Commission increasingly views its role as that of a traditional political executive in implementing the 1992 project. It is thus most predisposed to negotiations with integrated, centralized sources of political authority which reflect its own self-image. Just as EFTA lacks any true central authority, so does Eureka.

However, there are sensible and compelling reasons why the Commission should embrace Eureka more closely. A central goal of the 1992 project is to change the behaviour of governments *vis-à-vis* their national firms.[103] Eureka at least encourages national governments to fund R & D that fits with the goals of the 1992 project, even if they subsidize their national champions as they have always done and fund projects which do not fit with the central, strategic goals of the Framework programme. Eureka has forced the Commission to acknowledge that expanding its own powers and developing the internal market are separate goals.

The Commission in 1988 estimated that 'around half' of Eureka's projects had some link to EC-funded R & D, in that they extended EC projects closer to the market, covered different stages of R & D underway within Framework, or had some overlap.[104] Even this estimate seems low considering that there is virtually no area of R & D covered by Eureka which is not also covered under the Framework programme, and both have grown steadily since 1988. With more than 500 Eureka projects underway by 1992, certainly room existed for more synergy between Eureka and EC-funded R & D.

Doubts about the quality of many Eureka projects and the long periods required for many to reach their implementation phases pose constraints. But if the Commission's goal is to enhance the technological competitiveness of European industry, as opposed to simply increasing its own executive powers in innovation policy, Eureka holds much promise as a framework for doing so. Eureka shows how persistent national prerogatives in innovation policy remain. But equally it shows that the line between purely national and 'Europeanized' R & D has blurred. The Commission too often has acted as if a clear line between the two should be obvious to all, and that only R & D conducted under its own remit can truly promote the development of the internal market. Innovation policy emerges as an area where the Commission would be wise to consider the practical virtues of gradualism.

6   The participants' view

A range of views clearly persists among Eureka's Member States on the question of what the initiative should be trying to achieve. But it is only a mild exaggeration to argue that what public actors think of Eureka almost does not matter. Given its industry-led character, as long as governments find that Eureka's marginal utility to national innovation policies justifies its continued existence, what really matters are perceptions among Western Europe's industrial, research and scientific communities about how well Eureka works.

Early assessments of industrial attitudes towards Eureka, most of which were undertaken by individual Member States, limited themselves to the study of national participants or small, cross-national samples of participants.[1] This chapter focuses on the results of two more recent surveys of Eureka participants, each of which generated relatively large, cross-national data sets. Each survey's research design and methodology and the main features of their data sets are briefly reviewed in Section I. Section II culls the data for details on Eureka's partners, projects and the effect of its funding arrangements. In particular, this section sifts through the survey data for clues about Eureka's 'additionality' and added value. Correlations between participants' perceptions of Eureka and their national origins are explored in Section III. Section IV concludes by synthesizing the findings of the two surveys to generate clear statements about the nature of Eureka's partners and projects, the effects of its methodology, and its effectiveness as a system of incentives to encourage increased and accelerated innovation in Europe.

I. THE SURVEYS: DESIGN, METHODOLOGY AND DATA SETS

Early surveys of Eureka participants employed a 'case study' method, and relied on telephone or face-to-face interviews or responses to detailed written questionnaires. The two more recent surveys analysed

Table 6.1 Possible and actual sample sizes (independent survey)

Possible sample		Actual sample		Actual sample as % of possible sample	
Projects no.	Leaders no.	Projects no.	Leaders no.	Projects no.	Leaders no.
273	324[a]	107	121[b]	39	37

Source: Author's calculations based on information in Eureka project database as of November 1989.
Notes: [a]Some projects have multiple leaders. [b]A total of 14 respondents did not indicate which projects they were leading. It is thus impossible to determine how many of these respondents lead projects represented elsewhere in the data set. Based on the 8.4/10 ratio of leaders to projects for Eureka as a whole, these 14 'unknowns' are estimated to represent about 10 otherwise 'unsurveyed' projects.

here both used postal questionnaires to obtain data from as many participants as possible. The findings of both surveys were supplemented by extensive face-to-face interviews with Eureka participants.

One survey was conducted by the author for the purposes of this study independently of any Eureka institution or Member State. This 'independent survey' sought data on Eureka project leaders *only*.[2] A list was compiled of the addresses and contact persons of the leaders of all 273 projects contained in the Eureka database as of November 1989.[3] A pre-tested, trilingual questionnaire (in English, French and German) was posted in February and March 1990.[4] Table 6.1 shows the independent survey's possible and actual sample sizes for both projects and project leaders. The survey generated a data set on close to 40 per cent of all projects and a slightly lower percentage of all project leaders.

Since no reliable data exist on the organizational sizes and types of Eureka project leaders, Figure 6.1 compares data on *all* Eureka project participants with the independent survey sample of project leaders only. A large percentage of survey respondents were large industrial firms with more than 500 employees, but this share was smaller than the percentage of all Eureka participants who are large firms. Confirmed SMEs accounted for one of five leaders surveyed, which corresponded closely to the total SME share of all participants. Relatively few respondents to the independent survey were research institutes or university laboratories, which clearly participate in Eureka as subcontractors far more often than as project leaders. Many independent survey respondents (listed as 'no response' in Figure 6.1) chose not to indicate the size and type of their organization to preserve their anonymity.

A separate survey of all Eureka participants was conducted by a panel of industrialists assembled by Eureka Member States under the Dutch

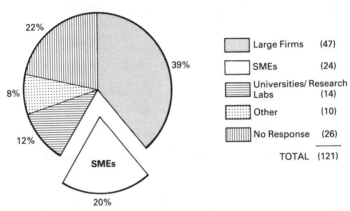

PROJECT LEADERS SURVEYED

Large Firms	(47)
SMEs	(24)
Universities/ Research Labs	(14)
Other	(10)
No Response	(26)
TOTAL	(121)

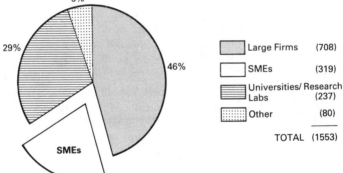

ALL EUREKA PARTICIPANTS

Large Firms	(708)
SMEs	(319)
Universities/ Research Labs	(237)
Other	(80)
TOTAL	(1553)

Figure 6.1 Size/types of Eureka participants

chairmanship of 1990–91. The assessment panel was headed by Wisse Dekker, a founding member of the Big 12 Roundtable and the former President of Philips. It distributed questionnaires to all Eureka participants via national Eureka offices in autumn 1990.[5] This 'official survey' generated a data set from a total of 874 completed questionnaires, which represented between 38 and 45 per cent of all participants and an unknown share of all projects.[6]

Table 6.2 Size and type of Eureka participants (official survey)

Size and type	Survey sample no.	%	All Eureka participants no.	%
Large firms	292	33	950	49
SMEs	311	36	394	20
Universities/research laboratories	239	27	495	25
Others/no response	32[a]	4	108	6
Totals	874	100	1947	100

Sources: Dutch chairmanship, *The Report of the Eureka Assessment Panel*, The Hague, 1991; Eureka secretariat, *Annual Progress Report 1990*, Brussels, 1991.
Note: [a]Data from questionnaires submitted by these respondents were omitted from the panel assessment's data analysis.

Far more universities and public research laboratories are represented in the official survey sample than in the independent survey (see Table 6.2). SMEs were substantially over-represented in the official survey data set and large firms were under-represented. The assessment panel took pains to analyse data on each set of respondents separately throughout its report.

Thus, the official survey produced a data set on a very large coterie of Eureka participants which is slightly more up-to-date than that of the independent survey. Its questionnaire covered a broader range of issues and often sought quite generalized responses. The independent survey generated a more in-depth and focused data set on a much smaller number of Eureka's primary participants. This chapter places somewhat greater emphasis on interpreting the results of the independent survey since it provides more detailed data on what motivates firms to participate in Eureka and the experience of the project leaders in managing projects, but the results of the two surveys are integrated whenever possible.

II. THE DATA: ANALYSIS AND IMPLICATIONS

The participants

The independent survey data strongly imply that most Eureka project leaders bring previous experience in collaborative R & D to their participation in Eureka. Almost exactly two-thirds of independent survey respondents reported having collaborated previously within Europe or internationally, and slightly fewer had participated in some type of EC-funded R & D (see Figure 6.2).[7] Most project leaders had

Previous Collaborative Experience Internationally

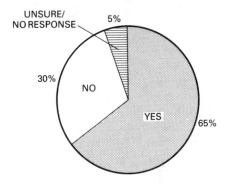

Previous Collaborative Experience in Europe

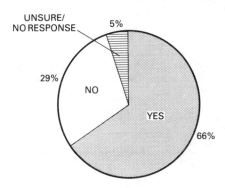

Figure 6.2 Collaborative experience prior to Eureka (independent survey)

collaborated in the past with at least one of their present Eureka partners and about half had previously worked with at least two (see Table 6.3).

More than 50 per cent of all project leaders indicated that they originally had proposed the project. A similar share of all types of participants told the assessment panel that they had become involved in Eureka through their 'own initiative' (see Table 6.4). These results confirm that Eureka is truly 'industry-led' and that firms rather than public agencies generate most project proposals.

The independent survey data suggest that project leaders over-whelmingly use their own pre-existing contacts to find their partners (see

Table 6.3 Number of current Eureka partners with whom project leaders had previously collaborated (independent survey)

Number of partners	% of total sample
Four or more	12
Three	7
Two	31
One	17
None	10
Unsure/no response	22

Note: Column does not add to 100% due to rounding.

Table 6.4 How organizations became involved in Eureka

How organization became involved	Independent survey[a] %	Official survey %
Project proposed by respondent[b]	55	51
Approached by another partner	21	32
Approached by own government	19	13
Other	9	3
No response	–	1

Notes: [a]Column adds to more than 100% due to multiple responses. [b] Independent survey questionnaire choice was 'our organization proposed project'; official survey questionnaire choice was 'own initiative'.

Table 6.5 How project leaders found partners (independent survey)

How partners were found	%
Own contacts	87
Partners contacted leader	15
National ministry	5
National Eureka office	4
Eureka database	2
Other	8

Note: Column adds to more than 100% due to multiple responses.

Table 6.5). However, in response to a separate survey question, nearly 40 per cent of all project leaders indicated that at least one of their current partners had contacted them during the 45-day period, or the time when proposals must 'circulate' to all national Eureka offices before they are granted Eureka status.[8] While the foundation for most projects is established links between organizations, Eureka seems to expand the number of partners taking part in many projects.

Data from the independent survey which correlate the size or type of project leaders to other variables must be treated cautiously since about one in five respondents would not reveal their own organization's size or type. However, clear distinctions between large and small firms are visible where their previous collaborative experience is concerned. Figure 6.3 shows that SME leaders were much less likely than large firms or other types of project leaders to bring previous collaborative experience to their participation in Eureka. If previous collaborative experience is viewed as something of a prerequisite for designing proposals which successfully become Eureka projects, SMEs operate at a disadvantage relative to large firms.

The independent survey data suggest that the formal and legal organization of projects poses more problems for SME project leaders than for large firm leaders (see Figure 6.4). Fewer SME-led projects operated under 'memoranda of understanding', a generally standard form of contract for collaborative business ventures, than did projects led by large firms. Fewer SME leaders had negotiated a memorandum of understanding which had legal status. Far more anticipated problems with intellectual property rights (IPRs).

The official survey found that 39 per cent of all participants experienced 'contractual drafting difficulties'. The data did not show large differentials between large firms and SMEs in the reporting of this problem or that of 'disagreements on property rights'.[9] The variation between the independent and official surveys on this question suggests that SME project leaders have far more problems than large firm leaders with the formal and legal organization of their projects, but that SMEs which participate as junior partners in Eureka projects are relatively untroubled by such problems.

The projects

With its focus on 'near-market' R & D projects, Eureka was created with the idea that it could take pre-competitive projects funded through the Framework programme or other international schemes 'closer to the market'. The independent survey results imply that Eureka generally fails to perform this function. Only a small (10 per cent) share of leaders indicated that their project had begun in some other international R & D scheme.

Most respondents to the independent survey (54 per cent) thought that links between Eureka and their country's national R & D programmes were 'adequate and satisfactory'. But less than one-third thought links between Eureka and EC-funded R & D programmes were

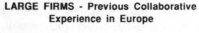

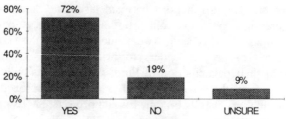

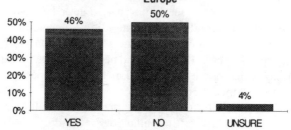

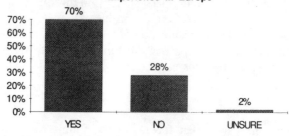

Figure 6.3 Size/type of project leader and previous collaborative experience (independent survey)

adequate, and only slightly more of those with previous experience in EC-funded R & D agreed (see Table 6.6).

The data from both surveys confirm that many Eureka projects do not perform downstream or 'near-market' R & D. It is too simple to say that the fewer the number of partners in any project or the shorter its projected life span, the more likely it is to yield a marketable product or process quickly. Yet, projects with relatively few partners are generally

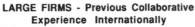

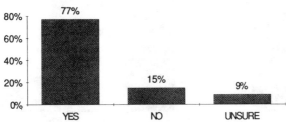

LARGE FIRMS - Previous Collaborative
Experience Internationally

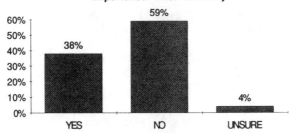

SMALL FIRMS - Previous Collaborative
Experience Internationally

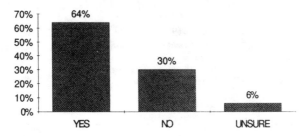

ALL OTHERS - Previous Collaborative
Experience Internationally

Figure 6.3 (continued)

more likely to develop tangible products in a short period of time because large, complex projects are logically more difficult to coordinate and finish quickly.

The independent survey data suggest that Eureka incorporates many large, many-partnered projects and relatively few simple bilateral projects (see Table 6.7). It might be inferred that leaders of infrastructure projects, which tend to include many partners, completed and returned

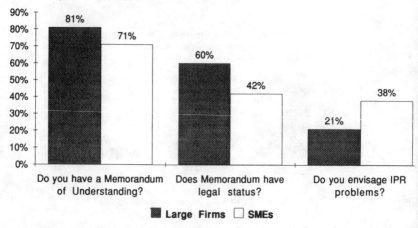

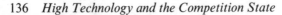

Figure 6.4 Formal and legal organization of projects (independent survey); percentages indicate 'yes' responses

Table 6.6 Adequacy of Eureka's links to EC-funded R & D (independent survey)

Subsamples	no.	Adequate %	Inadequate %	Unsure %
Respondents with previous experience in EC-funded R & D	(76)	37	32	32
Respondents without previous experience in EC-funded R & D	(36)	19	25	56
All others[a]	(9)	11	33	44
Total sample	(121)	30	30	40

Note: [a]Includes respondents who were unsure whether their organizations had previous experience in EC-funded R & D and those who did not respond.

Table 6.7 Project size (independent survey)

No. of partners	% of total sample
Six or more	41
Five	10
Four	16
Three	20
Two	13

the independent survey questionnaire more often than leaders of smaller, industrial projects. However, official statistics confirm that the

Table 6.8 Project leaders receiving public funds (independent survey)

Size/type of project leader	Yes %	No %	Unsure %
Large firms	83	11	4
SMEs	83	13	4
Research institutes/universities	92	8	–
Others	81	20	–
Total sample	84	13	3

Note: Rows do not add to 100% due to rounding or missing cases.

Table 6.9 Number of partners who receive public funds (independent survey)

No. of partners	% of total sample
Four or more	42
Three	11
Two	10
One	8
None	2
Unsure	23
No response	3

Note: Column does not add to 100% due to rounding.

average number of partners per project is about five.[10] Eureka clearly includes many large, complex projects.

The official survey found that nearly one-quarter of all participants expected no marketable results until five years or longer after their project's start date.[11] In particular, large firms appear to be involved in such projects quite often: 37 per cent expected commercial applications only after five years or more, compared with 22 per cent of SMEs.[12] The assessment panel noted that only twenty projects had been completed after five years of Eureka's existence and concluded that 'many Eureka projects involve pre-competitive research'.[13]

Project funding

The independent survey data reveal that, whatever else Eureka's projects have in common, a large majority receive public funding (see Table 6.8). It appears that all types of project leaders are about equally likely to receive government support.

Table 6.9 reveals that many respondents, more than 40 per cent of the total sample, indicated that at least four of their partners received public

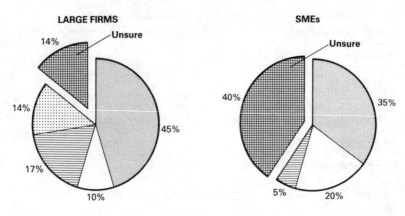

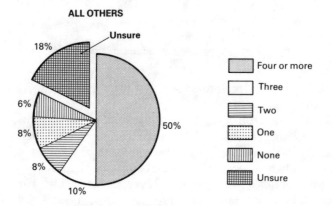

Figure 6.5 Number of partners receiving public funds by size/type of project leader (independent survey)

funds. However, nearly one-quarter claimed that they did not know how many of their partners were receiving government support.

As shown in Figure 6.5, projects led by SMEs tended to have fewer publicly funded partners than those led by other types of organizations. But what is most striking is the high percentage of SMEs who said that they were unsure how many of their partners received public funds. The independent survey data imply that Eureka's loose rules on information exchange between governments mean that many project leaders –

Table 6.10 Public funds as percentage of respondents' total and own R & D costs (independent survey)

Percentage of R & D costs	Total project costs			Own R & D costs		
	Large firms %	SMEs %	All[a] %	Large firms %	SMEs %	All[a] %
50–31%	34	50	45	43	58	46
30–21%	28	26	23	24	17	17
20–11%	13	17	8	4	17	7
10–1%	15	4	9	17	8	11
<1%	–	4	3	4	–	4
Other	6	–	10	8	–	12
No response	4	–	2	4	–	3

Note: [a] Total survey sample.

particularly SMEs – can only guess what levels and sources of funding each of their partners bring to their project.

Respondents to the independent survey were asked to estimate both the percentages of their project's total R & D costs and their own R & D costs that were covered by public funds. In both cases, the percentages were quite high (see Table 6.10). The responses of SME project leaders imply that proportionately more of their projects' total costs are covered by public funds than are those led by large firms. The differential narrows somewhat when the share of respondents' own R & D covered by public funds is considered. Generally, the independent survey data contain limited evidence that most national funding policies effectively discriminate in favour of SMEs.

A separate independent survey question asked respondents to indicate all the governments that, so far as they knew, contributed funding to their project. The data in Table 6.11 suggest that France provides funding to far more projects than does any other Member State. This finding reflects in part the proportionately larger share of the total survey sample (21 per cent) which was comprised of French project leaders. Yet, if broken down according to the national origin of each respondent, the sample can be seen to reflect with rough accuracy the actual division of project leadership between Member States (although the representation of German leaders is artificially high and that of Spanish and Austrian leaders is artificially low).

Table 6.12 shows that nearly one-third of independent survey respondents believed that having Eureka status had made it easier for them to secure private finance for their project. However, very few reported having been helped by their national Eureka office or a national ministry in finding private funds. While governments appear to provide

Table 6.11 Projects funded by each Member State, actual national division of project leadership, and national division of total sample (independent survey)

Member State	Projects funded[a]		Survey responses		Actual project leaders[b]	
	no.	%	no.	%	no.	%
France	54	45	26	21	73	23
Germany	41	34	18	15	30	9
Italy	38	31	14	12	35	11
Netherlands	30	25	15	12	38	12
UK	28	23	10	8	25	8
Spain	27	22	5	4	27	8
Denmark	18	15	6	5	12	4
Sweden	17	14	3	2	11	3
Norway	16	13	5	4	10	3
Austria	16	13	4	3	19	6
Finland	9	3	3	2	15	4
Belgium	11	9	3	2	11	3
CEC	10	8	0	–	2	1
Switzerland	8	7	2	2	10	3
Portugal	6	5	2	2	7	2
Greece	4	3	0	–	1	<1
Ireland	2	2	0	–	0	–
Iceland	1	1	1	1	1	<1
Turkey	1	1	0	–	0	–
Luxembourg	–	–	0	–	2	1
Totals	–	–	121	100[c]	323[d]	100[c]

Notes: [a]Columns indicate number of respondents and share of total survey sample which reported that their project received funding from indicated Member State; share column does not add to 100% due to multiple responses. [b]Based on information on 273 projects listed in Eureka central database as of November 1989. [c]Columns do not add to 100% due to rounding. [d]Some projects have multiple leaders.

Table 6.12 Eureka status and private finance (independent survey)

	Yes	No	Unsure/no response
	%	%	%
Has Eureka status made it easier to attract private finance to project?	31	48	21
Received help from Eureka office/ national ministry finding private funding?	10	79	11

a large amount of funding to the projects covered in the survey, they do

Table 6.13 Would the project exist without Eureka status?

	Independent survey %		Official survey %
Definitely	21	Yes	55
Probably	29		
Unlikely	32	No	40
Definitely not	13		
Unsure/No response	5	No response	5

not appear to act as a link between private funding and Eureka projects very often.

Eureka's additionality and added-value

Eureka is designed to give firms incentives to engage in R & D collaboratively which they might otherwise forego due to the high risks and costs involved in undertaking it on their own. Both surveys attempted to gauge Eureka's 'additionality' by posing simple questions about whether projects would exist without Eureka status.[14]

Table 6.13 reveals that about half of all respondents to both surveys estimated that their project definitely or probably would exist even if Eureka status had not been granted. The independent survey data suggest that many projects led by large firms would exist regardless of whether they had achieved Eureka status (see Figure 6.6). Meanwhile, SME leaders were far more likely to believe that their projects would *not* exist without Eureka status. The assessment panel's data generally support these findings. More SME participants (45 per cent) believed that their project would not exist without Eureka status than did large firms (39 per cent) or research laboratories and universities (34 per cent).[15]

The independent survey showed only a weak correlation between the previous collaborative experience of the project leader and the likelihood that their projects would exist without Eureka status. There was none at all if past involvement in EC-funded R & D is considered: many leaders who had never participated in EC-funded R & D claimed that their project's existence did *not* depend on its Eureka status.[16] However, Eureka's additionality *was* clear for project leaders who had never previously collaborated with their current partners: they were far more likely to believe their project would not exist if Eureka did not exist (see Table 6.14). The implication is that Eureka has the effect of creating new

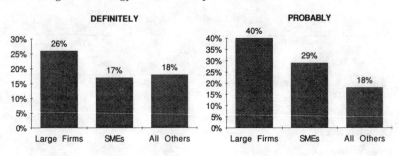

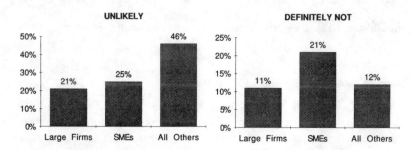

Figure 6.6 Would the project exist without Eureka status by size/type of project leader (independent survey)

collaborative links between firms who would not have chosen to undertake their current R & D project if they had not been able to share risks and costs with partners.

The data also suggest a rule of thumb: the larger the project, the less likely that it would have been launched without Eureka. One in five leaders of projects with five or more partners said that their projects would definitely not exist without Eureka. Only one in twelve leading projects with two or three partners responded similarly.[17]

Both surveys sought to determine the attitudes of present participants to future participation by posing the simple question: 'Does your organization intend to participate in more Eureka projects in the future?' The vast majority of respondents to both surveys thought they would or might partake in Eureka again, and only a handful ruled out future participation. There was no perceptible difference between the responses of large and small firms to this question (see Table 6.15). The independent survey data suggested that a significant determinant of attitudes toward future Eureka participation was whether or not respondents had collaborated in the past with their current Eureka partners (see Table 6.16). Project leaders who were new to their current

Table 6.14 Would the project exist by previous experience with current partners (independent survey)

Response	Previous experience %	No previous experience %
Definitely	24	16
Probably	32	24
Unlikely	30	37
Definitely not	10	21
Don't know	5	3

Note: Columns do not add to 100% due to rounding.

partners were far more enthusiastic about future participation in Eureka.

The independent survey also asked project leaders whether they would consider collaborating with their current partners again with no mention of any particular framework or scheme. A large majority (84 per cent) thought they might work with one or more of their Eureka partners again. Almost none thought future collaboration with their current partners was out of the question. Compared with responses to the question about whether leaders would consider future participation in Eureka, these figures indicate that project leaders value their current collaborative R & D experience more than participation in Eureka *per se*. However, Eureka has significant added value for organizations who had never collaborated with their current partners.

This observation is supported by data on the extent to which respondents' original ideas about the project's objectives and focus were altered after consultations with their partners. A majority estimated that their ideas had changed 'substantially' (18 per cent) or 'moderately' (43 per cent). Relatively few responded 'very little' (26 per cent) or 'not at all' (13 per cent). If Eureka acts to expand the number of partners which participate in its projects, the consequent exchange of ideas between organizations across borders obviously can alter, clarify or 'fine-tune' a project's objectives.

Determining what motivates firms and research organizations to participate in Eureka required more general or open-ended questions. The independent survey asked project leaders to indicate which perceived benefits of Eureka participation were most important in motivating them to participate in the scheme. The intent was to provide a question which linked the benefits associated with collaborative R & D generally to Eureka specifically. Respondents were given a list of sixteen potential benefits and an 'other' category and were asked to choose as many as were relevant and to rank them in order of importance (see

Table 6.15 Intention to participate in Eureka again

Participant size/type	Independent survey			Official survey		
	Yes	No	Unsure	Yes	No	Perhaps
	%	%	%	%	%	%
Large firms	66	2	32	43	3	54
SMEs	67	4	29	42	3	55
All others	72	8	20	58	2	41
Totals	69	5	26	47	3	50

Table 6.16 Intention to participate in Eureka again cross-tabulated with previous experience with current partners (independent survey)

	Intention to participate in Eureka again		
	Yes	No	Unsure
	%	%	%
Previous experience with partners	69	8	31
No previous experience	84	–	16

Table 6.17). Each potential benefit can be assigned a 'significance quotient' by assigning a value to its average ranking by respondents. This figure takes into account both how often it was chosen and how high it was ranked.[18]

The benefit which was valued the most by far was the 'cross-fertilization of ideas' that collaboration makes possible. The frequent choice and high ranking of the choices 'improvement of competitive position' and 'access to a larger potential market' suggest that, however many pre-competitive projects Eureka incorporates, a majority of all project leaders are participating in Eureka for commercial reasons. The high significance quotients corresponding to the choices 'R & D costs reduced' and 'better chance of project completion' imply that a significant source of added value for Eureka participants is that projects are more likely to be finished when costs and resources are shared between partners.

The independent survey data suggest that large firms and SMEs are motivated to participate in Eureka for different reasons (see Table 6.18). SME project leaders value Eureka's propensity to enlarge projects and speed their completion more than do large firm leaders. The more frequent choice and higher ranking by SMEs of 'improvement of competitive position', 'widens our product range', and 'access to a larger potential market' imply that SME project leaders are generally very

Table 6.17 Expected benefits of Eureka participation (independent survey)

Benefit	Frequency[a] %	Significance quotient[b]
Cross-fertilization of ideas	68	8.8
Improvement of competitive position	61	8.0
R & D costs reduced	57	7.9
Larger project/increased funds	50	6.5
Early access to new technology/knowledge	48	6.4
Better chance of project completion	48	6.2
Enhanced prestige	47	5.9
Access to larger potential market	40	5.5
Risks reduced	40	5.1
Widens our product range	39	4.8
Influence on development of standards	36	4.6
Elimination of duplicated R & D	36	4.5
Knowledge of partners' products/strategies	32	3.9
Supportive measures from Eureka	26	2.8
Protection from larger companies	12	1.4
Protection from foreign competitors	11	1.2
Other	7	1.1

Notes: [a]Column shows % of sample which chose each 'benefit' regardless of where it was ranked. [b]'Significance quotient' was calculated by assigning ranked choices a value between 1 and 16 in inverse order to the ranking respondents assigned to each benefit: ranking of 1 = value 16, ranking of 2 = value of 15, ... ranking of 16 = value of 1. Totals were then divided by the number of respondents which chose each benefit. No respondent chose all 16 benefits plus 'other'.

market-oriented. By contrast, large firms are motivated to participate in Eureka primarily by the need to share the R & D costs of expensive projects.

The official survey asked its respondents to choose from a short list of very general 'motives for participation in Eureka' (see Table 6.19). The choices offered to respondents do not shed much light on the question of what motivates participation in Eureka. However, SMEs do appear to value the 'business opportunities' offered by Eureka participation more than do other types of participants.

Table 6.20 lists responses to an official survey question which asked what respondents considered the 'most important aspects of Eureka'. Notably, public (or 'additional') R & D funds were considered to be less important than other aspects. The relatively low rate of choice of 'knowledge diffusion/sharing' does not support the independent survey's finding that 'cross-fertilization of ideas' is the most important benefit of collaboration via Eureka. However, the choices offered to respondents were rather vague and not very clearly differentiated. 'International cooperation' must be seen as subsuming at least in part

Table 6.18 Expected benefits of Eureka participation for large firms and SMEs (independent survey)

Benefit	Large firms	SMEs
Cross-fertilization of ideas	8.2	9.6
Improvement of competitive position	8.6	10.5
R & D costs reduced	9.0	9.4
Larger project/increased funds	4.3	9.3
Early access to new technology/knowledge	6.7	8.8
Better chance of project completion	6.6	10.0
Enhanced prestige	5.7	7.9
Access to larger potential market	3.6	7.3
Risks reduced	5.4	8.0
Widens our product range	3.9	8.0
Influence on development of standards	5.4	4.5
Elimination of duplicated R & D	5.5	6.5
Knowledge of partners' products/strategies	4.5	4.3
Supportive measures from Eureka	2.5	4.5
Protection from larger companies	1.0	4.5
Protection from foreign competitors	1.5	1.5

Note: N = 'significance quotient' (see Table 6.17)

the notion of 'cross-fertilization of ideas'. Moreover, the choice of 'cross-fertilization of ideas' as Eureka's primary benefit by independent survey respondents, and the importance of 'technology aspects' and 'technology development' for official survey respondents suggest a general observation: firms will collaborate in R & D projects when they can find partners whose assets in terms of technology and ideas complement their own.[19]

Both surveys included questions which were designed to pinpoint the specific effects of Eureka status on projects. The independent survey offered a rather short list of choices (although relatively few chose 'other') and invited respondents to choose as many as they thought relevant. The results shown in Table 6.21 show that project leaders generally viewed Eureka's effect on their projects as positive. Again, significant differentials existed between the responses of large firms and SMEs. In particular, SMEs appeared to value Eureka's 'marriage bureau' function more than did large firms.

The official survey asked participants to indicate Eureka's 'contribution' to their project. Respondents were offered no choices which implied that Eureka's contribution had been negative and, again, some choices overlapped. Differentials between large firms and SMEs were not substantial, but SMEs were more likely to cite 'new commercial applications' (70 to 62 per cent) and 'new distribution channels' (33 to 28

Table 6.19 Motives for participation in Eureka (official survey)

Motives	Large firms %	SMEs %	Total sample %
Technology aspects	88	81	86
Business opportunities	61	72	55
Financial aspects	50	45	52
Standardization	25	15	24

Table 6.20 Most important aspects of Eureka (official survey)

Aspect	Large firms %	SMEs %	Total sample %
Technology development	76	72	71
International cooperation	55	58	60
Additional R & D funding	43	53	47
Knowledge diffusion/sharing	37	36	39

Table 6.21 Effect of Eureka status on project (independent survey)

Effect	Large firms %	SMEs %	Total sample %
Increased financial size of project	60	58	59
Brought more partners into the project	34	71	53
Faster development of prototype	43	38	40
Made administration more difficult	38	33	34
Expanded market for eventual product	17	33	31
Delayed start of project	9	13	19

per cent).[20] The observations that most SMEs seem to be market-oriented and involved in genuinely 'near-market' projects are reinforced.

Both surveys sought to determine what had been the major problems that participants had experienced with Eureka. The independent survey presented project leaders with a list from which to choose as many as they found relevant, although many chose to write in their own choice under 'other' (see Table 6.22). By far, the problem most often chosen was 'different expectations among partners'. This result indicates that Eureka routinely brings together partners from different industrial cultures whose ideas about any project's time scale, methodology and goal are never one and the same. It also implies that negotiations over

Table 6.22 Major problems experienced (independent survey)

Problem	Large firms %	SMEs %	Total sample %
Different expectations among partners	55	42	51
Delays in project schedule	28	46	38
Intellectual property rights	28	33	26
Other	13	17	22
Risk of exploitation by competitors	19	21	17
Differences in accounting procedures	15	13	16
Language problems	17	13	12
Quality reduced to weakest partner	17	4	10
Negotiating location of project work	2	8	4

rights to exploit the results of projects are often difficult: a problem also subsumed under 'intellectual property rights', which was cited by more than one-quarter of respondents.

The frequent choice of 'delays in project schedule' appears to contradict with the relatively infrequent choice of 'delayed start of the project' as a primary effect of Eureka (see Table 6.21). The discrepancy may reflect the difference between delays in the start of projects and delays in a project's schedule once it has started. Public funding, which most projects clearly have, may help to launch Eureka projects sooner than projects which lack public support. But once R & D actually begins, the noted differences in national public funding policies – especially in time scales and points in time when funds are granted – can slow down the progress of projects. The data indicate that this problem is more acute for SME-led projects than for those led by large firms.

The official survey provided a quite different list of problems from which respondents could choose (see Table 6.23). All types of respondents thought 'contractual drafting difficulties' had been their most serious problem. Few clear differentials exist between the responses of large firms and SMEs, although a higher share of SMEs reported 'financial problems with partners'. This result provides some support to the independent survey's finding that SMEs experience problems leading projects because they often do not know whether their partners receive public funding or how much they receive. The official survey data do *not* support the hypothesis that SMEs have more problems with their project's formal and legal organization or with project delays. But these problems may be more common to projects led by SMEs, as opposed to those which only include SMEs.

The independent survey asked how governments could be more helpful in assisting the participation of project leaders in Eureka (see

Table 6.24). Predictably, what participants wanted most from their governments was more money. However, SMEs appeared to value the elimination of funding *delays* even more than *increased* funding. SME leaders also were more likely to want non-financial support from their governments, such as information on emerging standards and prospective partners. These findings suggest that public funding is not the only or even the most important source of Eureka' added value for its SME participants.

The official survey did not include a question which specifically asked how governments could be more helpful to participants. However, when asked which of Eureka's procedures most needed to be improved, vast majorities of both large firms (89 per cent) and SMEs (93 per cent) indicated a need for 'uniform funding procedures'.[21]

III. PARTICIPANT ATTITUDES AND NATIONAL ORIGINS

The official survey was designed to provide a quite generalized overview of participant attitudes toward Eureka. Due to the survey's inter-governmental sanction and the political sensitivity of passing judgement on national Eureka policies, the assessment panel did not provide any breakdown of responses according to the national origins of respondents. By contrast, the independent survey did generate subsamples from different Member States, even if they were quite small and comprised ten or more completed questionnaires only from France, Germany, the Netherlands, Italy and the UK (see Table 6.11). Some national characteristics and perceptions of Eureka are common to respondents from each of these states and are worth noting.

French project leaders came to Eureka with generally less previous collaborative experience or pre-existing relationships with their current Eureka partners than the sample as a whole.[22] More French respondents led relatively small projects (with two or three partners) than did their counterparts from other large states.[23] Nearly 70 per cent said their biggest problem was differing expectations among partners, compared with less than half of all other respondents.

By contrast, a very high share of respondents from Germany – more than 70 per cent – led large projects involving six or more partners.[24] Relatively few German leaders indicated that they originally proposed their project or implied that it was designed primarily to pursue commercial goals.[25] Responses from German project leaders on questions related to Eureka's effects and problems generally reflected the difficulties related to coordinating large, complex projects.[26]

Data provided by leaders from the Netherlands tended not to diverge significantly from that of the total sample. About the only perceptible national characteristic of Dutch participants was an unusually low propensity to complain about delays in receiving public funds.[27] The implication may be that mechanisms for the delivery of Dutch public funding are more efficient than those in other states.

Conversely, almost all respondents from Italy (93 per cent) wanted their government to speed up delivery of public funds, while fewer (64 per cent) complained about the amount on offer. A high share of Italian respondents also wanted their national Eureka office to provide better information on partners, more help in coordinating projects, and (especially) more help with standards compared with those of other Member States.[28] Italian participants generally appeared less happy with the performance of their national Eureka office than did those of any other large state.

Data collected from Italian project leaders also reflected a strong emphasis on commercial goals: more Italians said IPRs were a problem, more feared exploitation of project results by their competitors, and more claimed that Eureka had made it easier to find private finance compared with the mean for each response.[29] The wide implication is that most Italian-led projects are near-market, industrial projects.

As for Italian-led projects, those with UK leaders appear oriented towards commercial goals. Most British respondents said Eureka participation expanded their potential market and promised to lead to a prototype sooner.[30] However, the most striking characteristic of UK respondents was the frequency with which they reported problems related to public funding. Most comments volunteered in response to questions with an option of 'other' were complaints about a lack of public funds or delays in receiving them. Relatively more British respondents complained about project delays and complex administration than did those from other Member States.[31]

Subsamples for all other Member States included six respondents or fewer. However, several interesting observations come to light when the total survey sample is split between those from 'large states' – France, Germany, the Netherlands, Italy and the UK – and all others. This exercise allows two subsamples of eighty-seven project leaders from large states and thirty-four from 'small states' to be tested.

Small state project leaders generally reported less previous experience in collaborative R & D than did large state leaders. This finding was clear in all measures of previous collaborative experience, especially in the number of current partners with whom leaders had worked in the past (see Table 6.25).

Table 6.23 Major problems experienced (official survey)

Problem	Large firms %	SMEs %	Total sample %
Contractual drafting difficulties	38	39	39
Financial problems with partners	27	32	29
Partner(s) withdrew from project	30	25	26
Partner(s) failed to meet schedules	26	24	24
Delayed by supportive measure	16	15	16
Technical inability of partner(s)	9	11	11
Disagreement on product rights	12	12	10

Table 6.24 How governments could be more helpful (independent survey)

Response	Large firms %	SMEs %	Total sample %
Provide more public funds	68	58	68
Eliminate delays in funding	57	67	62
Provide more help with standards	13	29	18
Better coordinate other partners	13	13	14
Other	12	–	12
Provide better information on partners	2	13	8

Table 6.25 Small and large state respondents' previous collaborative experience with current partners (independent survey)

Respondents	Number of current partners					
	Four + %	Three %	Two %	One %	None %	Unsure %
Small state	6	3	29	32	15	15
Large state	14	9	32	12	8	14

Table 6.26 Shares of small and large state respondents' own R & D costs covered by public funds (independent survey)

Respondents	50–31% %	30–21% %	20–11% %	10–1% %	<1% %
Small states	35	15	15	12	12
Large states	49	17	3	11	1

Note: Rows do not add to 100% due to missing cases in Tables 6.25 and 6.26.

The most striking difference between the two groups was that small state respondents tended to lead smaller projects and receive less public

Table 6.27 Small and large state respondents' intentions to participate in Eureka again (independent survey)

Respondents	Yes %	No %	Unsure %
Small state	59	6	35
Large state	72	5	23

funds. For example, Table 6.26 shows that substantially lower percentages of small state leaders' own R & D costs were covered by public funds compared with leaders from large states. Despite this result, proportionately fewer small state leaders cited problems with Eureka, and more seemed pleased with the performance of their national Eureka offices, based on a relatively low rate of choice of 'suggestions' about how national offices could be more helpful. About the same percentage of small state respondents (80 per cent) as large state respondents (86 per cent) would consider collaborating again with their current Eureka partners.

Yet, substantially more small state leaders, over 40 per cent, said they would not consider future participation in Eureka or were not sure (see Table 6.27). This is a 'bottom line' finding which implies that small state respondents find that Eureka provides fewer benefits to them than it does to large state leaders, and that most small state leaders value their collaborative experience generally more than participation in Eureka specifically.

Dividing the total sample between respondents from EC states and those from EFTA states provides a less satisfactory basis for comparison for the simple reason that only 15 per cent of the independent survey sample were EFTA state firms. However, the data in Table 6.11 reveal that EFTA organizations account for a roughly similar share (13 per cent) of all Eureka project leaders. While EFTA participants lead relatively few projects, between 20 and 25 per cent of all Eureka projects include an EFTA partner.[32]

Most of the observations made above about small state project leaders as a subgroup also apply to EFTA state project leaders. But analysis of the subsample of EFTA respondents helps explain Eureka's surprising lack of additionality for project leaders who are new to collaborative R & D. Half (nine of eighteen) of EFTA respondents lacked any previous collaborative R & D experience. Most EFTA organizations who had collaborated in the past (six of nine) had never done so with their current Eureka partners. However, 83 per cent (fifteen of eighteen) said their projects would definitely or probably have been launched even if Eureka did not exist, compared with only 43 per cent of EC state leaders. Thus, most EFTA state leaders appeared to have decided that they wished to get involved in European collaborative R & D, perhaps in response to the launch of the 1992 project, regardless of whether they were granted Eureka status or even whether Eureka existed.

Review!

IV. SYNTHESIS AND CONCLUSIONS

The single characteristic of Eureka which is reflected most clearly in the survey data is its ambiguity. The initiative groups together a somewhat random collection of projects which often have little in common besides the Eureka label itself. The point is that any data set on Eureka – included the two analysed here – must be interpreted cautiously due to the eclecticism of its projects.

Yet, governments are very low on learning curves about how to organize and structure collaborative R & D programmes. The data sets analysed in this chapter are the most detailed ever collected on Eureka. The observations which spring from them have direct policy relevance because among them are clear, tested hypotheses about Eureka's major effects and problems.

The data provide a general 'snapshot' of Eureka's partners, projects and funding arrangements. Due largely to its 'industry-led' ethos, Eureka has built upon established patterns of collaboration more than it has prompted the creation of new ones. About two-thirds of all Eureka project leaders have previous collaborative experience. Project leaders clearly rely heavily on their own pre-existing contacts to find partners for Eureka projects, and most projects include at least two partners who have collaborated with each other in the past.

But Eureka's coterie of industrial participants is dichotomous. Large firm project leaders are far more likely than SMEs to bring previous experience to their participation in Eureka and they appear to have far fewer problems with the formal and legal organization of their projects. As many as one-third of large firm participants appear to be engaged in essentially pre-competitive projects, while SMEs tend to be very market-oriented and usually participate in genuinely 'near-market' projects. The assessment panel estimates that SMEs which participate in Eureka 'experience a more significant contribution to [their] competitiveness' than do large firms.[33]

Eureka's project list reflects a similar dichotomy. On one hand, Eureka includes many large, complex projects which are led by large firms (and public research organizations), and many of these projects clearly are not engaged in 'near-market' R & D. On the other hand, Eureka features a substantial number of projects led by SMEs which tend to include fewer partners and are more focused on short-term, commercial goals. One of the few characteristics common to most projects is that the vast majority are truly 'new' in the sense that they did not begin in some other international collaborative R & D scheme. This finding raises serious doubts about the adequacy of links between Eureka and the EC's R & D programmes.

The vast majority of Eureka's projects receive public funds and most project leaders seem to receive quite a lot. More than half of all Eureka projects feature at least two partners who are receiving public funds. The data confirm the broad estimate that as much as 35 per cent of the combined total costs of all Eureka projects are met by public funds. They also confirm that Eureka remains a largely French-led initiative. Far more of Eureka's projects receive public funding from France than from any other Member State.

Collaborative R & D, within or without Eureka, clearly poses special problems for those who take the collaborative plunge. The problem of different expectations among partners, which appears to be the most serious difficulty faced by most Eureka project leaders, must certainly be considered as endemic to collaborative R & D generally, not just to Eureka. The same must be said of the problems of keeping to project schedules and negotiating IPRs.

However, the data illustrate some clear effects of Eureka's distinct methodology. In particular, Eureka's strict intergovernmentalism clearly makes project definition and management difficult. Member State project selection and funding policies are distinctly 'nationalized' and are not very transparent between countries. A project proposal may conform with the criteria for granting Eureka status or funding set out by some Member States, but not others, thus leading to delays in the start of the project while different governments argue about whether the proposal deserves support. However, discrepancies exist between the two data sets on this question: the assessment panel stresses that 'different national funding procedures often causes [sic] problems in the definition and start-up of projects', while the independent survey suggests that getting projects started is less of a problem than managing them once they are underway.[34] Part of the explanation is that there is confusion about precisely what it means for a project to 'start': does it mean that it secures Eureka status and simply enters its 'definition phase' (which may involve mere discussions about the possibility of collaboration), or does it mean that a project enters its 'implementation phase' and R & D actually begins? A 'grey area' clearly exists between the granting of Eureka status and the implementation phase: a project may 'start' (depending on how that term is defined) at any point in between. The frequent citing of the problems 'different expectations among partners' and 'contractual drafting difficulties' by independent and official survey respondents respectively helps explain why projects may remain in this 'grey area' for a long time. In any event, the assessment panel estimates that about half of all projects have experienced problems with disharmonized national selection or funding policies.[35]

Both surveys imply that SMEs place a high value on non-financial supportive measures from their governments, which might help to compensate for their general lack of previous experience in collaborative R & D. But the independent survey data suggest that SME project leaders still have far more difficulties than other types of leaders in organizing projects, negotiating IPRs and keeping projects on schedule.[36] Eureka's lack of transparency is evident in the alarming number of SME project leaders who do not know how many of their partners are being funded. Eureka's national public funding policies do discriminate in favour of SMEs, but SMEs lead smaller and cheaper projects than do large firms, so a much larger percentage of their project's or their own R & D costs would have to be publicly funded before governments began spending anywhere near as much on SMEs as large firms. The data suggest that far less public money goes to SME project leaders than to other types of leaders, or to projects led by SMEs compared to those led by other types of organization.

The data contain real clues about how well Eureka works as a system of incentives created by public authorities to influence private sector behaviour. Many firms have responded to the existence of Eureka by proposing and undertaking collaborative projects which they would not have been able to perform on their own due to the high costs or risks involved. On the one hand, Eureka incorporates many projects – nearing one-half of the total – which *would* exist even if Eureka did not. Many of these projects include relatively few partners and are led by large firms who have previous experience collaborating with at least one of their present Eureka partners. On the other hand, 40 per cent of Eureka's projects appear to be truly 'additional', in the sense that they would not exist if Eureka did not exist. About half of these projects are led by SMEs, research institutes or universities. Most feature few partners or no partners who had collaborated with one another previous to their participation in Eureka.

Eureka's 'marriage bureau' function emerges as its most important source of added value. Eureka has the effect of enlarging at least one-third of all projects, a total which must include some which would exist even if Eureka did not. Often, projects are made larger because new partners become aware of proposals circulating during the 45-day period prior to the granting of Eureka status. A caveat is that larger projects may be more difficult to manage and keep on schedule. Because Eureka Member States offer different amounts of public funding according to different time scales, participants may find that the scope for delays and uncertainties increases each time a new partner is added to a project.

There is little evidence in the survey data that public funding is the only, or even the most important, factor motivating firms to participate in R & D that they would otherwise forego. The independent survey data show no strong correlation between the amount of public funding received and project additionality.[37] The assessment panel concludes that, 'surprisingly a relatively low value is attached to subsidies as such; public funding is used to execute the projects on a wider scale, to accelerate the project, or to overcome the extra costs of international cooperation'.[38]

The data also suggest that few Eureka projects are led by organizations which had never collaborated before and would not do so now without Eureka. A nuance which emerges from the independent survey data is that many leaders who lacked previous collaborative experience appeared to have decided to pursue collaboration before they knew they could work within Eureka or perhaps even before it was created. Eureka has not had a clear impact on the behaviour of these participants.

However, Eureka's additionality is clear for those project leaders, about 20 per cent of the total independent survey sample, who had never collaborated with any of their *current partners*. These leaders were about 50 per cent more likely than the rest of the sample to think that their project definitely or probably would not exist without Eureka status. Nearly all of these respondents are keen to participate in another Eureka project in the future.

A puzzle emerges: Eureka seems to motivate firms who had never worked *together* to undertake 'additional' projects more than it motivates firms who had never collaborated *at all* to engage in projects which owe their existence to Eureka. This anomaly may be explained in part by the fact that many EFTA firms have experience collaborating with other EFTA partners, but not with EC firms or in EC-funded programmes. Eureka has motivated many EFTA and EC firms to work together for the first time and many of the resultant projects are truly 'additional'.

Eureka is less a single system of incentives than an amalgam of national systems of incentives which are embedded in each Member

State's distinctive 'Eureka policy.' The independent survey data provide a window into the effect of national Eureka policies on the behaviour of indigenous firms. Clearly, the French have substantially expanded the European collaborative links of their R & D community through Eureka. Most French project leaders seem to be engaged in genuinely 'near-market' projects which are in line with Eureka's original goals. French leaders must routinely work with partners who receive less public funding than they do, which clearly can lead to problems of differing expectations. But the large amount of public funding committed by France to Eureka helps projects get started with few delays.

If the logic is accepted that Member States get out of Eureka what they put in, then the conclusion of an extensive survey of French Eureka participants undertaken in 1989 – that Eureka is a *succès indéniable* from the French point of view – is unsurprising. The French survey, conducted by IDS Consultants, seconds many of the conclusions of the present chapter.[39] For example, it found that Eureka had dramatically expanded links between French industry and other European organizations and increased the size of 'French' projects, particularly those led by SMEs.

By contrast with most French-led projects, a high percentage of projects with German leaders are large, infrastructure projects launched as a result of government initiatives. Many are led by non-industrial organizations and are only marginally related to commercial goals. The different political goals which the German and French governments brought to the making of Eureka in 1985 are thus readily perceptible in the nature of each state's actual participation in the scheme.

There is little which is distinctive about the responses of Dutch participants to the independent survey besides evidence of a high level of satisfaction with the Dutch Eureka office. Meanwhile, Italian project leaders complain more about the performance of their national Eureka officials than do respondents from any other large state. An important variable in explaining this difference in attitude may be that a high share of Dutch project leaders are large firms, while many Italian project leaders are SMEs, which rely more heavily on their national Eureka offices for support.[40]

Data collected from British respondents imply the UK is in a category of its own in terms of industrial attitudes. No other set of national leaders emphasize so strongly that their country's public funding policy is inadequate. Most British-led Eureka projects appear to be truly 'additional', but seem to cause more trouble than they are worth to their leaders. Previous surveys of British participants generally support the independent survey's findings that relatively few British participants are anxious to participate in Eureka again and many have difficulties keeping projects on schedule because 'a lot of time delays and bureaucracy are encountered'.[41]

Eureka's project list is very much dominated by the five largest states. A logical inference which could be drawn from the data is that this result is a product of small state firms' lack of previous experience in collaborative R & D relative to large state firms. Eureka seems to have provided a convenient vehicle to small state project leaders – particularly those from EFTA states – for establishing new collaborative links, particularly to firms in larger states. But while small state project leaders report relatively few problems with Eureka, they are less keen about the idea of participating in the initiative again. Now that new collaborative links are established, Eureka may have diminishing value for small state leaders, particularly because they receive less public funding than do leaders from large states.

Several observations from the preceding sections provide a foundation for the generation of prescriptions leading to the improvement of Eureka. First, the initiative certainly has helped far more SMEs to actually lead projects than could do so without Eureka. But SMEs still want more non-financial support, such as help with standards, intellectual property rights, information on potential partners and so on. The assessment panel recommends that 'more support should be given to SMEs in the fields of partner search, project definition, and feasibility studies'.[42]

Second, Eureka's strict intergovernmentalism is manifest in an extremely diverse project list. It is not at all clear that a majority of Eureka's projects operate 'close to the market' or aim to produce a marketable process or product quickly. The independent survey data generated from subsamples of national participants reveal substantial divergences between the project portfolios of different Member States (particularly between Germany's and those of other large states). On a political level, the assessment panel found 'no consensus among countries [about] whether the projects should be focused on market applicability or whether basic research is allowed as well'.[43] Political obstacles still exist which make it difficult to exclude all but 'near market' projects from Eureka.

It might be argued that there is no *a priori* reason why Eureka should not incorporate pre-competitive projects. National governments would fund many of these projects whether or not Eureka existed. Benefits may be had in terms of enlarged projects, accelerated technology transfer or cross-border standards development if such projects are performed collaboratively. Many EC governments would bridle at the suggestion that the Commission should have a monopoly power to decide which collaborative pre-competitive R & D projects in Europe should exist and which should not.

But other intergovernmental frameworks such as COST exist to fund such projects. Eureka was created to fill the gap in the range of existing collaborative schemes for an initiative which could promote European technological competitiveness in the short-term. If Eureka becomes a 'grab bag' for any type of R & D project, it becomes difficult for governments to promote Eureka as an initiative with a clear purpose. The assessment panel clearly had the problem of Eureka's fuzzy image in mind when it recommended that Member States pay 'special attention . . . to the commercial prospects' of its project portfolio'. Ensuring that Eureka incorporates only market-led projects would act to make Eureka's image much clearer and make it easier for Member States to 'sell' the initiative to their indigenous firms.

Third, the failure of governments to harmonize their Eureka policies is the initiative's most obvious weakness. The fact that projects may receive funding at different points in time from multiple governments causes delays and erodes the added value that subsidies should provide to projects. The assessment panel is particularly forceful in recommending that 'the timing of funding decisions in the different Member States as they relate to one project should be synchronised . . . this is a technical problem rather than a political one'.[44]

A related difficulty is Eureka's lack of transparency. It is undesirable that so many project leaders – especially SMEs – do not know how many of their partners bring public funds to their projects. Planning all projects but those with the shortest projected life span or fewest number of partners must become a guessing game in many cases. Echoing the recommendations of the authors of several previous surveys,[45] the assessment panel wants all Member States to make transparent their criteria and procedures for granting Eureka status and public funding to projects.[46] The idea that national funding commitments should be made simultaneously, multinationally and transparently when projects are approved is a blatant violation of Eureka's strict intergovernmental ethos, but it would clearly make project management much simpler and would probably encourage more firms to participate in Eureka.

Finally, Eureka and the Framework programme are clearly inadequately linked. Even though most independent survey respondents have previously participated in EC-funded R & D, an alarmingly low number believe that sufficient synergy exists between Eureka and the EC's programmes. The assessment panel observes that 'Eureka is not very often used to exploit the scientific and technological results from the EC programmes' and that 'co-operation between Eureka and the EC programmes is still weak'.[47] This problem requires careful study both by the Commission and Eureka Member States to determine what steps could be taken to ensure that the original vision of Eureka's complementarity with EC-funded R & D can be realized.

To summarize, the data suggest that Eureka as it is constructed provides incentives to firms which are sufficient to yield a substantial amount of 'additional' R & D. It has made a genuine difference in the overall European R & D effort by forging new links between firms and motivating more firms to engage in collaborative R & D than would do so otherwise. However, while industrial attitudes toward Eureka are generally positive, its participants are more enthusiastic about the experience of collaboration than they are about Eureka itself.[48]

This finding might be interpreted to suggest that Eureka is doing its job: one view would hold that Eureka exists only to convince firms to take the collaborative plunge for the first time and thus become accustomed to operating within a single European market for R & D. After firms see the benefits of collaboration, they should require no further incentives (i.e. subsidies) to conduct their R & D collaboratively in the future. In taking this view, one would welcome the finding that Eureka participants value their collaborative experience more than participation in Eureka *per se*.

But such a view seems myopic. The EC in the 1990s is not a classical economist's dream about to come true. European states which seek to promote supply-side innovation will always wish to provide more than verbal support for R & D projects that are of particular strategic importance. The emergence of the single market as a backdrop suggests that such projects will have more chance of success if they are undertaken collaboratively. European governments may wish to prompt private sector behaviour which leads to the conduct of such R & D, rather than relying totally on private sector initiative, particularly when non-European governments subsidize *their* technology producers in similar projects. Sometimes, European governments will wish to fund R & D that is impossible for the EC to fund because it is too close to the market, or involves non-EC firms, or serves the 'Community interest' of only a few EC Member States.

The point is that strong arguments will persist in the 1990s for the existence of a policy tool through which European governments can flexibly and collaboratively fund strategic R & D projects. As a system of incentives for influencing private sector behaviour, Eureka is by no means a failure. But neither is it the best of all possible worlds.

7 Inside the projects
Case studies

This chapter shifts levels of analysis from Eureka as a single initiative to Eureka as a collection of individual projects. There is no typical Eureka project. Thus, five projects which have been carefully selected and weighted to reflect the diversity of Eureka's activities are singled out for detailed evaluation. These projects' essential characteristics are summarized in Table 7.1.

Each case study below begins by assessing the project's fit with the national innovation policy goals of its 'lead' Member State(s). Eureka's 'added value' to each project is then summarized. The special problems encountered by participants in each project are considered. Finally, each case study grapples with the question of how Eureka's methodology has affected the management of the project and its chances for success.

I. MITHRA: WHAT THE SMEs THINK

The MITHRA project aims to develop and market mobile robots for 'tele-surveillance'.[1] Among the applications foreseen are robots which can detect and extinguish fires, sense intruders into warehouses or enter hostile environments such as a nuclear reactors. The project was launched with thirteen partners, all of whom are based in the Alps region 'technology triangle', whose corners are Lyon, Geneva and Torino. Its participants include one of the world's largest surveillance and security companies (the Swiss firm Cerberus), an affiliate of the Italian car-maker Fiat (SEPA), and a diverse assortment of robotics firms, several of which are very small. The project has an estimated value of 26 million ECU over five years.[2]

The MITHRA project was one of the first to be granted Eureka status which included SMEs in a leading role. The project has clear commercial aims: to produce three types of advanced robots for a total

Table 7.1 Five Eureka projects: essential characteristics

Project	Goals	Cost (MECU)	Major partners/ project leaders	Lead Member State(s)
MITHRA	Product-oriented	26	SMEs	France
RA-D	Product-oriented	12	Medium-sized oil drilling & engineering firms	UK
Eurotrac	Infrastructure	120	Universities, research laboratories	Germany
Cosine	Infrastructure	300	Research laboratories, national ministries	CEC
HDTV	Product-oriented/ infrastructure	625	Philips, Thomson	Netherlands, France, CEC

market worth an estimated 15–20 million ECU per year. One partner observed:

> We've spent almost an entire year on an operational study to verify how to make a product which corresponds exactly to the needs of the client. But not with the robotics people, not with the scientific university people, but with the people who make and sell security products.[3]

The project's fit with French national innovation policy goals was evidenced by the avid interest taken in the project from an early stage by the MRT. Prior to achieving Eureka status, several French partners had direct contact with Curien.[4] For political reasons, the French were concerned to dispel the notion that Eureka was an initiative only for large, MNC-led projects. For policy reasons, the MITHRA project was consistent with the MRT's general push to 'regionalize' French innovation policy and encourage the development of an entrepreneurial corps of French SMEs. The project included two SMEs and a *polytechnique* located in Grenoble's high-technology park, the *Zone pour l'Innovation et les Réalisations Scientifiques et Techniques* (ZIRST), which was designed to link industrial firms with the local university and was the first of its kind in France.[5]

The Italian interest in launching MITHRA was catalysed by the Torino-based *Centro Estero Camere Commercio Piedmont* (CECCP), which is an actual partner in the project and has extensive links to the Grenoble *Chambre de Commerce et d'Industrie*. The CECCP has worked to develop for the Torino area a strong reputation as a centre of excellence in innovation. It also has nurtured the Lyon–Torino–Geneva triangle's international reputation.

The Swiss government's interest in the project stems from the involvement of the extensive Swiss surveillance and security industry. Although Switzerland provides no public funds to private firms participating in Eureka, the Swiss government has funded the participation of the *École Polytechnique Fédérale de Lausanne* in MITHRA. The commitment of all three governments to the project was symbolized by the public signing of a project 'protocol', which formalized work-sharing arrangements between the project's partners, in the presence of NPCs from all three countries in July 1987.[6]

According to two partners surveyed, Eureka's added value stems primarily from its expansion of the eventual market for the project.[7] For the project's SMEs, Eureka provides public funds without the onerous administrative work associated with the EC schemes and allows its partners managerial autonomy. A spokesman for one partner complained:

> It's very annoying for an SME because if you consider the extra administrative work together with your chance of getting [EC] funds, you can demonstrate that it's not advantageous for an SME to even try. The administrative work is enormous. Even in Eureka about 30 per cent of the money we've received goes on paperwork. For Esprit, it's more than half. But Eureka is a lot better than the other European programmes. The second fundamental advantage of Eureka is that normally the management of the project isn't done by public administrations. Basically, they give their approval and the money ... then you can say 'buzz off'.[8]

Eureka also allows MITHRA to include Swiss, non-EC participants, and to retain French as its *lingua franca*. One partner explained:

> The partners all speak French, with the exception of the Turinos, who speak the local language, *patois*, which is almost French. So everybody understands each other directly. The problem of language in European programmes is very important. I know one project between Spaniards and Germans where the language is English, and it's very awkward. Especially in small firms, and more particularly among French small firms, it's very rare that people speak other languages.[9]

Despite the benefits MITHRA's partners associate with Eureka, the project ran into difficulties almost immediately after it started. First, the show of solidarity by all three relevant governments in launching MITHRA produced no coordination of funding decisions. Three project partners reported problems in keeping the project on schedule due 'the staggering of several years of the points when public finance was released by different governments'.[10]

Second, coordinating a project with thirteen diverse types of participants proved problematical. Several partners suggested that the early involvement of a myriad of public administrations in the project's definition created pressures to allow more firms into the project than were really necessary.[11] IPRs were negotiated soon after the project started, but several partners foresaw future problems with profit-sharing, and one said, 'We all sit around a table with our machine guns. It's not easy'.[12]

Finally, the project illustrates the acute financial problems faced by many European SMEs. The project's original 'technical pilot' was the French robotics firm AID, which employed seventy people when the project was launched. Both AID and another Grenoble-based SME in the project, ITMI, nearly collapsed when their credit lines expired in September 1987. AID was forced to withdraw from the MITHRA project and eventually transformed itself into a consulting firm.[13] ITMI's participation in MITHRA was re-evaluated and eventually reduced.[14] The project as a whole was set back considerably in the process.

The MITHRA project points to the particular difficulties faced by SMEs that choose to engage in near-market R & D instead of basic R & D as sub-contractors to large firms or public research laboratories. Development R & D usually promises profits only in the long term and even then receipts are often irregular, which makes self-financing for SMEs extremely difficult. As a spokesman for AID lamented:

> The problem is that in Europe you don't have the financing that you have in the US . . . We'll be able to exist on the work we have now for just a couple more months because we have very good products but not the finance. For a project like this, it's a disaster, because it's only partly financed, and it's necessary to find the rest of the finance ourselves. And it's absolutely impossible for us to find as much as we need. It's not at all like in Japan, where there's a synthesis between the technology and the finance.[15]

Reaching a verdict on the effect of Eureka's methodology on the MITHRA project is difficult. Two partners estimated that it was 'unlikely' that the project would have been launched without Eureka. The project's partners clearly prefer Eureka's industry-led ethos to the *dirigisme* of most EC programmes. But early political interest in the project did not translate into coordinated funding decisions between three governments or sufficient finance for the French SMEs involved. European governments have paid much lip service to Eureka's value as a forum for extending the benefits of collaborative R & D to SMEs. However, the creation of new technological liaisons without new liaisons between product-oriented SMEs and sources of funding may be counterproductive. The effect may be to condition potentially innovative SMEs to conclude that collaborative 'near-market' R & D is simply not worth the risks involved.

II. RA–D: THE TEXTBOOK PROJECT

The Rig Automation Drilling (RA-D) project seeks to apply novel mechanical handling techniques to off-shore gas and oil drilling. Its goal is to develop a highly mechanized and automated drilling system which can be easily assembled off-shore and then quickly moved away to new drilling sites. RA-D is a relatively small and exclusively Anglo-Norwegian project involving five large oil companies, a Norwegian drilling contractor and a British engineering firm.[16]

The RA-D project has clear commercial goals and aims to develop a marketable product. The two lead firms are medium-sized (each with about 1500 employees) and are collaborating together for the first time. The project receives public funding from both the British government and the EC's Thermie programme into new energy technologies. It is one of a relatively small number of Eureka projects which are led by British firms, and is described by a British Eureka official as a 'textbook example of the kind of project we think should be conducted under Eureka'.[17]

The RA-D project is germane in the context of British and Norwegian national innovation policies because North Sea oil is a critical source of export and tax revenues for both countries. North Sea oil reserves are far more costly to extract than those in the Middle East because the drilling environment is extremely hostile and dangerous and requires very complex engineering. The UK has provided public funding for R & D into deep-water drilling techniques since 1976.[18] The world-wide market for off-shore operations is worth more than 50 billion ECU per year, with actual drilling worth about a quarter of the total.[19]. Norway and the UK each have world-class oil drilling and engineering industries.

The RA-D project is three-cornered. Strachan and Henshaw are the rig designers and managers of the project. Large oil companies, who are cash-rich and own the platforms, provide funding and eventually will use the system. Smedvik, a Norwegian firm with a global reputation in engineering, actually operates the drilling equipment.

The added value of Eureka for the project stems first from its inclusion of Norway as a Member State. A participant from a UK participant claimed:

We needed the Norwegian papal blessing as well as the British. I honestly don't know if the Norwegian government is contributing to the project, but I doubt it. Remember, though, that Statoil, who are a major partner, is a state-owned oil company. So just having them involved is a sort of public support from their government.[20]

Second, Eureka has allowed the RA-D partners to pool EC subsidies with those offered by the UK. The project leader suggested, 'I think had we not got Eureka status together with the EEC support, which of course is different, I don't think we would have carried the project. But we are getting a lot more money from Brussels than from the British government'.[21]

Finally, the circulation of the project proposal during the 45–day period before Eureka status was granted generated interest in the project from French, Italian, Dutch and Finnish firms. While none joined the project, one project partner speculated, 'hopefully through these contacts, we will be in a position in the future to talk to them about maybe being our licensee and maybe, say, the Italians could reach a different overseas market than we can in Britain'.[22]

The RA-D project's most serious problem has been coping with the intricacies and frustrations of obtaining support from a poorly resourced and ill-coordinated British administration. The project leader explained:

To enable the DTI to look at giving us any money at all, we had to have Eureka status. So we picked up the Eureka status . . . We applied through the DTI for funding as a manufacturer under the Support for Innovation scheme. We found that to be a horrendously complex business. Although we had a lot of sympathy for the DTI officials, it was a very onerous exercise. We obtained Eureka status in Copenhagen, but then it was agreed by the British administration that it might be a better thing if the Department of Energy sponsored this, not the DTI. Having got to the stage where the DTI was actually able to give us some money, when we actually got approval, we switched to the Department of Energy.[23]

Reflecting on this experience, a spokesman for Strachan and Henshaw complained:

A plea from the contractor: compared with the French, the Italians, probably the Norwegians, there is a lack of coordination and cohesion in this country for those seeking public support. Between ministries, and between ministries and non-ministries, such as some of the pseudo-venture capitalists that we have such as the British

Technology Group. In every direction there is no coordination. So one has to become an expert oneself. You can't just go see a man in Whitehall and he'll do it for you ... So the action for me right now is in Brussels ... Even though I'm not quite sure where Eureka stops and where the EC begins, the way I view it ... Eureka is status. The EC is money.[24]

A second problem is simply the high risks involved, which are mostly borne by the two lead partners. Public support from the EC and Department of Energy was secured only until the land-testing phase of the project. After that, as the project leader noted, 'how much will it cost to do new testing, marketing, demonstration and convincing to get it accepted by the oil industry is completely impossible to know'.[25] Crucially, a chance to spread the risks to partners beyond Norway and the UK was missed in 1988. A project partner recalled:

We engaged in quite serious discussions with organizations in Italy, Holland, France and in Finland for working out a way that we could collaborate under Eureka such that each government would support its own contractor in sharing in this automation of drilling. I think we did not place enough importance at the time on using the correct words to make those other European contractors eligible for support from their governments ... There's a learning curve involved here, and we haven't always got it right ... But there's nobody around in British government offices that can help you on this learning curve.[26]

While Eureka's methodology provides new collaborative opportunities to European firms, many may be missed simply due to inexperience. The RA-D project shows that Eureka participants depend on public administrations for more than just public funding.

The RA-D project brings together partners with clear complementary assets who had never worked with each other before. Eureka has been used as a policy foil by two governments for directing R & D support to industries which matter greatly to their national economies. However, the picture which emerges from the British side is one of a lack of coordination with other domestic and European R & D schemes, and virtually no public administrative support for expanding the project to include additional partners, even though the partners wished to do so. If the RA-D case typifies the experience of partners engaged in a 'textbook example' of a project which merits British public support, one must wonder how firms fare in R & D sectors where the justification for support is not as compelling.

III. EUROTRAC – THE KITCHEN SINK INCLUDED

Eurotrac is a snappy acronym for the ponderous project title 'European Experiment on Transport and Transformation of Environmentally Relevant Trace Constituents in the Troposphere over Europe'. Its goal is to determine how pollution in the lower atmosphere contributes to acid rain, the 'greenhouse effect' and depletion of the ozone layer. All Eureka Member States (except Luxembourg and Iceland) plus the Commission are members of the project.

Eurotrac was the first environmental project to achieve Eureka status. It is by far the most expensive Eureka project in the sector and the vast majority of its funding comes from public sources, with some of its subprojects receiving 100 per cent public funding. Nearly all of Eurotrac's partners are universities and public research laboratories.

Public statements by Eurotrac participants stress that the project seeks 'to promote the technological development of sensitive, specific and fast response instruments for environmental research and monitoring'. Yet, its organizers admit that Eurotrac is essentially 'a basic research project'.[27] Eurotrac has only long-term industrial applications, no clear commercial goal and little pretence of being a 'near-market' project.

Eurotrac consists of a complicated umbrella framework for coordinating fourteen individual subprojects. An International Executive Committee includes a representative from each Member State and has overall responsibility for the project. It is advised by a Scientific Steering Committee which evaluates project proposals, progress and results. An international secretariat manages Eurotrac and coordinates its subprojects.

Eurotrac was launched on a German initiative in 1985 when conflicts between Member States abounded about whether or not Eureka should incorporate pre-competitive projects. Eurotrac is very much a German-led project and the BMFT provides more than 40 per cent of the project's total public funding (see Table 7.2). German research teams lead five of twelve subprojects.

A German–Dutch bilateral project into tracking atmospheric pollution, the Photochemical Oxidant and Acid Deposition Model (PHOXA), predated Eurotrac. The original German 'push' to launch Eurotrac within Eureka in 1985 was supported by the Netherlands,[28] where the political saliency of environmental issues is nearly as high as in Germany. Austria, Finland and Norway, countries where acid rain caused by industrial pollution from East European countries was a major concern, also immediately signed onto Eurotrac in 1985. Sweden

Table 7.2 National direct grants to Eurotrac (1989)

Member State	Total	Share of total project cost
	(100 ECU)	%
Germany[a]	5261	42
CEC[b]	1907	15
Netherlands	1132	9
UK	1051	8
France	725	6
Sweden	692	5
Switzerland	475	4
Norway	440	3
Others	922	7
Total	12605	99[c]

Source: Eurotrac International Scientific Secretariat, *Annual Report Part 1: General Report*, Garmisch-Partenkirchen, Fraunhofer Institute, 1990.
Notes: [a]Germany exclusively funds the Eurotrac Secretariat (45,500 ECU in 1989). [b]Indicates total value of Joint Research Centre contribution plus direct grants. [c]Column does not add to 100% due to rounding.

joined soon after Eurotrac was launched and now plays a leading role in two Eurotrac subprojects.

While British negotiators in 1985 resisted opening Eureka to non-industrial projects such as Eurotrac, the UK possesses substantial scientific expertise in the atmospheric sciences. For both the UK and France, combining national projects with Eurotrac had the effect of widening their potential impact and reducing their costs. British and French research teams lead five Eurotrac subprojects between them. However, all funding from the UK and France has been re-directed from pre-existing national programmes and neither funds permanent staff working on the project.[29]

The Commission's support for Eurotrac was slow in developing. One Eurotrac principal admitted 'things were strained at first but relations are much improved and getting better'.[30] The EC's Joint Research Centre (JRC) was already involved through the COST framework in R & D related to Eurotrac's proposed activities in 1985 and extensive exchange between scientists in different academic disciplines and national settings was routine in the atmospheric sciences. Close professional links between JRC researchers and those operating in national settings served to permeate the boundaries between EC and national policy networks and effective pressures developed for ensuring that the JRC had a primary role in Eurotrac.

Eureka's added value stems first from the flexibility it allows its participants in determining the project's aims and activities. A member of the Eurotrac secretariat explained that the Eureka label originally was sought for the project because 'there was a desire to be free of the CEC and to use a 'bottom-up' approach where groups of working scientists could fashion their own goals within a given framework'.[31] Environmental R & D was not a priority area within the Framework programme when Eurotrac was launched and most EC environmental schemes had goals which were quite centrally defined.

Second, Eureka accommodates cooperation which cuts across both national borders and scientific disciplines. The effective study of transboundary pollution obviously is impossible for any single European country. At the time of Eurotrac's launch, the Luxembourg accord was still far from full implementation and thus there was no easy method for incorporating EFTA states into EC environmental R & D. More than 13 per cent of Eurotrac's total funding is now provided by EFTA states.[32] By nature, the work involves 'almost all disciplines of the natural sciences (meteorology, physics, chemistry, biology, etc.)'.[33]

Third, Eurotrac's broad membership provides the potential for a more unified European voice at the level of international policy. One of Eurotrac's stated objectives is 'to improve the scientific basis for taking future political decisions on environmental management in the European countries'.[34] The convening of the International Conference on Global Warming in 1990, which resulted in a new international protocol on the emissions of chlorofluorocarbons, highlighted the need for reliable information on the transport of atmospheric pollutants across frontiers.

Finally, Eureka provides the Eurotrac partners with the opportunity to combine national subsidies with EC funds. Despite the increased profile of environmental R & D in Framework III, EC funding levels are still quite modest. For example, the EC's Step and Epoch (European Programme on Climatology and Natural Hazards) programmes receive combined funds totalling less than 29 million ECU per year, compared with Eurotrac's annual budget of 30 million ECU.[35] The JRC is a major contributor to four different Eurotrac subprojects, and two are considered 'joint projects' with the Commission, which funds about one-third of each.

Maintaining a stable flow of funding to the project is constantly cited by participants as the project's most serious problem. Eurotrac's governing bodies echo complaints familiar throughout Eureka about 'difficulties in coordinating the subprojects' because 'administrative processes in some countries are slow'. The Eurotrac organizers urge that 'coordination of the work in different countries . . . needs simultaneous funding [decisions] throughout the project'.[36]

Second, Eurotrac's political profile within the Eureka network has been quite low since it was launched. Recent Eureka environmental initiatives, such as Euroenviron, have far clearer commercial aims than does Eurotrac. Launched in 1989, Euroenviron catalyses projects to develop the next generation of pollution control equipment. Political support is bolstered by the fact that SMEs are often major players in the pollution control industry and because 'the demand is real'[37] for clean technology. The British DTI estimates that the UK market is growing at a rate of 9 per cent per year and will be worth 12 billion ECU by the end of the century.[38] At a political level, the UK, Italy and Denmark appear to be far keener on Euroenviron, with its clear commercial aims, than on Eurotrac. By contrast, new 'national committees' were created by France, Germany, the Netherlands and Sweden in 1989 to monitor more closely the use of national funds devoted to Eurotrac. The project's organizers expressed fears that they would end up 'providing an additional hurdle over which an investigator must climb in order to fund his work'.[39]

Eureka's methodology has suited Eurotrac insofar as it has allowed a group of atmospheric scientists to create their own subprojects with substantial financial support from Germany. Over time, Eurotrac has successfully attracted financial and scientific commitments from the Commission, the JRC and the UK. Yet, the complexity of inter-governmental funding arrangements has caused frustration within Eurotrac, as is often the case within Eureka more generally.

The primary lesson of the Eurotrac project seems to be two-fold. First, continued political support is clearly quite crucial to the success of pre-competitive projects. Eurotrac was created with political as well as scientific goals: its founders aimed to ensure that the project had an impact on environmental public policy. By 1990, Eurotrac accounted for close to 14 per cent of the total value of all Eureka environmental projects. The scientists who launched Eurotrac appeared to appreciate that existing funding commitments could come under threat as more 'near-market' projects were granted Eureka status. By 1990, they were forced to admit that 'the data so far collected and the understanding so far achieved are not yet sufficient to contribute appreciably towards the.. . objective of providing a good basis for political decision-making'.[40] Eurotrac's organizers continued to remind its researchers that to keep the project going, participants needed to keep sight of its political as well as its scientific goals.

Second, the German insistence that environmental R & D is appropriate for inclusion within Eureka has become more widely accepted over time, but the idea that Eureka should incorporate basic or pre-competitive projects has not. One Eurotrac partner commented,

> It's still a surprise to me that they accepted Eurotrac at all. We're clearly doing basic R & D, although we're working on instruments that may have commercial value. But we don't fit in with them. We're a nuisance to them. The [UK] Department of Environment gives us funds, but the DTI wants nothing to do with us.[41]

While acknowledging his government's political support for Eurotrac, one Eureka official argued, 'That project never should have been accepted. It has nothing to do with the rest of Eureka'.[42] Eurotrac's status as a Eureka project and its considerable expense lend credence to the view that Member States have indeed thrown whatever has suited their national innovation policy into Eureka, including the kitchen sink. It is little wonder that Eureka remains an initiative whose central objectives and image are blurred.

IV. COSINE: WHEN THE COMMISSION LEADS

The Cosine project is the only Eureka project for which the Commission is the clear leader. Its goal is to 'federate' European science and technology computer network services and databases using the Open Systems Interconnection (OSI) standard developed by the International Standards Organization. The total value of all international and national actions related to Cosine is estimated at 300 million ECU.

The politics of OSI are nearly as complex as the technology involved. In 1983, the standard was endorsed collectively by the Big 12 Roundtable, which then formed the Standards Promotion and Application Group (SPAG) primarily to push for the widespread adoption of OSI. The dominant, *de facto* standard for interworking systems, Systems Network Architecture, had been developed by IBM in the early 1960s to provide complete network services using a coherent computer architectural framework. The effect was to 'lock in' customers to IBM's proprietary standard. By contrast, OSI offers the benefit of linking systems corresponding to the different and often incompatible architectures that have emerged in Europe and elsewhere. Customers thus may build information systems with different products from different vendors if all use the OSI standard. European producers benefit from being able to offer customers hardware and software which is compatible with that produced by other manufacturers.[43]

The OSI model fits neatly with the Commission's policy to liberalize the telecommunications services sector. Before 1987, national postal and telecommunications authorities (PTTs) held a monopoly on most data transmission services and developed divergent network standards based on national custom. Compared with the USA and Japan, Europe lacked a wide range of international data network services and connectivity between separate national networks was poor.[44]

Similar problems plagued the telecommunications equipment sector, where highly nationalistic patterns of public procurement meant there was little cross-border trade in the EC. In 1986, intra-EC exports of equipment made in the EC were worth only 803 million ECU, compared with more than 1.5 billion ECU in extra-EC exports.[45] What Sharp termed the 'highly damaging and chauvinistic attitudes'[46] of national PTTs fuelled the Commission's determination to create a single market in both telecommunications services and equipment.[47]

Cosine was designed to attack one part of the problem. European researchers often lack access to research networks beyond their borders because they use incompatible architectures. The federation of research networks using OSI would provide researchers with widespread inter- active access to remote computers and databases across Europe.

The question of how Cosine fits with national innovation policies is complex. All Eureka Member States participate, but several bring distinct national priorities to the project. While the German BMFT originally proposed Cosine in 1985, the Bundespost has been particu- larly stubborn in asserting its prerogative to set telecommunications standards. The BMFT's enthusiasm for Cosine fits with its general self- image as a force for the modernization and Europeanization of German innovation policy. The EFTA Member-States view Cosine as a method for further integrating their research communities with those of the EC. Less technologically advanced states, such as Greece, Turkey, and Portugal, see Cosine as a means for linking their research communities with those in large Eureka Member States.

However, Cosine is more properly viewed as an element of the Commission's own innovation policy. Despite its general aversion to Eureka in 1985, the Commission became persuaded that Eureka's methodology had functional value in promoting acceptance of the OSI standard. Establishing OSI throughout Europe, according to a Com- mission official, requires all EC and EFTA Member States 'to be in one boat rowing all at once in time'.[48] Cosine is a tool that the Commission can use in its effort to persuade the European telecommunications community – defined in its widest sense – that adoption of common standards is a non-zero sum game.[49]

Cosine has encouraged extensive exchanges between the project's primary partners – which are mostly public research laboratories and national ministries – and national PTTs, European standards bodies such as CEN/CENELEC and the Conference of European Post and Telecommunications administrations (CEPT), and hardware and software manufacturers. The project seeks to contribute to a single market in products such as research networks and 'value-added' telecommunications services. First, it contributes to the 'market pull' of OSI by creating incentives for industry to develop new supported products using OSI standards. For example, the Cosine Policy Group has convinced partners in at least five other Eureka projects and three Framework projects to use the standards developed during Cosine's early 'specification phase'.[50] It also encourages governments to arrive at common procurement specifications for research networks.

Second, Cosine strengthens 'the position of buyers and users ... *vis-à-vis* IT and telecommunications suppliers'.[51] Neither network users nor suppliers have traditionally had much of a voice in telecommunications standards-setting, which has remained a prerogative of national PTTs and their 'national champion' suppliers. The Commission has a long history of trying to convince PTTs to create a coherent trans-European 'backbone' network standard for their national research databases. The focus of the Commission's efforts traditionally has been CEPT, a collective association of national PTTs. However, CEPT is loosely organized and under-resourced and lacks even a central office.[52] National PTTs have guarded their independent discretion to set standards and deliberations between them on common standards-setting have often been arduous and unproductive.

The Commission has fought back by creating the European Telecommunications Standards Institute (ETSI), whose membership includes a diverse collection of users and suppliers. It also has encouraged and helped to fund RARE (*Réseaux Associés pour la Recherche Européenne*), an association designed to provide European research network providers and their users with an institutional voice.[53] RARE has been the main contractor for the technical work involved in Cosine's specification phase, to which the Commission provided 20 per cent funding, and a secretariat for the Cosine policy group on which all Eureka Member States are represented. Cosine entered its implementation phase in 1990, and the Commission agreed to fund most of its first pilot project using Esprit funds.[54]

Third, Cosine promises to intensify cross-border links in the European research community, with positive knock-on effects for its own collaborative R & D programmes as well as Eureka. It also enhances

European credibility within the Coordinating Committee for International Research Networks (CCIRN), created in 1987 to promote the interconnection of research networks between the US and Europe. RARE is the main interlocutor for Europe within the CCIRN, which has emerged as a key forum for the eventual development of a seamless system of interconnected research networks.

Eureka's added value to the project stems from the need to persuade national PTTs and network service suppliers to adopt the OSI standard voluntarily. A complex array of other actors must also support the idea, including international standards authorities, telecommunications equipment suppliers, network service users, etc.[55] To some extent, this task requires a 'bottom-up' approach. However, as explained by a former member of the Cosine policy group:

> There are also very strong top-down elements to Cosine. Eureka's bottom-up approach is very much designed for industrial collaboration. Cosine is not an industry-led project, it's largely a government-led project with an infrastructure aim . . . One of the things we want is common specifications and certain number of common services which conform to [OSI] standards, but with extra user specifications. Industry is being invited to follow and provide products according to them . . . It should lead to industrial products which are supported by industry and evolve according to the standards. It's got to be bottom-up in a certain sense, but also top-down in a certain sense.[56]

An essential problem for the Cosine project as well as for EC telecommunications policy more generally is that both national governments and PTTs have proven remarkably reticent in setting their own agenda in telecommunications. Progress toward common standards has been slow due to the strength of vested national interests, the technical complexities involved and the underdevelopment of international standards organizations. National telecommunications policy networks – which typically include national ministries, standards authorities and telecommunications equipment manufacturers – have had stable memberships over time and have remained largely impervious to outside influence.[57]

The point is illustrated in the very high market shares enjoyed by domestic equipment manufacturers in key product sectors such as those for central office switches (see Table 7.3). While the industry underwent significant rationalization in the latter half of the 1980s, national governments were tempted to leave in place as long as possible conflicting national equipment standards which protected domestic

Table 7.3 Market shares for central office switches in Europe (1986)

Supplier	France %	FRG %	Italy %	UK %	Denmark %	Sweden %	Norway %
ITT	0	35	30	20	10	0	100
CGE/CGCT	100	0	0	0	0	0	0
Ericsson	0	0	21	15	90	100	0
Siemens	0	65	0	0	0	0	0
Italtel	0	0	49	0	0	0	0
Plessey	0	0	0	35	0	0	0
GEC	0	0	0	30	0	0	0

Source: Adapted from G.C. Lodge, *Comparative Business–Government Relations*, Englewood Cliffs NJ, Prentice Hall, 1990.

firms, especially when the EC as a whole maintained a trade surplus in telecommunications equipment, albeit a dwindling one.[58]

The Commission often has been accused of engaging in 'protocol wars' in its standards policy for data transmission. Debates between Member States and between states and the Commission are 'very technical and also of course very political, one using the other as an excuse'.[59] The stakes are high, as the telecommunications sector will generate up to 7 per cent of EC GDP by the year 2000, up from two to three per cent in the late 1980s.[60]

Despite considerable differences of views between different DGs, the Commission as a whole has tried to cast itself as an honest broker between national governments, PTTs, RARE and equipment suppliers. In pushing for adoption of OSI standards, the Commission has on its side the moral weight of the argument that the lack of interconnectivity between network services isolates researchers in Denmark from those in Portugal, or those in Germany from those in Turkey, when all involved in debates about OSI must agree that they should be able to communicate with one another. Politically, the Commission has allied itself with the Big 12 on the OSI issue, who form an extremely powerful political constituency when they are able to identify their common interest.

Eureka's methodology has allowed the Commission to coordinate national OSI-related actions with its own more readily than it could have if Cosine was incorporated within the Framework programme. Because it is a Eureka project, Cosine helps the Commission to refute the claim of several Member States that it is going beyond its powers in pushing for rapid liberalization of the telecommunications sector. In the words of a Commission official:

If the European research effort is less effective than it might have been because of the parcelization or lack of application of certain standards, hence effectively breaking the thrust of our standards policy . . . then it is perfectly legitimate for us to intervene and try to do something about it . . . We have a constant battle between Member States wanting to maintain all of the power themselves yet wanting the Commission to open up foreign markets for them . . . Cosine is part of our more general effort to get the telecommunications community to act as a Community instead of acting as a lot of squabbling kids.[61]

Clearly, Cosine is a very special case within Eureka. Viewed in the context of the Commission's wider mission to liberalize and restructure the European telecommunications industry, Cosine itself has quite modest aims. But the project remains a microcosm of the volatile politics of European telecommunications policy.

V. HIGH DEFINITION TELEVISION: PLUS ÇA CHANGE?

Along with Jessi, the HDTV project forms the most critical litmus test for Eureka's success. If all of the project's planned investments are realized, the project will be the largest single investment project in Europe besides the Channel Tunnel.[62] The assessment panel convened to evaluate Eureka in 1991 cited the HDTV project as a textbook example of the type of cooperation between government and industry that Eureka should promote. It noted that industry is 'in a bottom-up way responsible for the development of technology and products', but applauded wider political efforts to establish a common European technical standard for HDTV which, it is hoped, will develop into a global standard.[63]

The HDTV project brings together Europe's only three globally competitive consumer electronics firms – Nokia of Finland, Philips and Thomson. The project seeks to develop the next generation of colour television (CTV), which is by far the most important single product sector within the European consumer electronics market (see Table 7.4).

In key respects, CTV is a classic case of a European industry dominated by national champions who have been protected from foreign competition by a range of measures, particularly incompatible national standards. When CTV was first introduced to Europe in the 1960s, French broadcasting authorities chose a system called SECAM (*Séquence à Mémoire*) as a national broadcasting standard. Most other European states opted for the PAL (Phase Alternation by Line) system, which was originally developed in Germany. Previously, the USA and

Table 7.4 EC consumer electronics consumption and share imported by product category (1989)

Product	Consumption (BECU)	Share imported %
Colour television	6.5	20
Video cassette recorders	2.9	46
Video camcorders	0.8	99
Audio products	3.2	89
Compact disc players	0.8	74
In-car entertainment	1.4	58

Source: European Commission cited in A. Cawson and P. Holmes, 'The new consumer electronics' in C. Freeman, M. Sharp and W. Walker (eds) *Technology and the Future of Europe: Global Competition and the Environment in the 1990s*, Frances Pinter, 1991.

Japan had adopted the technologically inferior NTSC (National Television System Committee) standard in the 1950s. NTSC produces a picture of lower quality because it projects a signal which uses fewer lines (525) on a television screen than SECAM or PAL (625). Since all three standards are technically incompatible with one another, decisions related to their adoption were as political as they were technical. For example, the adoption of PAL by most of Europe gave European firms the opportunity to license PAL technology to foreign producers only for the manufacture of small-screen (less than 20 inch) sets.[64] The effect was to 'freeze' foreign CTV producers out of much of the European market.

However, Japanese producers began to expand their European market shares in the 1970s by manufacturing PAL standard sets more efficiently than Philips and other European competitors. Over time, Japanese firms were able to seize on economies of scale which derived from production for the Japanese and American markets to manufacture small-screen PAL standard sets at a low marginal cost. The adoption of the SECAM by France acted to insulate the French market and Thomson from Japanese competition for a longer period. However, Japanese producers had developed dually compatible PAL–SECAM CTV sets at a relatively low cost by the early 1980s. This development, combined with the expiration of European patents on the PAL standard in the late 1980s, left Philips, Thomson and lesser European manufacturers dangerously vulnerable to cheap Asian imports.

Large profits and the technical expertise gained in the video cassette recorder (VCR) market in the early 1980s were critical to the Japanese assault on the European CTV market. The current global standard for the video products industry, 'Video Home System' (VHS), was developed by a subsidiary of Matsushita, the world's largest consumer electronics group. Philips backed its own V2000 standard, as well as the short-lived consumer laserdisc system, with disastrous results. It was nearly forced out of consumer electronics altogether by the losses incurred.

The rapid growth of consumer demand for VCRs in the mid-1980s produced a general atmosphere of crisis among European CTV producers. By 1988, Japanese firms had secured partial or total ownership of sixty-three consumer electronics plants in Europe.[65] South Korean and Taiwanese producers also began to invest heavily in Europe. In response, Japanese firms began to concede markets for 'mature' consumer products to lower cost producers from newly industrializing Asian countries. The focus of Japanese efforts became innovation in new, high value-added products such as camcorders, digital VCRs and HDTV.

The annual global market for HDTV could be as high as 100 billion ECU by the late 1990s. HDTV technology promises to have applications for a broad range of industrial and military industries. Among the secondary markets for HDTV which already are emerging are those for electronic cinema broadcasts of sporting and musical events, medical imaging and 'tele-auctions'. The implications of HDTV for semi-conductor producers will be enormous, as the IC content of HDTV receivers will be approximately five times that of conventional CTVs.

The Japanese state broadcasting organization NHK began research on HDTV in the early 1970s. By 1986, NHK and its industrial partners had developed the 'Hi Vision' HDTV system, and were ready to present its transmission standard, MUSE (Multiple Sub-Nyquist Encoding), for adoption as a world standard by the International Consultative Committee (CCIR) of the International Telecommunications Union. However, because the MUSE standard was incompatible with existing TV broadcasting standards, fears emerged that the intent was to create a huge consumer market for Japanese-produced receivers. Fierce lobbying by France, Germany and Britain led the CCIR to postpone the adoption of a global standard until 1990.

Later in 1986, the Commission unveiled a directive which imposed the British-developed 'MAC packet' of standards for all direct broadcasting via satellite (DBS) in the EC. Crucially, the MAC standards allow an evolutionary approach to the adoption of HDTV. In the short term, they provide an interim system to transmit pictures and sound of substantially better quality than current systems. Consumers may receive the improved signal using conventional CTVs provided they have a satellite dish and tuner. Otherwise, conventional sets receive and display MAC signals with ordinary definition. Eventually, a full-blown digital high definition MAC (HD-MAC) system is foreseen which would project on 1250 lines, or twice as many as are now used for conventional broadcasts in Europe.[66]

DBS is the enabling technology for HDTV. Channels which broadcast via satellite use a wider frequency bandwidth (12 MHz) than terrestrial TV channels (6 MHz). The MAC standard uses the wider bandwidth to transmit more 'information.' The result is larger, cinema-quality pictures and digital sound. Eventually, the extra bandwidth could accommodate the transmission of up to eight languages simultaneously. This aspect of HDTV promises to yield a truly common European market for multilingual TV programmes.

After acceptance of the 1986 EC directive, the MAC standard was endorsed by the European Broadcasting Union (EBU), which represents all major European broadcasters. European CTV producers thus were provided with the opportunity to develop a 'home-grown' HDTV system based on MAC standards. An increase in the number of frequencies for broadcasting and services – another consequence of technological advance – promised to result in over 200 new European DBS channels by the mid-1990s. The launch of the Eureka HDTV project in 1986 thus took place as part of a frantic and extensive mobilization of European political and industrial resources to develop a technology with critical implications for a wide range of broadcasting, electronics, defence and aerospace industries.[67]

The Eureka HDTV project brings together more than forty organizations from ten countries. A central project directorate, with headquarters at Philips, coordinates interactions between project partners, the EC, the EBU and the national governments of the major participants. Project partners are divided into 'type A' and 'type B' participants. The former (predominantly Philips, Thomson and Nokia) are responsible for developing HDTV hardware, while the latter are subcontractors, programme-makers or national broadcasting authorities.[68]

As the oldest and largest consumer electronics firms in Europe, Philips is the lead firm in the HDTV project. It has an unmatched global reputation as a product innovator, after pioneering the audio cassette and compact disc. Yet, the VCR debacle highlighted how Philips chronically fails to develop its own innovations. Consumer products activities accounted for 47 per cent of Philips' total turnover in 1975, but only 23 per cent by 1985. The group embarked on a wholesale restructuring of its management, which was widely viewed as inefficient and sclerotic, to develop a more global marketing strategy in 1981. However, Philips continued to depend heavily on the European market, which still accounted for about 60 per cent of its total sales by the early 1990s.[69]

Philips has traditionally sought close links to the Commission in order to compensate for the disadvantages – both in terms of political weight and home market base – of having its headquarters in the Netherlands. It maintains a large and highly influential lobbying organization in Brussels. Between 1983 and 1987, Philips obtained 157 million ECU in EC subsidies and secured more Framework programme contracts than any other firm in Europe.[70]

Thomson holds the Vice-Presidency of the HDTV directorate and is the main link between the project and several subprojects funded through the Framework programme to develop enabling technologies for HDTV. After being nationalized in 1981, Thomson began an intensive effort to become a global producer in consumer electronics. It began spending heavily on R & D and acquired a wide range of foreign interests, including the Ferguson division of the UK's Thorn-EMI.

Eureka's added value for the HDTV project is clear in the way the project has mobilized political and financial support from all the large EC Member States as well as the EC. A principle figure in the HDTV directorate observed:

> The main difference Eureka made was that it got governments really involved, not just because they give us money, but because they're in the project themselves. Because they have the transmitters, they have the PTTs, and they can't solve the problem themselves just as we on the industrial side can't solve the problem alone. The trick is that Eureka gave us a framework to bring all these partners together.[71]

Eureka provides added value in that it allows EC and national subsidies to be pooled on R & D which is very expensive. Yet, the primary contribution of the Commission to the project has been its pursuit of a comprehensive industrial policy for HDTV which goes far beyond the Eureka project itself. On a political level, the Commission was instrumental in engineering EC-wide consensus on the need to lobby for acceptance of HD-MAC as a global standard by the CCIR. A common EC position was adopted in November 1989 and reaffirmed in 1991.[72] The Commission also convinced Member States that the European HDTV effort required a 'cultural policy'. The explosion of new cable and satellite channels foreseen for the 1990s promised to open up huge new markets for programming which could only be met by large-scale imports, regardless of the development of HDTV. As recalled by a spokesman for Philips:

It was strange the way it was suddenly realized in the political area, and I think the Commission encouraged this, that television is more than technology and more than programmes: it has a social and cultural impact, especially among the French, for whom it's *la culture*, and there goes Monsieur Mitterrand.[73]

The establishment of a common standard for HDTV was a central element of the EC's first 'audio-visual policy' to develop a pan-European 'audio-visual media products industry' which could attack an expanding market presently dominated by US, Brazilian and Japanese programme producers.[74] For his part, Mitterrand proposed the creation of an 'Audio-Visual Eureka' in 1989 to promote the production of programmes using HDTV technology.[75] In something of a replay of 1985, the French initiative was seen as competing with the Commission's own 'Media' policy to promote European audio-visual production. But Audio-Visual Eureka eventually got off the ground as a twenty-eight-member initiative which exists independently of Eureka but shares a similar structure. It is primarily used to associate as many non-EC states as possible in implementing the EC's HDTV strategy.[76]

Thus, political support for an indigenous European capability in the manufacture of HDTV hardware has been mirrored in the development of a complementary EC audio-visual 'software' policy. A key milestone was acceptance of the 'Television Without Frontiers' directive in October 1989.[77] It earmarked funds to HDTV programme-making while reserving a majority of EC satellite transmission time for programmes of European origin.

The HDTV project's fit with national innovation policies is analytically muddied because technological change has eroded the protection offered by incompatible standards, with the effect of obscuring European CTV producers' national identities.[78] The major Eureka HDTV partners include several of Europe's only truly multinational firms. For example, Philips has divisions or affiliated companies in Germany, France, the UK, Italy, Austria and Belgium, all of which participate in the HDTV project.[79]

Yet, the interest of the Dutch government in the project is clear. Philips continues to spend more than half of its R & D budget in the Netherlands and the Dutch government subsidizes about 40 per cent of Philips' total Eureka project costs.[80] Encouraging Philips to engage in HDTV research collaboratively reduces the costs of national subsidy and helps ensure that other European firms do not develop systems with alternative standards, as Thomson did with CTV in the 1960s.

The French national innovation policy interest is reflected in the funding of HDTV subprojects by four different Ministries, the tripling of domestic funding for HDTV in 1989 and the launch of Eureka Audio-Visual. Resort to state protectionism for Thomson has become less politically tenable in the post-SEA period. Eureka has become a national innovation policy foil to 'push' Thomson toward innovation in CTV with a view to a wider European market.

For the governments of other 'Type A' participants, the logic of subsidizing their national firms' involvement in the project is unambiguous. The German government has incentives to induce Bosch to participate because it is the only option for securing a German role in the development of HDTV. The same might be said for the Scandinavian governments which fund Nokia's participation. The entry of an Italian consortium as a collective 'Type A' participant in 1990 was accepted by the principal partners in part because the Italian state broadcasting authority, RAI, had previously funded HDTV demonstration projects using the Japanese Hi Vision system.[81]

The HDTV project may appear to be a rare case of multiple European industries, national governments, and the EC pursuing a mission-oriented, Japanese-style industrial policy. Key public actors in the project – particularly the French government and the Commission's DG XIII – are strong proponents of such *grands projets* and admirers of Japan's MITI. However, the HDTV project shows that obstacles to the successful commercialization of home-grown European innovations remain remarkably persistent even in the altered political environment which surrounds the 1992 project.

First, despite general European endorsement of the MAC standard, key European telecommunications authorities have adopted different varieties of the standard. In 1988, the French and German PTTs chose 'D2–MAC' – the variant backed by the Eureka project partners – for their national DBS channels. Compared with other variants of MAC, it allows less data to be transmitted (i.e. limiting the number of languages which can be transmitted simultaneously) so that its signals can be carried through terrestrial cable networks. The trade-off is a sensible one on the European continent, where extensive cable networks already exist. However, the UK still has very limited cable networks. Thus, a variation called D-MAC, which can accommodate more sound and data, was chosen for broadcasts by the new DBS channel, British Satellite Broadcasting (BSB) in 1988. The adoption of two variations of MAC should not matter in the long term since both are intermediate stages on the path toward the fully digital HD-MAC system, which is probably still years away. But the short-term effect was to 'split' the MAC standard, and to delay production of the very sophisticated integrated circuits used in MAC receivers. Consequently, industry confidence in the MAC standard was weakened. In June 1988, Rupert Murdoch announced that new DBS channels due to come on-line in February 1989 for his Sky Television system would use the existing PAL standard owing to concerns that MAC chips might not be available by the time of their launch.

The use of PAL by Sky clearly violated the spirit of the 1986 EC directive which required that all DBS transmissions use the MAC standard. Yet, Sky could legally broadcast in PAL by using a satellite called Astra, which operated on such low power and frequencies that it was not covered by the Commission rules. Murdoch had the choice of broadcasting Sky via Astra only because recent advances in reception technology greatly expanded the areas which could be covered by low-powered satellites. Later in 1989 four German channels also elected to broadcast in PAL using Astra.

BSB began broadcasting using the MAC system in early 1990, but it fell into deep and immediate debt and was purchased by Murdoch and merged with Sky to form 'BSkyB' within the year. BSkyB continues to broadcast using the PAL standard. One upshot of the continued use of PAL in Europe is that Asian producers are free to mass-produce CTVs with built-in PAL standard satellite receivers. These sets have advantages over the present European MAC system, which requires that consumers place bulky receiving equipment on top of their TV sets. Moreover, the European strategy for limiting the inflow of MAC-format imports and favouring European IC producers also comes under threat. Philips, Thomson, and other European firms have pooled their patents on MAC technology. The licence agreement they would offer to Asian firms which elect to build MAC sets would strongly encourage the use of ICs produced in Europe.[82] But domestic producers will receive no such protection unless MAC is established as the European standard.

A second problem for the HDTV project is the general corporate health of Philips. The group was forced to take 'drastic measures' after an entirely unpredicted collapse in profits in 1990, with the effect of further sapping industry confidence in the MAC standard. What Philips' executive chairman termed a 'crisis of confidence' led to renewed criticism of the group's management and financial controls, and even prompted the taking of legal action against the group by its own shareholders.[83] Grave doubts were cast on Philips' ability to continue making the huge capital investments needed to stay in the IC business. The group previously had insisted – particularly to the Commission – that its consumer electronics division generally and the HDTV project specifically depended on its ability to make its own chips.[84]

As part of the emergency measures taken in 1990, Philips also vastly reduced its participation in the Jessi project. Raimondo Paletto, the Chairman of the Jessi Board, asserted that Philips remained 'a major participant in several fields, especially in applications linked to HDTV'.[85] But Jessi's overall budget for 1992 was slashed by one-quarter after Germany cut its funding under the budgetary strain of unification, and other participants followed suit. The continued existence of the Jessi project was uncertain beyond the end of its current phase in 1996.[86]

Third, the Eureka HDTV project started later than did similar Japanese efforts. To some extent it has benefited from the delay, as the HD-MAC standard was able to incorporate technological advances in both transmission and reception which occurred after the Japanese Hi Vision system was developed. But the HDTV project partners were reckoned to be at least two years behind Japanese HDTV producers in the race to develop a fully digital MAC system in 1990.[87] At this point, Sony claimed that it would mass-produce Hi Vision sets, perhaps by forming an industry consortium to spread costs, in a strategy reminiscent of that which established VHS as a global standard for VCRs.

NHK began to broadcast three channels in Hi Vision in November 1991. By 1992, the price of Hi Vision receivers was still an exorbitant 7500 ECU. However, to make Hi Vision compatible with existing sets, NHK developed a decoder which, although still expensive, was seen as a precursor to cheaper second-generation versions expected to be on the market by late 1993. Japanese proponents of Hi Vision also began to target high-profit markets for teleconferencing, medical uses and auctions. European governments expressed anxiety about the possibility that Hi Vision might penetrate the EC's market as European providers of these services are forced to buy Japanese equipment to compete.[88]

Meanwhile, commercial Japanese broadcasters – which compete with NHK – encouraged the development of a separate system called 'Clear Vision'. It exploits the full potential of the conventional NTSC standard by using HDTV technology to record programmes on 1125 lines, then electronically converting pictures to 525 lines in the studio. The result is a far clearer picture. The price of sets with Clear Vision reception systems was less than half that of sets equipped with the European D2–MAC system by 1992. As with D2–MAC, old sets worked as before with the Clear Vision system, ignoring the additional 'information' that was transmitted. Since conventional European broadcasts use 625 lines instead of 525, Clear Vision pictures would be even clearer in Europe. While European technology similar to Clear Vision exists for use with 625–line TVs, political commitment to HD-MAC has deterred its development. Yet, Clear Vision's debut has led influential voices in the

European broadcasting industry to call for abandoning the EC-backed plan to move towards a full HDTV system by using D2–MAC now.[89]

For its part, the CCIR at its 1990 Düsseldorf meeting again decided to postpone a decision on adopting a global HDTV standard until 1994. A key factor was the American position, which had evolved considerably since the USA leaned toward endorsing Hi Vision in 1986. Handicapped by a lack of public funding, no US-developed system appeared to be a serious contender in the HDTV competition by as late as 1990, when only the Japanese and European systems seemed viable.[90] Pressure from US broadcasters for an evolutionary standard then tilted the US CCIR delegation toward the MAC standard.[91]

Yet, the picture had changed significantly within a year. The US Federal Communications Commission (FCC) began testing six different HDTV systems in 1991, including several which were all-digital. Dramatically, a report leaked by the French Foreign Ministry argued that the D2–MAC system – a hybrid digital/analogue system – had been made obsolete by a new all-digital system developed by the Massachusetts Institute of Technology and General Instruments.[92] Both Philips and Thomson became involved in two 'non-MAC' US projects and started working on enhanced versions of PAL. They also openly argued to the FCC that they could deliver a working all-digital system by 1995, while still insisting that the EC should support the MAC system because a fully digital system was still many years away.[93] The European HDTV partners at times seemed to be hedging their bets while conceding that D2–MAC was probably a loser.

The combination of developments in the USA and Japan, the demise of BSB, and the expiration of the 1986 EC directive on DBS provoked much political manoeuvering in Europe on HDTV in late 1991. The Commission had to decide whether to renew its efforts to establish D2–MAC as an interim standard. Certainly, strong arguments had developed in favour of abandoning *dirigisme* and allowing the market to choose between competing standards. However, the Commission unveiled a new proposal which required that all new DBS channels use D2–MAC. BSkyB and others using PAL would be allowed to continue doing so as long as they 'simulcasted' in D2–MAC, or broadcast in both standards at once. The Commission proposed that the EC subsidize the costs of simulcasting – estimated at 5 million ECU per channel annually – until January 1994. The proposal also required CTV receiver and set manufacturers to build in D2–MAC circuitry by 1994.[94] The Commission planned to ban PAL broadcasts in any country at the point when 70 per cent of receivers were compatible with MAC.

The practical effect of the plan was to double the cost of broadcasting and halve the number of transmitters in Europe. It also required huge subsidies. In response to widespread industry criticism, the Commission proposed that the amount of money committed to promotion of the MAC standard be doubled. Pandolfi said he would ask for nearly 1 billion ECU to be earmarked to pay for the conversion of existing programmes into the new format and to ensure that all DBS companies used MAC only by 1994.

The proposal gave British manufacturers and satellite broadcasters (including BSkyB) an extra two years to comply. Still, with close to 1.5 million PAL-standard receivers already installed in the UK, the switch to MAC by 1996 clearly could not take place without outraging many British consumers. A similar row was foreseen in Germany, where the two-year grace period for the UK was not extended, and eight German broadcasters immediately said they would refuse to cooperate with the directive.[95]

Predictably, Murdoch and many German DBS broadcasters argued that the interim D2–MAC system should be abandoned until a fully digital HDTV system could emerge. Meanwhile, Philips and Thomson lobbied the Commission to ban PAL transmissions even sooner than 1994. The Commission thus was caught in the middle of an intense cross-fire between powerful and self-interested actors all playing for high stakes. In the event, the Commission was forced to stitch together an awkward and expensive compromise to sustain the viability of the MAC standard, and to claim that it would end all PAL broadcasts in 1994 (1996 in the UK) by 'market or mandate'.[96]

Debate within the EP on the Commission's proposal baldly revealed how much technical or market considerations had been overridden by politics in the HDTV debate. The *rapporteur* of the EP's Science and Technology Policy committee, Gérard Caudron, admitted that 90 per cent of the EP's Members had reservations about the proposal. But he nonetheless recommended approval on the grounds that 'a text, if only average not to say mediocre, is preferable to further quibbling'.[97]

The dispute was settled at least temporarily when the EC's Council of Ministers rejected the Commission's proposal in favour of a watered-down directive in December 1991. It required manufacturers to provide a socket for connection to MAC circuitry instead of actually the building the MAC system into all satellite receivers and TV sets. Only new satellite services which began transmissions after 1 January 1995 were required to broadcast in MAC as well as PAL, and the question of subsidies for simulcasting was left open.[98] When asked in 1991 if the

Eureka HDTV project was effectively dead, a Eureka official involved in the project since its launch replied, 'Probably. But it was a nice try'.[99]

However, the political climate continued to change as fast as the technologies involved. The MAC system was given a potentially important boost in June 1992 when the Commission secured the commitment of an association of European broadcasters, satellite operators, cable distributors, CTV manufacturers and programmme producers on a Memorandum of Understanding in which all pledged to develop the D2–MAC standard. The Commission insisted that the agreement was 'concrete proof that market forces share the Commission's strategic vision for a European response'.[100] Together with the 1991 transmission directive, the Memorandum put in place two of three 'pillars' of the Commission's industrial policy for HDTV. All that remained was agreement on an 'action plan' for HDTV, or a financial commitment from Member States to subsidize the transition away from PAL to the MAC standard. But the Commission's agreement with industry remained non-binding until deals were reached with individual broadcasters on subsidies. While Pandolfi's revised bid of 850 million ECU for HDTV support was received enthusiastically by Germany, France, Luxembourg and the Netherlands, it was resisted furiously by the UK. A British minister called the proposal 'totally unacceptable' and complained that it had not 'come anywhere near a convincing business case'.[101] His views were not easily dismissible considering that over 90 per cent of all European households with satellite TV still used PAL dishes.

The final outcome of the race to develop HDTV remains uncertain. Yet, a number of broad lessons may be gleaned from the European HDTV experience to inform future attempts to synergize European efforts in industrial policy. First, the project shows that Eureka has the potential to catalyse European political resources when both national governments and the EC see vital industrial interests at stake. The only criticism leveled at Eureka's methodology *per se* by HDTV project participants has been a familiar one: project partners generally have to re-apply for public funding each year, thus complicating the task of keeping the project on schedule.[102] Yet, with technologies changing so fast, the Commission and national governments could legitimately argue that multiannual funding commitments would be inappropriate.

Most of the setbacks suffered by the European HDTV project may be attributed to the severe competitive weaknesses which plague European producers. Neither Thomson nor Philips have shown they can effectively integrate their corporate structures or strategies in the style of Sony and Matsushita. Philips' pull-out from Jessi is indicative, as is Thomson's admission that it cannot compete with Japanese manufacturers in developing high-definition VCRs. The proven ability of Asian producers to outcompete European producers in CTV manufacturing may mean that European consumers simply end up paying more for Japanese sets even if HD-MAC is adopted world-wide. Sony and Matsushita have long insisted that they are technically ready to manufacture CTVs using any standard which may be adopted overseas. Philips, Thomson and Nokia might claim the same, but they are unlikely to be able to compete on price terms in manufacturing anything but a MAC system.

Second, the EC role in the HDTV project shows that encouraging collaboration and then seeking protectionism for all involved may seem to be a 'way out' of dilemmas posed by the Commission's conflicting industrial and competition policy priorities. The Commission has chosen to lead EC governments in legislating into existence a European standard, instead of leaving the decision to the market as was done with VCR standards. It has paid for the looseness of its 1986 directive, which neglected to make provisions for low-powered satellites such as Astra. The argument has been made – particularly by Philips – that the Commission should have realized that their 1986 directive contained a loophole which could be lethal to the establishment of D2–MAC. But the advances in reception technology that make DBS possible using low-power satellites such as Astra were difficult, if not impossible to foresee in the mid-1980s. The episode points to the fundamental difficulties involved in favouring domestic producers in sectors where technological change occurs rapidly.

Third, the HDTV saga reveals that Europe's most politically powerful industrial firms have learned that substantial benefits can be had when they identify their common interests and insist that all of Europe faces a common threat from abroad. Claims that the original Japanese MUSE standard was permanently incompatible with current receivers were always dubious. Advancing chip technology eventually promises to make conversion between standards possible at a low added cost to receivers. The rhetoric employed to justify political support for the European HDTV project has at times bordered on the comical:

> [The MUSE] promoters set their sights high. Tempted by the potential scale of the HDTV market, they opted for a system which would be totally incompatible with existing 'traditional' TV equipment. In other words, the Japanese 'revolution' would have thrown some 600 million TV receivers throughout the world on the scrapheap . . . The goal of the Japanese industry appeared to be uncontested domination of a market of massive proportions.[103]

Fourth, the HDTV project has been a testing ground for the concept of supportive measures within Eureka. A report on the subject by the Finnish chairmanship in 1992 pointed to severe discord between Member States with vested industrial interests in the project – notably France, the Netherlands and Finland – and most others, who argued against imposing a standard on the market.[104] The report also high-lighted Eureka's lack of authority or resources for standards development:

> Eureka cannot and is not meant to bind its members, nor has it funds within its reach to be offered, whereas the European Commission do have these assets . . . It suffices to note the practical limitations of Eureka and dependence on other bodies when Eureka products and systems are entering the market.[105]

Finally, the European HDTV partners have succeeded in developing MAC technology, but have done so at considerable public expense in a manner that still does not have clear benefits for consumers. It is unclear whether the Eureka project partners, which have developed specialties which could easily evolve into market-sharing arrangements, truly will compete as they have promised in marketing HDTV once the project is complete. The somewhat contrary statements of a representative of Philips are revealing:

> When the project is over, we'll meet again on the marketplace as normal competitors. That of course is not the whole story. Whether Eureka had existed or not, there were going to be discussions between the corporations about bringing the system to market beforehand. And it's also obvious for us to start making receivers earlier than Thomson or Nokia before the transmission system is ready makes no sense. But basically we stop collaborating after the prototypes are built.[106]

Perhaps the primary lesson of the HDTV project is that despite the shift from purely national to integrated European industrial policies, very little has changed about the fundamental character of government–industry relations when politically powerful firms are involved. Much political entrepreneurship has been invested in sustaining public support for the Eureka HDTV project. The technical arguments surrounding the development of HDTV are politically loaded. They have been used effectively by European CTV producers to set the agenda for an EC audio-visual policy which neatly fits with their own commercial interests. In short, the scale of European innovation policies may be shifting to the regional level. But the political dynamic of public support

Table 7.5 Case study findings: Eureka's added value

Project	Inclusion of EFTA states	National & EC funds combined	Increased market	Expanded project size
MITHRA	X		X	X
RA-D	X	X	X	
Eurotrac	X	X		X
Cosine	X	X	X	X
HDTV	X	X	X	X

for technological innovation in the run-up to 1992 is remarkably consistent with that of the bad old days of national champions.

VI. CONCLUSION

Detailed analysis of individual Eureka projects shows – no less than the more extensive analysis in Chapter 6 – what a complex mosaic of activities are subsumed by Eureka. One of the few traits shared by all of the projects considered in this chapter is that each reflects a specific and quite distinct R & D priority of the Member States (including the Commission) which are its main sponsors. Put simply, Eureka generates projects which serve the goals of national innovation policies, but allows them to be conducted collaboratively.

Eureka status is a common denominator inasmuch as it has brought similar benefits to a very diverse set of projects (see Table 7.5). The single feature of Eureka which provides 'added value' to all five is its inclusion of EFTA Member States. National funding has been pooled with EC funding in four of the five projects. Partners in four of the projects ascribe to their Eureka status two benefits which are intertwined: expanded project size and increased potential markets for the products or services that are foreseen upon project completion.

However, the five projects have encountered very disparate problems. Table 7.6 points to the myriad of things that can go wrong with collaborative R & D projects and suggests that the benefits of Eureka status must be weighed against problems experienced as a direct consequence of the initiative's methodology. For example, political interest in MITHRA helped make the project's launch possible in 1986. But the initial involvement of a myriad of public agencies in organizing the project may have acted to make it larger than ideal for political reasons, and partners have had severe difficulties coping with unco-ordinated deliveries of national funding commitments. The RA-D project probably would not exist if not for the participation of Norway,

Table 7.6 Case study findings: problems and effect of Eureka's methodology

Project	Problems	Effect of methodology
MITHRA	Uncoordinated public funding commitments; project complexity; problems of SMEs generally	Neutral/ negative
RA-D	Weak UK public administration; lack of non-financial supportive measurers	Negative
Eurotrac	Project complexity; uneven political commitments due to project's precompetitive nature	Neutral
Cosine	Vested national interests; wider disputes in EC telecoms policy	Positive
HDTV	Foreign competition; management; 'splitting' of MAC standard	Positive

a non-EC state, and funding from both national and EC sources. However, the drawbacks of Eureka's reliance on small and often under-resourced national public administrations emerge quite starkly in the case of RA-D. Eurotrac clearly benefits from its ability to pool national and EC funding, but it seems clear that the project would stand a better chance of success in a framework with more secure and centralized funding arrangements.

By contrast, in the cases of Cosine and HDTV, Eureka has worked as intended. Projects were organized from the 'bottom-up' and then attracted support from a range of public actors extending far beyond the realms of the projects themselves. The most serious problems experienced within both projects are not clearly attributable to Eureka's methodology.

Thus, the 'Eureka input' into each of the five projects has varied considerably, as have the dynamics of government–industry relations at play within each project. The model of policy networks developed in Chapter 1 provides a guide for understanding these dynamics. Each Eureka project may be located in wider, sector-specific networks which exist to make policies designed to promote the innovative capacity of that sector. Each network may be assessed according to the three variables used to conceptualize policy networks: the relative stability of relationships between actors, the relative insularity of the policymaking setting and patterns of structural dependencies, or the extent to which public and private interests depend on one another for resources (see Table 7.7). The policy network model makes it possible to understand

Table 7.7 Locating Eureka projects in wider policy networks

Project	Wider network	Membership	Permeability/ insularity	Structural dependencies
MITHRA	Robotics	Fluid	Permeable	Weak
RA-D	Energy	Stable	Insular	Strong
Eurotrac	Environment	Fluid	Highly permeable	Moderate
Cosine	Telecommunications	Expanding	Permeable	Moderate
HDTV	Information technology	Stabilizing	Highly permeable	Very strong

how government–industry relations within different sectors are manifest at the level of individual projects.

The robotics policy network into which MITHRA falls has a fluid membership. The robotics sector is marked by a relatively large number of SMEs and research laboratories which compete for public funds and policy influence. The creation of Famos in 1987 initially revealed a split between Europe's industrial and 'academic' robotics communities, with the MITHRA robotics partners firmly in the former category. One claimed, 'The university people and research lab people want to take over Famos, and that's completely wrong . . . We're returning to Esprit and Brite. It's a disaster'.[107] Eureka's robotics activities subsequently became dominated by actors who already were active in the EC's own more pre-competitive robotics activities funded through Brite.[108] MITHRA's exclusion from Famos meant that when the project nearly collapsed, it received no support from the Famos umbrella structure. More generally, the policy network in which decisions about European robotics R & D are taken is marked by rather weak dependencies between government and industry. The widespread adoption of new flexible automated manufacturing techniques may be crucial for post-Fordist economies, but individual R & D projects in the sector are usually quite small and private actors have incentives to pursue near-market R & D regardless of whether they receive public support. The robotics network is quite loose, disaggregated and subject to shifts in policy priorities. MITHRA has suffered from the shift in political support to Famos and its diminishing symbolic value as an SME-led project.

The British RA-D project leader managed to ensure that its client-ministry would be the British Department of Energy, not the DTI, which was crippled by the squeeze put on its policy resources by a government which appeared unconvinced that the UK even needed an industry ministry in the 1980s. Sponsorship by the Department of Energy meant

Seanus-book,

that the RA-D project could be subsumed within a established British energy R & D policy network in the UK, whose membership intersected with a similarly routinized EC network, which had presided over a large cache of EC funding for many years. Memberships in these networks are stable due to the oligarchic nature of the oil industry and the limited number of well-established firms which compete in the oil-drilling and engineering industry. The British RA-D project leader, for example, is over 100 years old. Structural dependencies between public and private interests are strong in energy R & D policy networks owing to the importance of the industry for both national and regional economies. Public and private interests are thus bonded together and this fusion is reflected in the funding the RA-D project has secured from both the UK and the EC. Compared with most of the other projects under study, the RA-D project is relatively insulated from shifts in political priorities and secure in its resources.

Within Eurotrac, structural dependencies are weaker. For example, events in 1991 led to concern among the project's organizers about whether the Germans would continue as the project's paymaster in the face of demands to help fund the Gulf war effort and economic reconstruction in eastern Germany. As a member of the Eurotrac secretariat observed, 'People want to be seen to be funding this sort of R & D. There really is a symbolic aspect to this that works in our favour ... But we're susceptible to basic changes in political priorities'.[109] While the political salience of environmental issues has generally increased in Europe, environmental protection tends to become a less urgent public policy priority during periods of recession or fiscal austerity.[110] Moreover, near-market R & D into clean technologies has become viewed by many Member States as a more urgent priority than basic R & D of the sort undertaken within Eurotrac. Thus, membership in the European environmental R & D policy network has been fluid as the dominant role of research laboratories and universities has been challenged by market-oriented firms, especially SMEs, which attract an increasing share of funding. Eurotrac leads a precarious existence as an expensive project within a loosely integrated network which is buffeted by changes in broader political and fiscal priorities.

Cosine allows liberalizing influences – such as data network service users – to cohere in associations such as RARE and develop a voice in a network previously dominated by a relatively small number of PTTs, telecommunications ministries and equipment suppliers. Cosine thus reflects the Commission's goal of expanding the membership of the European telecommunications policy network to reflect a wider array of interests. While the project's goals are narrowly defined and highly technical, the technocratic nature of the project contrasts with the Commission's highly controversial and politicized mission to liberalize the telecommunications sector more generally. Despite the Commission's insistence that establishing OSI standards is a 'non-zero sum game', many national actors, such as the German Bundespost, see their interests threatened by the Commission's general strategy in telecommunications liberalization. Cosine must be widely inclusive and incorporate a diverse collection of actors, and thus the project is permeated by wider disputes in the EC telecommunications policy network. On one hand, structural dependencies within the network are limited. The most powerful actors in the network – the Commission, PTTs, telecommunications suppliers – all have substantial independent resources of their own. For example, the Bundespost's independence is guaranteed in the German Basic Law. On the other hand, Member States and national telecommunications suppliers depend on the Commission to open foreign markets for them and protect them from foreign suppliers. This dependency helps the Commission in its effort to convince national actors to 'row together' in embracing OSI and liberalization of the telecommunications sector more generally.

The HDTV project generally has consolidated the power of Europe's consumer electronics oligarchs in a wider European information technology policy network. Yet, in important respects, the HDTV project is a 'stand alone' network in which substantial financial and political resources have been compartmentalized in the pursuit of a specific and ambitious goal. The project shows that when Big 12 firms successfully identify a common set of objectives, Eureka offers a lever for mobilizing public support behind them. In the case of HDTV, European governments are highly dependent on a few producers to develop a critical technology, and the massive investment of effort and public money made in the effort to 'save' the MAC standard reflects these strong dependencies. But as much as Philips and Thomson have 'captured' the HDTV network, an ersatz collection of actors, including Rupert Murdoch, German DBS companies and European governments which lack CTV producers, are in a position to influence the project's outcome. Not all share a similar interest in establishing the MAC standard. Moreover, the HDTV policy network remains highly permeable by outside influences – including the US FCC, the CCIRN, Sony and Matsushita, and so on. The Eureka project partners are unable to insulate themselves from wider developments in the global race to develop HDTV. Single-minded public and private action is a necessary, but not sufficient, condition for the project's success.

To summarize, this chapter yields three key observations about how Eureka projects work 'on the ground'. First, actors who seek Eureka status often do so to attract political support to their R & D activities; they then seek to insulate themselves from policy shifts which may threaten their project. The MITHRA partners succeeded in achieving the first, but failed to achieve the second goal. The RA-D partners succeeded in achieving both. The Commission has used Eureka to try, as far as possible, to insulate Cosine's specific mission from wider, acrimonious telecommunications policy disputes. A Eurotrac spokesman admitted, 'We were happy to have the [Eureka] label because it gave us political support at the beginning, but I hope that now our funding comes from sufficiently different sources that we're safe'.[111] HDTV partners want multiannual funding commitments from their governments because these would help to insulate the project from scrutiny. They resent the Commission's compromises with PAL-dedicated interests and want the MAC standard simply to be forced upon broadcasters.

Second, these case studies have all, in different ways, revealed the limitations of Eureka's 'bottom-up' approach. The MITHRA project provides evidence that Eureka is a useful forum for the generation of projects by regional policy networks which cut across national boundaries, as does the Rhône–Alpes triangle more generally. Yet, it also reveals that Eureka is in no sense a panacea for the chronic financial problems of potentially innovative SMEs. The RA-D project shows that the effectiveness of Eureka as a 'marriage broker' is limited if public administrations cannot provide support and advice to industrialists who are new to collaboration. Cosine cannot work without strong 'top-down' elements. The HDTV project would be dead in the water if political commitment to the MAC standard was any less strong. In short, developing collaborative communities in technology-intensive industries usually requires active public input which goes beyond the simple provision of public funds.

Finally, this chapter makes clear that if there is one key prescription for making Eureka a more effective policy tool, it is that funding decisions should be harmonized in time, if not amount. All of the projects treated in this chapter receive funding from multiple sources. All suggest that substantial effort is required for partners to secure funding commitments and then to plan their projects around them. Urging Eureka's Member States and the Commission to coordinate the timing of their funding decisions does not require a suspension of scepticism about what inspires industrialists to complain about the public support they receive. If Member States are unwilling to back up political commitments with more than haphazardly timed delivery of funds, then a large number of Eureka participants will always waste critical time as projects slip off schedule. It bears reminding that Eureka was launched in the first place because European industry could not turn innovations into products fast enough to compete with the Japanese and Americans in key technology-intensive industries.

8 Conclusion

This chapter moves toward a final assessment of Eureka. First, Eureka must be placed in the context of the 1992 project. The EC as a whole has determined that domestic industries should be subjected to more market forces and give up competitive advantages which spring from barriers to trade across frontiers. Yet, Eureka provides national subsidies to 'near-market' R & D projects. Eureka reflects the uneasy coexistence of free markets and public intervention at the heart of the 1992 project.

A separate set of paradoxes is contained within new competition state strategies at the national level. States have developed new interventionist policy tools to bolster national competitive advantage through innovation, but innovation increasingly springs from transnational partnerships. Programmes designed to foster innovation are often 'para-governmental' in structure and provide wide discretion to private interests in decisionmaking. Yet technological innovation and competitiveness are increasingly important sources of state power in the 1990s. Eureka subsumes these paradoxes quite clearly.

Governments have 'disaggregated' their industrial policy tools in order to intervene more selectively and strategically in a wider range of industrial sectors. Policy analysts thus must disaggregate innovation policies to understand them. The policy network model allows innovation policies to be dissected not only between sectors, but also at different levels of analysis where the relative salience of political or technical rationality varies considerably. The model is used here not only to place Eureka in the context of developments in European innovation policies more generally, but to help explain the very eclectic patterns of government–industry relations which are encompassed by the initiative. This chapter concludes by evaluating Eureka according to the criteria for analysis developed in Chapter 1.

I. THE 1992 PROJECT: TENSIONS AND CONTRADICTIONS

Eureka is in many ways a microcosm of the tensions and contradictions which are endemic to the 1992 project. The potential benefits of the internal market – a 5 per cent increase in EC GDP and the creation of five million new jobs – have always been clear. After the ratification of the SEA in 1987, no serious contender for political authority in any of the twelve EC Member States could credibly urge that the 1992 project be abandoned or that national support for its core objectives be withdrawn.

But consensus on the ends of the internal market is not the same as consensus on the means for its creation. The 1992 project implies substantial political and economic upheaval and cannot promise to benefit all European industrial and political actors equally. Political actors are naturally loathe to watch the lowering of barriers to trade lead to the decline of national industries and the subsequent loss of jobs, investment and tax revenues that may result as new competitive forces are unleashed. Industries which have benefited from protected national markets will seek political support to maintain their advantages while they simultaneously look to exploit new opportunities beyond national frontiers. The argument of politically powerful firms such as Philips, Renault or Siemens that their US or Japanese competitors stand to benefit most from the internal market cannot be dismissed out of hand by political authorities. While much lip service has been paid to the urgent need to create the internal market, its implementation is a highly political process which invokes short-termism and intransigence in bargaining between economic actors whose interests are threatened.[1]

The pace of European political integration is influenced by a diverse array of public and private actors operating at both the regional and national levels. Few have clear interests in simply maintaining the status quo or, alternatively, forging ahead to achieve a full political union. Most have interests best served by creating a political environment somewhere between these two possibilities. A myriad of new regional institutions – many outside the formal organizational confines of the EC itself – have emerged since the Community was 'relaunched' in the mid-1980s. Many serve the interests of those actors who seek closer European unity, but wish to retain the benefits which accrue from their purely national identities. Clearly, Eureka is one such institution.

For EC Member States, accepting the principles of the internal market does not mean accepting that national prerogatives should be surrendered in a process of 'scaling up' and Europeanizing innovation policies more generally. At the same time, states now accept that innovation increasingly is a product of transnational linkages between firms, and that collaborative R & D reinforces the common objective of establishing the internal market. European innovation policies thus have converged and become informed by common goals. But the existence of Eureka shows that they still are motivated far more by national self-interest than by lofty political ideals.

For its part, European industry clearly has benefited from the growth of Eureka. It provides what the Framework programme cannot: links to national administrations, funding for near-market R & D and opportunities to receive subsidies for projects which do not fit with the strategic goals of EC programmes. The interests of many European firms – particularly the Big 12 but increasingly SMEs in a wide range of sectors – are served by the existence of both the Framework programme and Eureka since subsidies from each may be pooled and projects refused funds by one may be funded by the other.

The internal market cannot be freed simply through the use of blunt instruments such as EC legislation to ban national protectionism and state aids to industry. National governments, and especially the Commission, somehow must convince European firms to act in the interests of the 1992 project while still pursuing their own narrow self-interests. The challenge for European industrial policies is daunting. Many of Europe's most globally competitive firms in technology-intensive industries have prospered only because they have exploited protected national markets as a springboard for global strategies. Many of Europe's most important 'home-grown' technological successes – such as Concorde, Airbus or Ariane – would have been failures if national governments had not suspended market forces or directed vast amounts of state funding to R & D subsidies. Collaborative R & D programmes have emerged as a policy response. They allow national governments and the Commission to reconcile the goals of freeing the internal market and providing state support for technological innovation.

Chapter 1 argued that collaborative R & D and the internal market are mutually reinforcing because of their complementary supply and demand side effects. In theory, Eureka complements the supply-side goals of the 1992 project by encouraging pan-European marketing strategies, convincing firms to undertake more R & D and eliminating duplicated, inefficient R & D efforts. Contact with wider market opportunities is a primary reason why firms choose to collaborate via Eureka. Eureka has made possible a substantial number of R & D projects that firms could not fund or risk without partners. Eureka's efficiency-promoting effects are impossible to gauge precisely, but there is at least anecdotal evidence to suggest that its largest projects – the

HDTV project, Prometheus, ES2 and Jessi – have acted to synergize the actions of the few European MNCs which have the resources and market shares needed to innovate in the relevant sectors.

On the demand side, Eureka's contributions to the development of common standards and the opening of public procurement markets have been relatively modest outside of the HDTV and Cosine projects. The EC faces a long, uphill battle in these policy areas generally. However, contrary to the hopes expressed in its Declaration of Principles, Eureka has done little by itself to produce 'an acceleration of ongoing efforts to elaborate industrial standards at an early stage [and] open up the system of public procurement'.[2]

It is difficult to reach a clear verdict on how much Eureka has altered national champion-centred innovation policies to make them consistent with the 1992 project. The question of whether governments generally have received good value for money from their subsidies also cannot be answered definitively. Chapter 6 revealed that the vast majority of Eureka project leaders receive government subsidies. Most receive quite a lot. It is singularly difficult for governments to gauge the minimum amount of subsidy needed to induce firms to collaborate in the interests of promoting innovation or the 1992 project. Moreover, the motivations of Eureka's national governments in subsidizing their home firm participants are mixed and impossible to disentangle. Eureka is both a tool for hastening the construction of the internal market as well as a method by which governments may continue to subsidize their domestic national champions while 'hiding' subsidies within a pan-European framework.

Eureka may be viewed as a sort of 'halfway house' in the Europeanization of national innovation policies. It allows European governments to pursue their own distinctive innovation policy agendas, but also to encourage private behaviour which is consistent with the objectives of the 1992 project. Eureka has yielded truly common actions within some projects and purely national actions, only marginally altered to accommodate the principle of promoting collaborative R & D, in others. But Eureka clearly is more than just as an amalgam of national innovation policies. It also incorporates a series of distinct, sector-specific, nascent pan-European innovation policies which are most purely reflected in umbrella frameworks such as Famos or Jessi. In short, Eureka exists at the point where the goals of national innovation policies converge without becoming collective.

The Commission's early suspicions that Eureka was simply a way for Member States to provide state aids to national champions without being challenged by the EC's competition authorities have never gone

Seanss book!

away. There is no single 'Commission view' on the need for or benefits of subsidized collaborative R & D. This point comes clear when one first visits DG IV in Brussels and is told, 'Philips and Thomson have these DG XIII people in their pockets', and then literally crosses the street to the palatial DG XIII building to hear, 'I'm sorry to say this, but European companies need money if they're going to compete with the Japanese'.[3] The growth of the Framework programme's budget means that DG XIII is now responsible for the second largest single item of EC expenditure after the Common Agricultural Policy (CAP). Meanwhile, DG IV continues to frustrate its next-door neighbours by, for example, launching investigations into the legality of state aids to Thomson or publicly warning that the HDTV project could produce a cartel of television equipment producers.[4] This divergence of views illustrates the extent to which the Commission itself has become a dynamic political system – marked by internal rivalries and competing agendas – due to the conflicting goals of the 1992 project. Eureka sits uncomfortably at the confluence of these competing agendas.

A purely free market solution to the problem of European technological competitiveness would simply mandate the removal of all internal and external barriers to trade within Europe. All R & D subsidies, whether they were directed to purely national or collaborative R & D, would be disallowed. In order to remain competitive, European firms would have to fund their own R & D. Since the costs and risks of R & D are reduced through collaboration even without public subsidies, European firms logically would have incentives to engage in collaborative R & D without any prompting by their governments.

The argument against such a solution is one of political practicality. Many European firms in key technology sectors – microelectronics, consumer electronics, robotics, etc. – simply could not stand up to Japanese and US competition if all subsidies were withdrawn. More generally, the very nature of the relationship between technology and competitive advantage in international trade naturally gives birth to 'forms of industrial organisation that differ from perfect competition and, hence, also 'strategic' behaviours by individual agents', particularly governments.[5] On grounds of national and regional economic security, European governments are simply not willing to succumb to technological dependence on foreign suppliers in key sectors.

Thus, as Sharp and Shearman have argued, collaborative R & D is 'a second best option'[6] to an entirely free market solution. It provides a bridge between the bad old days of national protectionism and the brave new world of the internal market. In innovation policy as in trade policy, 'the challenge . . . is to *avoid* reinforcing through protection the existing rigidity of the industrial sector or sectors in question, while at the same time fostering or even imposing adaptation in return for temporary protection'.[7] In some respects, the Framework programme and Eureka may be viewed as fundamentally protectionist, but at least they encourage firms to adapt to the internal market and the increasingly urgent need to innovate in order to compete. They generally do not reinforce the rigidities to which pre-1985 national innovation policies contributed.

From the Commission's point of view, Eureka may be seen as a 'second-best option' to a truly common European innovation policy. Since it funds collaborative projects, at least national subsidies act to encourage recipients to become familiar with market opportunities beyond their borders and to identify obstacles to the pan-European marketing of their products. Eureka has induced a broad range of collaborative R & D activities which the EC itself either could not or would not have been able to induce on its own (as well as activities it would not wish to induce!). It is a method of protectionism which is less inconsistent with the goals of the 1992 project than are traditional methods.

At a basic level, Eureka has grown because it is flexible enough to promote free competition between many firms or encourage market 'closure' to consolidate the dominant market position[s] of a few firms.[8] This dualism is also present in the 'dialectic of 1992': as the post-SEA period has seen conflicts between the EC's competition and industrial policies, EC and national innovation policies, and competition and closure become perceptible in bold relief.[9] Because it contains the means to achieve entirely contrary policy ends, Eureka is broadly consistent with the 1992 project.

To understand why Eureka exists and works as it does, the conclusion of an ambitious study of the relationship between innovation and international trade is apt:

> There is certainly a wide variety of economic inducements to innovation, but these belong to the necessary, although not sufficient, conditions. Sufficiency is provided by the degree of matching/ mismatching between these generic market opportunities and the institutional conditions related to scientific/technological capabilities available in each country, the 'bridging institutions' between pure science and economic applications, the expertise embodied in the firm and the pattern of organisation of the major markets.[10]

Eureka is a new type of 'bridging institution': it seeks to bridge the traditional gap between Europe's proven capacity to innovate and the actual commercialization of European innovations. Eureka is unique in relying on the expertise of firms to set its agenda. It is an attempt to induce European technology-intensive industries to adjust to major changes in the pattern of organization of their 'home market', the internal market. Above all, it reflects the assumption that the internal market is a necessary, but far from sufficient condition for inducing enhanced European technological competitiveness.

II. MESO-CORPORATISM, PARA-GOVERNMENT AND SYMBOLIC POLITICS

Eureka engenders a complex pattern of different policymaking arrangements. Explaining why begins by recalling a principle which is central to the study of government–industry relations: the process of interest formation shapes and is shaped by the organization of state structures. Traditional innovation policies focused state subsidies and attention on a few national champions. These policies fitted neatly with broader macro-corporatist strategies, which pursued economic growth by creating formalized structures for negotiations between government and 'peak associations' which were given monopolistic power to represent the interests of industry and labour. National champions often were provided with monopolistic power to represent the national interest in technological development. Innovation policies were relatively easy to plan and execute when policy resources could be focused on a relatively small number of large firms in key technology-intensive industries such as telecommunications, computers and aerospace.[11] Macro-corporatist strategies encouraged the emergence of industrial structures in technology-intensive industries which were dominated by national champions, whose dominance in turn made the pursuit of macro-corporatist strategies seem logical.

In the 1990s, competition state strategies are more sophisticated. They accentuate 'the dualism between competitive and corporatist processes [which] is an increasingly important cleavage in contemporary capitalist democracies'.[12] Competition state strategies may be viewed as 'meso-corporatist', in that they create a 'fusion of the processes of interest representation, decision-making and policy implementation to a more restricted range of issues than the 'system-steering' concerns of macro-corporatism'.[13] Many of the high ambitions of macro-corporatist strategies have been abandoned because states are far less able to 'steer' national economies which are interpenetrated by unpredictable trans-national forces. But in many respects, meso-corporatist strategies must be *more* ambitious and embrace the highly technical and uncertain policy task of harnessing national capabilities to attack future markets for technologies that are changing fast. Policies must be responsive to a far wider coterie of firms, which usually cannot be organized into 'peak associations', and which compete in a more diverse and disaggregated range of niche markets for technology-intensive products. More generally, as Hilpert argues, 'the state when dealing with techno-industrial innovation is completely different from that which designs Keynesian programmes in economic and social policy . . . the state does not react to strong social interests or an economic crisis: the state is active, it takes a leading role'.[14]

Promoting innovation involves vast uncertainties and requires access to much specialized information which governments lack. Policies must be selective and responsive to different technological trajectories in different sectors. They must seize on private sources of specialized information and expertise and put them to work in pursuit of the public policy goal of promoting competitiveness. Governments must disaggregate their policy tools to make policy tasks manageable. The most logical way to do so is to develop distinct policy goals and tools in specific industrial sectors. Policies such as Eureka are distinctly meso-corporatist in character, with government–industry relations increasingly played out in distinct sector-specific policy networks.

Government needs to be contextualized for government–industry relations to have meaning. Differences must be acknowledged between political executives, or ministers in power, and the administrative agencies of the state.[15] Within telecommunications and consumer electronics policy networks, Cawson *et al.* conclude that government–industry relations

> tended on the whole to be between . . . agencies and the firms, and often involve ongoing, rather routine contacts where the views and actions of the members of the political executive have little direct impact . . . Given the party political nature of political executives, they seem far more to relate to a broad orientation towards the future shape of society and the nation's place in the world.[16]

Clearly, a gulf exists between political executives and administrative agencies and each has its own distinct form of rationality. In the political realm, choices are largely determined by the will to remain in power. In the administrative realm, particularly where innovation policy is concerned, choices are largely determined by technical knowledge. Links between these two realms are often tenuous.[17]

Critics of macro-corporatism stressed the powerful agenda-setting capacity such strategies typically assigned to private interests and unelected administrators[18] As the focus of state support for industry becomes more sector-specific and driven by technical rationality, private firms and administrative agencies clearly may take on an even more powerful agenda-setting policy management role. Eureka empowers administrations and firms in precisely this manner. Its ministerial conference formally grants national ministers the power to choose which projects to approve or fund, but in practice it is national administrations which make and implement most of these decisions. These administrations are 'shallow, even in the larger countries'.[19] Eureka reflects consensus among its Member States that innovation cannot successfully be promoted by rules-bound, discretionary national administrations who try to pick winners or 'manufacture' the technological goals and transnational linkages of individual projects. Administrations simply choose among proposals which emanate from industry itself. It is up to private actors to choose their own goals and partners.

Eureka thus has the effect of promoting the unification of many private interests at a transnational, sectoral level. It rewards actors who can identify their collective sectoral interests, develop mechanisms for self-scrutiny and convince national administrations that their activities promise to yield competitive advantage. Political commitment to promoting sector-specific activities often has translated into tranches of funding which are compartmentalized and 'sector-dedicated', as in the cases of Famos, Jessi, Euroenviron or the HDTV project. Private actors are granted much scope to influence distributional decisions within these large, programmatic or umbrella projects because they retain goal and agenda-setting within them. Such projects operate at levels far removed from national political or administrative scrutiny because Eureka itself operates far from any locus of central political authority. Collective scrutiny by Member States is almost non-existent due to the weakness of Eureka's central institutions.

Eureka's methodology and structure are consistent with the trend toward disaggregated, sectorized post-Fordist innovation policy strategies which support favoured private sector activities with the minimum public power necessary. The initiative resists traditional typologies of national or international organizations, just as 'quasi-governmental' organizations at the national level often straddle the traditional distinction between public and private organizations. Eureka is one of a growing and diverse collection of transnational, para-governmental organizations (PGOs) which have emerged at a pan-European level. Many exist due to the growth in the size and scope of the EC's own activities. Others reflect the need to promote exchange between groups of states which are larger than the EC twelve on issues that do not fit easily within the EC's remit. For example, the CSCE's profile has been raised considerably as a forum for intergovernmental exchange on European security and human rights issues since the fall of authoritarian governments in Eastern Europe in 1989. In technical standardization, CEN/CENELEC subsumes all eighteen EC and EFTA Member States. The Council for European Cultural Cooperation and Audio-Visual Eureka each include more than twenty-five Member States, although the work of both is very much determined by the development of the EC's own audio-visual policy.

Recalling the early debates about what role the Commission would play in Eureka, Hilf's explanation of the rise of transnational PGOs in Europe is apt:

> The use of PGO-like structures rather than units of the core institutions makes it possible to escape from the complex bureaucracy-wide rules affecting pay, finance and audit; makes it possible to cross group boundaries by involving non-EC member countries; allows interest groups to participate in EC operations; and may have significant presentational and public relations advantages[20]

All of these are reasons why Eureka's administrative structure and methodology emerged as they did. Eureka was designed to be free of what was viewed as the Commission's rigid and inflexible bureaucracy and to include non-EC states. Governments wished to have a framework for funding R & D that was 'industry-led' and which allowed private interests to determine what sort of new cross-border liaisons should be struck. But explaining why mechanisms for central political direction or control were not 'built into' Eureka requires understanding the rationality which political leaders bring to the design of innovation policies. The symbolic political value of initiatives such as Eureka may matter more to political executives than do their actual outcomes. Political executives can claim political advantage if they are perceived as adopting innovative new policies which promote national technological modernization, competitiveness and a role for indigenous firms in the vaguely explicated Third Industrial Revolution. Eureka is not a centralized, supranational programme because governments would lose their abilities to use it as a tool of *national* innovation policies if it were. Eureka is not an EC programme largely because its symbolic political value would be minimal for national governments if they had simply handed over authority for managing the initiative to the Commission. A broad conclusion of this study is that while technological modernization and competitiveness are prerequisites of state power, they are not the only or even the primary motivators of governments when innovation policies are designed.

Eureka also is indicative of the trend toward more diverse, alternative forms of functional administration in Europe. It solves a collective action problem for governments who wish to retain national prerogatives in policymaking, yet promote the development of the internal market and cross-national alliances between indigenous firms. For its industrial participants, Eureka provides a forum for attracting public support to private sector activities with minimal intervention by public authorities. Eureka has no organizational precedent, but neither do many other European PGOs. A key lesson which emerges from study of Eureka is that the politics of European integration cannot be understood merely by studying the institutions and policies of the European Community.

III. POLICY NETWORKS AND GOVERNMENT–INDUSTRY RELATIONS

Eureka reflects the increased transnational focus of European innovation policies. It points to the insufficiency of the 'weak' or 'strong' state distinction which still dominates the industrial policy literature.[21] Searching for common, sector-specific patterns of government–industry relations across a range of countries is now often more profitable for the policy analyst than focusing on the national setting as the key unit of analysis.

Several distinct levels of analysis must be delineated to understand the recent transformation of European innovation policies (see Table 8.1). The policy network typology, originally developed as a meso-level concept, may be applied at all of these levels. First, the model has heuristic value at a 'macro-level'. Recalling how Eureka, SDI and the Framework programme competed for political backing in 1985, a European innovation policy network at the highest political level may be discerned in which decisions are made about how Europe's finite technological resources are deployed. The Commission and national governments compete for authority, and thus the Framework programme and Eureka compete for resources at this level. Political rationality is a key determinant of outcomes. The Commission's goal of expanding its *acquis* and the British goal of preserving national autonomy in innovation policy have a perceptible impact on general agenda-setting.

Industrial interests at this macro-level are fragmented by sectors as well as by nationalities, but generally they are adaptive. In 1985, the Big

Table 8.1 European Innovation Policy: levels of analysis

Network	Level	Dynamic of government–industry relations
European innovation policy	Macro	Competition between Commission and national governments for authority; industrial interests fragmented and adaptive
Framework programme	Initiative	Competition between EC Member States and between industrial interests for scarce policy resources
Eureka	Initiative	Competition between Member States to shape Eureka's goals and structure; industrial interests compete for scarce policy resources
Sectoral	Meso	Commission–industry or national administration–industry alliances; competition for resources dependent on strength and durability of political commitment to sector and ability of industrial participants to identify their collective interests
Project	Micro	Commission–industry or national administration–industry alliances; resources dependent on outcomes in wider networks

12 firms and large manufacturers threw their weight first behind the European participation in SDI, then the Commission's proposals for the Framework programme, then Eureka. The European robotics industry has benefited from the growth of the EC's Brite programme, but the Famos framework has targeted national subsidies to a scheme in which industry has more independent discretion. In crude terms, many firms are unconcerned whether the EC or Eureka brings them subsidies. They will cash the cheque no matter who writes it.

Outcomes of interest mediation at the macro-level of European innovation policy set the stage for relationships between actors within Eureka and the Framework programme, which each may be viewed as a distinct 'initiative-level' policy networks. Political rationality still matters at this level. Within the Framework programme, Member States compete to ensure that scarce policy resources are directed to sectors where the competitive advantage of their indigenous firms is strongest. Industrial interests compete for EC subsidies by lobbying both their national governments and the Commission to increase funding for programmes which fund R & D in their sector. The Commission must act as an 'honest broker' and seek to satisfy the interests of both national governments and industry, since it is dependent on both in its effort to expand the EC's 'own resources' in innovation policy. But it still seeks opportunities to guard and expand its own independent discretion in innovation policy.

Within Eureka, Member States compete to influence the initiative's general policy goals and structure. The Germans continue to insist that Eureka is an appropriate forum for infrastructure projects such as Eurotrac. The British and Swiss argue that the industry-led character of Eureka must be preserved and that it should be perform nothing more than a 'marriage bureau' function. The French view is that more centralized mechanisms, such as collective, multiannual funding decisions, are needed for Eureka to work effectively. The Italians and Danes want Eureka to do more for SMEs. The Greeks, Turks and Irish simply want to participate in more projects.

Sectorized industrial interests may compete for funds at the initiative-level. For example, protagonists in the Jessi project have criticized the new emphasis of Eureka on promoting environmental R & D:

> It would be dangerous . . . if some politicians responsible were to hesitate and think of increasing their support for other objectives which appear more pressing, to the detriment of the strategic option that Jessi represents. To take, for example, the problems posed by the environment, which I myself believe are very important, I do not think there can be a European ecological policy without the technological means to support it . . . the control of information technologies is that 'hard core' which determines all the possible choices.[22]

However, competition for resources between sectoral networks is muted by Eureka's lack of centralized funding structures. More often, competition for funds is between actors *within* particular sectors. Participants in Eurotrac are reminded by the project's secretariat that the project has political goals, not just scientific ones, which cannot be ignored if the project is to receive large subsidies as new Eureka environmental projects emerge which have clearer commercial goals. European manufacturers and universities in the robotics sector pushed for the launch of the Famos umbrella project to transform political commitment to FMS into money, thus effectively insulating them from competition with other sectors for public funds. Now, these actors compete for generally finite pools of funding which Member States have committed to the robotics sector.

Thus, the explanatory power of the policy networks model remains most powerful at a sectoral or 'meso-level' of European innovation policymaking for three essential reasons. First, the growth of collaborative R & D programmes and the industrial policy role of the EC mean that differences in patterns of policymaking are often more pronounced in different sectors than in different states. Varying degrees of 'Europeanization' in different sectors means that the sector in question often matters in determining patterns of government–industry relations more than the national origins of the firms competing in it.

Second, as policies have become disaggregated, public strategies have become more uniquely tailored to the specific technological imperatives which characterize individual industrial sectors. The extent of governments' involvement depends mostly on the perceived strategic importance of each sector for more general technological development or competitiveness. Much also depends on the extent to which the market itself does not allocate resources for the R & D needed to generate innovations. Governments intervene with more resources in sectors where 'market failure' deters firms from expending the resources needed to innovate.

Third, sector-specific networks have emerged which are distinguished from one another by breaks in the structure of their resource dependencies. Governments have committed specific policy resources to the promotion of different sectors, such as robotics or biotechnology. Policy resources are normally compartmentalized and 'sector-dedicated' within wider R & D budgets.

Sector-specific policy networks correspond to individual subprogrammes within Framework, such as Esprit, Race or Brite. At this level, decisionmaking structures are often highly technocratic and insular, with the Commission and industry enjoying substantial autonomy from national governments. Esprit, which is still largely managed by a Commission–Big 12 alliance, is the textbook example of a tightly integrated policy community at the initiative level. Its membership is stable, it is largely isolated from outside influences, and it is characterized by powerful structural dependencies, as both the Commission and the Big 12 face severe pressures to make high-cost projects into critical technologies produce results in order to justify further funding commitments. By contrast, Brite and the EC's biotechnology schemes are loosely integrated issue networks with a diverse collection of SMEs, research laboratories and universities participating. A diverse range of projects is subsidized and there is no unified industrial constituency in either sector. Funding levels remain quite low and firms have clear incentives to fund their own R & D, so resource dependencies between private and public actors are quite weak.

Eureka also contains meso-level networks, which often correspond to umbrella projects such as Famos or Euroenviron, or large, complex projects, such as the HDTV project or Jessi. The development of umbrella projects within Eureka has often been motivated by the desire of networks of industrialists and officials to heighten their discretion to set goals and allocate funding based on technical rationality. Alliances between the DTI and British robotics firms in Famos and the BMFT and European atmospheric scientists in Eurotrac are illustrative.

Finally, each individual Eureka or EC-funded project may be viewed as a policy network in itself: a distinct arena for the mediation of public and private interests. Once resources are committed to individual projects, technical rationality governs relationships between public and private actors within individual projects, as all share a common interest in making the project succeed. But project-level networks are linked by resource dependencies into meso-level networks, and participants often must adopt political strategies to achieve their objectives, as the HDTV and Eurotrac partners have done.

This study has revealed change in the dynamics of government–industry relations at all of these levels of analysis since the mid-1980s. At the macro-level, political and technical rationality converged between 1985 and 1987. This convergence had powerful implications for early distribution of benefits at the initiative level, as the Commission sought to get the Framework programme established and the French and their supporters scrambled to get Eureka up and running. Industry saw its interests served by both initiatives. The Commission–Big 12 alliance successfully used widespread political concern about European weakness in information technology to convince EC governments to launch the Framework programme and to earmark most of its funds to Esprit and Race. National governments also depended on the support of former national champions to successfully launch Eureka. Actors in pre-existing sectoral networks, especially in the information technology sector, were keen to use Eureka as a launching pad for new, ambitious projects which could not be easily funded through the Framework programme due to its limited resources and pre-competitive restrictions. Thus, Eureka's early project lists were dominated by large, expensive projects, and contained relatively few small projects led by SMEs.

But collaborative R & D is still a relatively new feature of European innovation policies. The Framework programme, Eureka and most meso-level networks which exist with them are still permeable by wider political influences. For example, ICL was summarily ejected from the Big 12 Roundtable as well as several Jessi subprojects after the Japanese firm Fijitsu purchased 80 per cent of its shares in 1991. The DTI claimed the decision by the Jessi board to reduce ICL's participation in Jessi was politically motivated and designed to find favour with protectionist elements within the Commission.[23] An ICL representative commented, 'We've truly seen the Commission as a political agent at their worst and at their best'.[24]

The permeability of Eureka by wider political agendas is still considerable. Pressures to open up Eureka to Eastern European states after 1989 are illustrative. The idea that Eureka should promote environmental R & D, originally pushed by the Germans and resisted by other Member States, is now well established because environmental issues have become more salient in national politics.

Industrial interests have become unified within several sectors at the initiative level, but there is little evidence that the key unit for analysis for government–industry relations at the transnational level has become industry associations or alliances as opposed to individual firms. Despite linkages developed through multiple collaborative R & D projects, Philips and Thomson are still rivals in many respects and relations between them are uneasy and potentially conflictual. Even at the level of domestic economies, recent work by Cawson and others stresses that industry associations in Britain, France and Germany play only a small role in policymaking or the determination of broad industrial policy strategies. However, the associational weakness of interest organization in critical industries such as electronics or telecommunications does not mean that private interests are not extremely powerful in determining policies.[25]

Structural dependencies remain complex between networks at the different levels specified in Table 8.1. However, Eureka shows that once policy resources are committed to funding certain types of R & D, actors in sectoral networks seek to fortify and routinize policymaking structures at the meso- and micro-levels. Any proposed changes to these structures can be resisted on the grounds that they would be costly in terms of administrative efficiency or continuity in the pursuit of specific avenues of innovation. Eureka has prompted the development of several quite distinct sectoral networks – in microelectronics, environmental technologies, robotics, etc. – which are often far removed from central political authority and operate quite independently. Since Eureka's activities are so diverse, its rules of process are few and its central administration is minimal, networks at the meso- and micro-levels can often 'stand alone', with clear breaks in the structure of their resource dependencies. These networks have become more routinized and entrenched over time, and less permeable by political influences present at the macro- or initiative-levels.

Existing models of policy networks emphasize resource dependencies which transcend organizational boundaries in national settings.[26] A key point of this study is that the existence of transnational policy networks often allows actors within them to break from dependencies on political authorities or international organizations because they operate at a level where political authority and transnational administrations are weak. Both are particularly weak in Eureka's case. Once resources are committed to sectoral activities within Eureka, corresponding networks can become self-sustaining because interests are transnational and independent.

Others who have employed the policy network model to study European government–industry relations or EC policymaking have come to similar conclusions about the ability of networks to insulate themselves on a European level. Schneider and Werle find that 'European policy networks are selective and there exist 'entry barriers' which tend to exclude actors not represented by powerful corporate actors . . . such as environmentalists and consumers'. Moreover, 'bureaucracy gains influence at the expense of both the European and national parliaments'.[27] Extensive investigation of European industrial policies in the consumer electronics and telecommunications sectors leads Cawson to observe 'existing political practices in many settings have tended to exhibit a dualism between corporatism for the powerful and pluralism for the powerless, and it would be surprising if the totality of interest group politics in the new Europe turned out to be much different'.[28] In an era when the EC's democratic legitimacy and penchant for technocratic forms of policymaking are under intense scrutiny, the policy network model is a valuable tool for assessing the extent to which specific interests can use the European level to 'hide' from pluralistic pressures which persist at the national or subnational levels.

At the same time, it must be acknowledged that a complex constellation of vulnerabilities still persists for many sector-specific policy networks. A minority of Eureka's Member States have budgets 'dedicated' to Eureka, so the amount of funding available to its participants is dependent on wider budgetary and industrial policy decisions which are made in a national political contexts. Sectoral networks cannot insulate themselves entirely from changing political agendas. The success of one network in producing innovations could still produce a rapid shift of resources away from others. The lesson of the 1980s is that policy analysts will need to be preoccupied with explaining change in European innovation policies as much as continuity in the 1990s. The value of the policy network approach is that it resists determinism and is flexible enough to accommodate such change.

IV. GOVERNANCE WITHOUT GOVERNMENT?

This study has sought to evaluate Eureka critically and has found a great deal about Eureka to criticize. Yet, any critique must acknowledge that Eureka and other collaborative R & D programmes are still quite new. As a British Eureka official argues:

> It's really in its very early days. There's an enormous learning curve to be gone through, because it demands that national administrations collaborate together in handling projects through procedures, even though it recognizes that each government has autonomy in terms of funding provisions. So you've got an officialdom that has to go through a learning curve, and you have an industrial clientele who are used to a much more focused R & D support effort. They're used to having the goalposts cast in concrete and being able to shoot in a line that's set for them by governments and that's not what we have in Eureka.[29]

As this study neared completion, the Dutch chairmanship of 1991 engaged in its own performance analysis of Eureka after five years of its existence. In addition to the survey undertaken by the Eureka assessment panel, Eureka NPCs held a series of 'X-Ray' sessions on Eureka's sector-specific activities as well as what were termed its 'four corner flags': synergy with the EC's R & D activities, supportive measures, umbrella projects and support for SMEs. At an operational level, these corner flags set the 'playing field' for Eureka as a distinct programme. It is worthwhile to review the present study's findings on each of these issues before evaluating Eureka according to the criteria developed in Chapter 1: its provisions for enhancing the participation of SMEs in collaborative R & D, its additionality to the wider European R & D effort, its contribution to the 1992 project and its administrative efficiency.

The issue of synergy between the EC's R & D programmes and Eureka continues to be approached with much caution by Eureka Member States. EC–Eureka relations have a history of tension and Pandolfi's commitment to strengthening EC links to Eureka has yielded few tangible results. There is hope that the Commission in future will deem the results of Eureka projects suitable for support as 'Community R & D activities' through the Value programme, which commits 9.5 million ECU annually to the dissemination and utilization of the results of collaborative R & D.[30] But the central problems of EC–Eureka relations are ensuring that the Framework programme and Eureka do not duplicate each other, that the Commission 'push' EC-funded projects towards Eureka as they are completed, and that the Commission and Eureka officials are aware of each others' activities.

This study has produced clear evidence that there is room for far more synergy between the EC's R & D programmes and Eureka. The idea that Eureka would take many pre-competitive projects conducted within the Framework programme 'closer to the market' has not materialized in practice. Eureka and the Framework programme, except in the case of projects involving Big 12 firms such as HDTV and Jessi, do not complement each other very well at present. The problem of overlap between the Framework programme and Eureka is 'not of any real concern' in the eyes of the assessment panel.[31] But the more that Eureka and the Framework programme grow in size, the more scope there is for wasteful duplication.

As the Commission prepared its plans for Framework IV in 1992, Pandolfi conceded that the problem of synergy with Eureka had never been properly addressed by the EC. He and Delors both urged that EC funding should become 'more focused on targeted projects in key technologies' and cited Eureka as 'something we must consider in adapting our own R & D programmes to the needs of industry'.[32] For the first time, the Commission seemed prepared to systematically co-ordinate EC funding for 'horizontal activities to develop generic technologies' with Eureka projects which were 'more sector-specific, located further down the process'.[33] The Commission seemed to be acknowledging as never before that Eureka – despite its solidly intergovernmental structure – had real potential to contribute to the effectiveness of its own innovation policy. Meanwhile, new liaisons were created between Famos and Brite and between the biotechnology activities of Eureka and the EC.[34]

Supportive measures have always been a rather vague concept. This ambiguity helps explain why Eureka has done little to seize on the increased opportunities it should offer for defining new pan-European standards, opening public procurement, identifying barriers to trade and matching private financing with collaborative R & D projects. The Dutch-led review produced an admission that enthusiasm for supportive measures

> has somehow weakened within the Eureka framwork [sic] over the last years, after the initial political statements. This is in part due to the vagueness of the idea and its political implementation . . . and to an evident lack of structures and procedures by and between various actors involved (who does what towards who?).[35]

The evaluation undertaken by the Dutch chairmanship laid a basis for making supportive measures a more tangible source of added value for Eureka participants. The assessment panel found great confusion among participants about what supportive measures were, mainly due to the failure of Eureka Member States to clarify the concept.[36] But the X-Ray sessions which focused on Eureka's sector-specific activities acknowledged the

> dual character of Eureka . . . the Eureka of more strategically oriented projects with bigger companies in the lead and SMEs in their slip-stream and the Eureka of the somewhat smaller project-initiatives with in many cases SMEs even in initiating roles'.[37]

The sessions produced the sensible conclusion that supportive measures should be 'regrouped' into direct market-opening measures for large projects such as HDTV, and 'help of a more day to day nature' for SMEs seeking finance, help with standards or assistance in the commercialization of their innovations.[38] However, it remains to be seen whether supportive measures will ever be more than a vague and ineffectual element of Eureka given its lack of central mechanisms for defining and implementing them.

The general view on umbrella projects within the Eureka network is that 'if and when umbrellas are properly organized and managed these initiatives could significantly contribute to a more efficient and effective use of the very limited manpower within national Eureka offices'.[39] But there is also much concern that umbrella projects, including large, complex projects such as Jessi and the HDTV project, have become 'empires within empires' over which public officials have little control. Most have their own information systems, with wide varieties of hardware and software, which leads to duplication and incompatibility between them and Eureka's central database. The effect is often that Eureka's central database lists very little information on subprojects underway within umbrellas. To join a project, interested potential partners must then seek information from umbrella project boards or working groups, which are often cabalistic and resistant to new partners. Several of Eureka's environmental umbrella projects have provisions written into their constitutions which may be used to bar the entry of new partners.[40] The Dutch chairmanship noted 'serious concern . . . with regard to the low level of industrial participation' in many of them.[41]

The lack of transparency within large projects such as Jessi, HDTV and Prometheus, especially as regards decisionmaking about which subprojects receive funding and how much, are another source of concern for Eureka NPCs. The Dutch-led X-Ray review urged that new 'rules of the game' had to be defined and implemented to make umbrella and large strategic projects more accountable to Eureka as a whole. But it ultimately and rather haplessly concluded that 'NPCs are not in a position to enforce recommendations or to interfere with actual project-management'.[42] A general conclusion appeared to be that while little could be done to influence umbrella projects that were already in existence, 'in the future great care must be taken when establishing new umbrella-initiatives . . . by defining clearly the scope of their work and labelling the initiative for a restricted definition period only'.[43]

Several of Eureka's umbrella projects must be counted among its success stories. Famos has worked to synergize the efforts of a large number of diverse actors, including many SMEs and public research laboratories, working in robotics, software engineering, CAD, manufacturing and so on. The Eurolaser umbrella has led to the definition of common health and safety standards which could yield substantial competitive advantage for its participants. Large-scale, strategic projects such as Jessi, Eurotrac, Prometheus and the HDTV project certainly have synergized R & D efforts that might otherwise be fragmented. It makes sense that umbrella projects are a good idea in sectors where Europe has little history of collaboration, many types of actors are needed for innovation or the eventual market is the public sector. But umbrella projects are also a way that project participants can hide from scrutiny by Eureka as a whole. Concern about umbrella projects makes it abundantly clear that quite insular meso- and micro-level policy networks have emerged within Eureka. Umbrella projects highlight the initiative's general incapacity to ensure that all projects granted Eureka status are consistent with objectives which may be centrally agreed between its Member States at a political level.

Enhancing the participation of SMEs in Eureka has been adopted as common goal of nearly all Member States. SMEs which participate in Eureka are keenly market-oriented, but less experienced in collaborative R & D than large firms and other types of organizations. They clearly have more problems with the formal and legal organization of their projects, and suffer more than other types of project participants from haphazardly-timed deliveries of public funding and Eureka's lack of transparency. SMEs would stand to benefit most from more effective non-financial supportive measures.

At the same time, Eureka's additionality is most clearly revealed in the substantial number of SME-led projects which might not exist if Eureka did not exist. The initiative clearly provides significant added value to projects which feature substantial participation by SMEs. Eureka is not simply lining the coffers of cash-rich national champions.

However, the Eureka assessment panel described the rate of SME participation as 'increasing but still modest'.[44] Whatever the 'optimal' level of SME participation, there is certainly more that could be done to assist SMEs which presently participate. The 'regrouping' of supportive measures to provide more non-financial assistance for SMEs and the 'increasing tendency' for Member States to earmark funds for the proposal phases of projects were both encouraging developments on this front between 1991 and 1992.[45]

As for its contribution to the 1992 project, Eureka generally has promoted behaviour amongst both governments and firms which is consistent with the goal of establishing the internal market. Eureka's contribution to the transformation of what Prakke has called the 'cultural and competitive environments'[46] in which European technology-intensive firms operate has not been insignificant. While few project leaders report having been helped by their national Eureka institutions in attracting private finance to their projects, about one in three claims that Eureka status has made it easier to secure private funds. Eureka has had positive technology transfer effects both between industrial sectors and across national borders. The initiative has quite clearly established many collaborative links between EFTA firms and their EC counterparts which would not otherwise exist.[47] It has done more than any of the EC's own programmes to promote the development of a 'European technological space' which extends beyond the boundaries of the EC twelve.

In assessing Eureka's administrative efficiency, the tension between efficiency and political accountability must be acknowledged. Eureka is industry-led because governments placed higher value on the former than the latter in 1985. The trade-off between efficiency and accountability highlights a question which has lurked behind much of the analysis in this study: whether or not Eureka would be a more effective innovation policy tool if it was more centralized, supranational and, in a word, *dirigiste*. The idea of turning Eureka into a central R & D funding agency which pools national resources and develops strong public institutions to monitor Eureka's activities is quite clearly not on its agenda. But a strong argument could be made that Eureka Member States have paid far too little attention to its operational means, as opposed to its political ends, in creating and designing the initiative. Moreover, the political ends of Member States differ: they bring their own domestic political agendas to bear on Eureka and they often clash. Eureka would work more effectively if these conflicting objectives could be better-reconciled. The key is to find as much common ground as possible in national policy agendas. Eureka's institutions need to be revamped to provide for the clearer articulation of precisely where national interests converge into common interests, and how resources could be better mobilized to pursue them.

At the operational level, even when Member States agree on common policy goals, Eureka often lacks the institutional power to implement them. Eureka's promise to offer supportive measures to projects remains a hollow one because the initiative is not equipped to provide much public support to most projects beyond public funding. Clearly, the granting of project status to many poor quality or clearly pre-competitive projects has muddied Eureka's image.

At the project level, managers are low on learning curves about how projects can best be managed and what potentially can go wrong after commitments to collaborate are made. The failure of Eureka's Member States to harmonize the timing of their funding policies has further complicated the task of project managers. There is no question that the initiative would be more efficient and more enthusiastically embraced by industry if the time scales of funding policies were harmonized to the point that Member States made synchronized national commitments to approve and fund project proposals. The planning of projects would be enormously simplified if funding commitments were made for longer periods of time, with provisions for releasing funds at pre-determined points in a project's evolution. Project management would be less an exercise in shadow-boxing if Eureka was more transparent so that each project leader knew how much public funding his partners had to contribute to the project.

Eureka needs more transparency and predictability if it is to maximize its potential to help SMEs. What they most want from Eureka is the elimination of uncertainty about whether they will have the resources needed complete their R & D projects. SMEs clearly have special problems with project planning, coordination and scheduling compared with other types of actors. They often lack the resources to vet other firms to find out which will be effective partners and which will not. Common, transparent, multiannual funding commitments would especially benefit SMEs.

Critics would argue that funding projects in this manner would violate Eureka's intergovernmental ethos and would require sweeping changes in the way that budgeting and planning is carried out within national administrations. National budgets for R & D are often adjusted up or down as part of general annual public budgeting processes, thus making multiannual commitments difficult. Harmonizing national Eureka policies would require substantial political will.

But Eureka's member-governments have advanced far enough on their learning curves to realize that the initiative is plagued by problems of delays, coordination and lack of transparency. Eureka's strict intergovernmentalism carries costs in terms of time and efficiency which cannot be ignored in judging the initiative's performance. If its Eureka governments are truly as concerned with the initiative's outcomes as its symbolic political value, they should try to eliminate as much as possible the uncertainties which obtain at the project level. Eliminating these uncertainties while ensuring that partners are accountable for the use of public funds requires more stringent and, in many cases, collective assessment of proposals. If governments pooled resources for technology assessment, they could make firm and collective political commitments to fund projects throughout their anticipated life span, with funds delivered at designated points in time. Much of the uncertainty faced by project participants is a direct product of the fact that Eureka only marginally harmonizes twenty-one distinct funding policies.[48]

The case study method of policy analysis often carries the unspoken assumption that significant policy change or reform is impossible. A key methodological difficulty is that the contingent aspects of policies under study often are taken for granted. More specifically, much of the new government–industry relations literature is sceptical about the ability of governments to impose state-determined goals on patterns of technological change. Cawson *et al.* conclude that 'governments may decide themselves to act as 'collective venture capitalists' in the early stages of the development of new technologies, but our experience suggests that sooner or later such enterprises fail or develop the autonomy of firms'.[49]

This study has made a conscious effort not to assume that the contingent features of Eureka are cast in stone. The relative 'youth' of collaborative programmes makes them reformable for the simple reason that the newer the policy, the less that inertia is a deterrent to policy change. It is not enough to simply criticize the way Eureka works without considering how it *could* work, or how it could be reformed to work more effectively.

The author was invited to present the findings of this study to Eureka NPCs in April 1991. He was specifically asked to present ideas for enhancing the participation of SMEs in the initiative, but also to share more general ideas on how Eureka might work more effectively. The prescriptions which were offered (summarized in Appendix I) are feasible, not utopian. They are sensitive to the complex intergovernmental politics of Eureka, its minimal administrative resources and continued controversy at a political level about exactly what Eureka should be trying to achieve.

The response of delegations ranged from near-total agreement to laughing the author 'out of court'. One delegate accused the author of taking a 'Peter Pan' approach to Eureka, and prescribing changes that would require political will and action when 'we never get anywhere when we talk about politics'.[50] But the prescription most urgently recommended by the author and nearly all other analysts of Eureka was eventually implemented in the collective decision of six Member States – France, Spain, Finland, Sweden, Denmark and the Netherlands – to synchronize as much as possible their Eureka project approval and funding decisions for a one-year trial period in 1992.[51] The idea had been under discussion for some time[52] and its intent was simply designed to make Eureka more administratively efficient. In no way did it address wider problems such as Eureka's lack of accountability for the private use of public resources. However, the synchronization experiment along with the generally effective evaluation of Eureka undertaken in 1990–91 illustrated two crucial points: Eureka needs reform and is reformable. It is too cynical to conclude that it must fail because most previous collaborative initiatives have failed, or that it can only lead to the 'capture' of states by narrow, unaccountable private interests. Above all, assuming that Eureka as presently constituted is the best of all possible worlds means taking the opposite of the Peter Pan approach to public policy: one closes one's eyes and assumes that because policy change is difficult, it is not worth attempting or even wishing for it.

Appendix
Prescriptions for the re-design of Eureka

This appendix summarizes recommendations presented to a meeting of NPCs on 10 April 1991 as part of the general review of Eureka by the Dutch chairmanship. The prescriptions are designed to achieve four key goals: longer-term general policy initiatives, harmonization of the timing of public funding commitments, more rigorous technology assessment and more effective supportive measures.

Chapter 4 made clear that one of Eureka's problems is the lack of continuity between the policy initiatives of successive chairmanships. This problem was acknowledged when the troika system was developed to link successive chairmanships. In order to facilitate longer-term policy initiatives, each of the three troika Member States should have a representative working alongside the secretariat in Brussels. Chairmanships could then use the secretariat as a resource to prepare and implement policy initiatives. Eureka's institutional memory would be strengthened and its attention span lengthened.

Implementing time-synchronized, multiannual funding commitments does not require collective acceptance of the idea by all Member States. Synchronized funding commitments could be made inter-governmentally. 'Kick-off' meetings should bring together all governments and firms implicated in project proposals at the project approval stage. Member States which cannot offer such funding commitments to their project participants – either by choice or necessity – could opt out of kick-off meetings. The upshot of synchronized funding commitments would be to inject far more certainty into the project-funding process, which would make the planning and management of projects easier.

Longer-term funding commitments generally require more effective technology assessment. Technology assessment within Eureka presently occurs on a purely national basis and this need not necessarily change. If governments made firmer and longer-term funding commitments at the approval stage, it would have the desirable effect of inducing them to take technology assessment more seriously and would help to ensure that all Eureka projects are 'quality projects'.

A general prescription is that Eureka requires a more powerful and better-resourced secretariat. It could remain purely functional, yet take central responsibility for the implementation of a number of policy tasks. It makes sense that all twenty-one Member States should be represented on the secretariat. One official seconded from each national Eureka office and DGs XII and XIII of the Commission would mean that the secretariat would consist of twenty-three officials, which is not an unwieldy number. Linking the chairmanship with the secretariat would give the latter what it now lacks: a hierarchical structure and a central authority for actually managing it.

There are five essential reasons why a stronger secretariat should be considered. First, it could provide institutional support to facilitate synchronized, multiannual funding commitments. The secretariat could be given responsibility for collating and synthesizing the results of separate national technology assessments before projects are approved. It could provide operational support to facilitate 'kick-off' meetings.

Second, supportive measures are obviously a problem of collective action. Few requests for supportive measures have been taken up at an intergovernmental level, where they obviously must have effect to help project results find markets. The secretariat is Eureka's only supra-national institution and logically is best able to make supportive measures a less ambiguous concept and develop clear provisions for their implementation. Particularly, the secretariat could sensibly be given resources to gather information on new developments in standards-setting, which often emanates from the national level. Similarly, most actions which aim to link Eureka to sources of private finance, identify barriers to marketing the results of Eureka projects and pry open public procurement markets are most effectively carried out centrally. Even if venture capital continues to seek primarily companies to fund instead of projects, the secretariat could keep and update a database on SMEs and start-ups which need finance but also happen to be involved with Eureka. The secretariat could be directed to identify barriers to trade and discrimination in public procurement which limit markets for Eureka-produced products. If it had responsibility for communicating its findings annually to the Eureka ministerial conference, national trade or industry ministries would find it hard to avoid taking action to eliminate such barriers at the national level.

Third, Eureka needs a source of advice for SMEs on Memoranda of Understanding and IPRs. The secretariat could provide consultancy services to partners on how to organize and manage their projects. A central source which consolidates the management experience of past Eureka projects could help prospective project leaders advance more quickly on learning curves about how they manage their own project.

Fourth, the problem of insular umbrella projects and large, strategic projects requires a central institution with sufficient resources and a broad knowledge of Eureka's activities to ensure accountability. There is interest within the Eureka network of fixing project 'milestones', or points in time when project progress and activities are reviewed by relevant Member States. A better-resourced secretariat could be given responsibility for coordinating project reviews at set intervals. This would logically induce Member States to make multiannual public funding commitments with more confidence.

Finally, the secretariat generally could promote greater transparency within Eureka. Data on proposals and announced projects contained in the Eureka database are often vague and without detail. Sensitive questions of industrial secrecy are at play, but prospective partners currently may be discouraged from seeking to participate in proposed projects. It is often impossible to tell whether projects duplicate R&D underway elsewhere or even within another Eureka project, or to see how projects might relate to one another in terms of standards, shared goals, multi-technological links, etc. Circulating proposals for 45 days in the Eureka data base already has the effect of enlarging about one-third of all projects. More information on proposals in circulation would expand even more projects. But the Eureka network almost certainly will need to go out and consciously seek it. The secretariat could usefully take on this task and enhance Eureka's ability to encourage technology transfer, as well as provide scrutiny of meso-level policy networks.

Notes

1 HIGH TECHNOLOGY AND THE COMPETITION STATE

1 Eureka secretariat, 'Declaration of Principles relating to Eureka adopted at Hanover, 6 November 1985', Brussels, p. 1.

2 While the total value of all Eureka projects is actually higher than the EC's budget for R & D, Sharp is right to observe that the figures for Eureka are highly speculative and include both government and industry commitments, while the Framework budget shows only expenditures from the EC's budget. See M. Sharp, 'The single market and European technology policies' in C. Freeman, M. Sharp and W. Walker (eds) *Technology and the Future of Europe: Global Competition and the Environment in the 1990s*, London, Frances Pinter, 1991, pp. 71–2.

3 This analysis is inspired by Strange's argument that the accelerating pace of technological change, the liberalization of international finance, and the lowering of the real costs of transborder transport and communications are the three 'driving forces' of the internationalization of production in the world economy. However, the argument here is that technological change is the most crucial of the three and that it 'drives' the other two. See S. Strange, 'States, firms and diplomacy', *International Affairs*, 1992, 68, pp. 1–15.

4 S. Strange, *States and Markets*, London, Frances Pinter, 1988, p. 162.

5 See J. Lesourne, 'The changing context of industrial policy: external and internal developments' in A. Jacquemin (ed.) *European Industry: Public Policy and Corporate Strategy*, Oxford, Clarendon Press, 1984, p. 21.

6 G.C. Mowery and N. Rosenberg, *Technology and the Pursuit of Economic Growth*, Cambridge and New York, Cambridge University Press, 1989, p. 210.

7 LAREA/CEREM, *Les Strategies d'Accordes des Groupes Européennes: Entre La Cohesion et l'Eclatement*, Nanterre, Université de Paris X, 1985, p. 1.

8 See F. Meyer, *International Trade Policy*, London, Croom Helm, 1978, pp. 13–24.

9 See M. Olson, *The Rise and Decline of Nations*, New Haven, Yale University Press, 1982; A. King, 'The problem of overload' in A. King (ed.) *Why is Britain Becoming Harder to Govern?*, London, BBC, 1975.

10 See M. Piore and C. Sabel, *The Second Industrial Divide*, New York, Basic Books, 1984; R. Jaikumur, 'Post-industrial manufacturing', *Harvard*

Business Review, 1986, 64, pp. 69–76; A. Roobeck, 'The crisis in Fordism and the rise of a new technological paradigm', *Futures*, 1987, 19, pp. 129–54; B. Jessop, 'Neo-conservative regimes and the transition to post-Fordism: the cases of Great Britain and West Germany' in M. Gottdiener and N. Komninos (eds) *Modern Capitalism and Spatial Development: Accumulation, Regulation and Crisis Theory*, London, Macmillan, 1989; B. Jessop, *State Theory: Putting Capitalist States in Their Place*, Cambridge, Polity Press, 1990.

11 A.D. Chandler, *Scale and Scope: the Dynamics of Industrial Capitalism*, Cambridge MA, Harvard University Press, 1990, p. 607. See also S. Cohen and J. Zysman, 'Manufacturing innovation and industrial competitiveness' in U. Hilpert (ed.) *State Policies and Techno-Industrial Innovation*, London, Routledge, 1991, pp. 270–1.

12 B. Jessop, Thatcherism: the British Road to Post-Fordism?, *Essex Papers in Politics and Government*, 1990, 68, pp. 23–4.

13 L. Tyson and J. Zysman, 'American industry in international competition' in L. Tyson and J. Zysman (eds) *American Industry in International Competition*, Ithaca NY, Cornell University Press, 1983, p. 28.

14 Strange, 'States, firms and diplomacy', p. 3.

15 P. Cerny, *The Changing Architecture of Politics: Structure, Agency, and the Future of the State*, London, Sage, 1990, chapter 8.

16 See S. Cohen, D. Teece, L. Tyson and J. Zysman, 'Competitiveness', *BRIE Working Papers*, 8, 1984.

17 P. Cerny, 'The limits of deregulation: transnational interpenetration and policy change', *European Journal of Political Research*, 1991, 19, p. 183.

18 G. Dosi, K. Pavitt and L. Soete, *The Economics of Technical Change and International Trade*, London, Harvester Wheatsheaf, 1990, p. 3.

19 R. Rothwell and W. Zegveld, *Industrial Innovation and Public Policy: Preparing for the 1980s and 1990s*, London, Frances Pinter, 1981, p. 1.

20 See C. Freeman and L.L.G. Soete, *Technological Change and Full Employment*, Oxford, Basil Blackwell, 1987; S.J. Kline and N. Rosenburg, 'An overview of innovation' in R. Landau and N. Rosenburg (eds) *The Positive-Sum Strategy: Harnessing Technology for Economic Growth*, Washington DC, National Academy Press, 1986; I.M. Kirzner, *Discovery and the Capitalist Process*, Chicago, University of Chicago Press, 1985; A. Heertje, 'Can we explain technical change?' in S. MacDonald, D. McL. Lamberton and T. Mandeville (eds) *The Trouble with Technology: Explorations in the Process of Technological Change*, London, Frances Pinter, 1983.

21 C. Freeman, *The Economics of Industrial Innovation*, London, Frances Pinter, 2nd edition 1982, p. 195.

22 J. Levinsen and P.H. Kristensen, *Small Country Squeeze*, Copenhagen, Forlaget fur Samfunds-konomi og Planlaegning, 1983, p. 27. See also R. Rothwell, 'The difficulties of national innovation policies' in MacDonald *et al.* (eds) *The Trouble with Technology*, p. 47.

23 Studies which linked rising levels of R & D spending with higher rates of innovation in the 1960s include E. Mansfield, 'Rates of return from industrial R & D', *American Economic Review*, 1965, 55, pp. 310–22; M. Brown and A.H. Conrad, 'The influence of research and CES production relations' in M. Brown (ed.) *The Theory and Empirical Analysis of Production*, New York, Columbia University Press, 1967; J. Minasian,

'Research and development, production functions, and rates of return', *American Economic Review*, 1969, 59, pp. 80–5. Research which points to the absence of any correlation after 1970 includes E. Thomas, 'Recent research on R & D and productivity growth', paper presented to OECD conference on science and technology indicators, 1980, Paris, May, mimeo; R. Rothwell and W. Zegveld, *Innovation and the Small and Medium-sized Firm*, London, Frances Pinter, 1982, p. 3; Z.J. Acs and D.B. Audretsch, 'Innovation in large and small firms: an empirical analysis', *American Economic Review*, 1988, 78, p. 679. On this discussion generally see J. Aubert, 'Innovation policies: a three way contrast', *OECD Observer*, 1984, Paris, OECD, 131, pp. 6–11.

24 Strange, *States and Markets*, p. 132.
25 *Ibid.*, p. 127.
26 See M. Sharp, *The New Biotechnology: European Governments in Search of a Strategy*, Brighton, Sussex Policy Research Unit, 1985, p. 37.
27 M. English, 'The European information technology industry' in A. Jacquemin (ed.) *European Industry: Public Policy and Corporate Strategy*, Oxford, Clarendon Press, 1984, pp. 228–9.
28 Quoted in C. Lockwood, 'Telecommunications: rewiring the world', *The Economist*, 17 October 1987, p. 7.
29 Chandler, *Scale and Scope*, pp. 618–19;
30 H. Håkansson, *Industrial Technological Development*, London, Croom Helm, 1987.
31 D.R. Roman and J.F. Puett, Jr, *International Business and Technological Innovation*, Oxford, North-Holland, 1983, pp. 162–4; U. Hilpert, 'The state, science and techno-industrial innovation: a new model of state policy and a changing role of the state' in U. Hilpert (ed.) *State Policies and Techno-Industrial Innovation*, London, Routledge, 1991, pp. 11–14.
32 See H. Ward and G. Edwards, 'Chicken and technology: the politics of the EC's budget for research and development', *Review of International Studies*, 1990, 16, pp. 37–54.
33 A good summary of post-war 'national champion' strategies in Europe and their ultimate failure is W. Sandholtz, 'Esprit and the politics of international collective action', *Journal of Common Market Studies*, 1992, 30, pp. 6–11.
34 See A. Jacquemin, *Collusive Behavior, R & D and European Policy*, Brussels, Commission of the European Communities, EC Economic Paper 61, 1987, p. 16.
35 P. Cecchini with M. Catinat and A. Jacquemin, *The European Challenge 1992: the Benefits of a Single Market*, Aldershot, Wildwood House, 1988, p. 17.
36 This analysis is inspired by B. Balassa, *The Theory of Economic Integration*, London, Allen & Unwin, 1961.
37 R.F. Elliot and P. Wood, *The International Transfer of Technology and Western European Integration*, University of Aberdeen, Department of Political Economy, occasional paper no. 79–07, 1987, p. 37.
38 See K.W. Grewlich, 'EUREKA – eureka?', *Aussenpolitick*, 1986, 37 pp. 24–36; B.L.R. Smith, 'A new "technology gap" in Europe?', *SAIS Review*, 1986, 6, pp. 233–6; M. Sharp and C. Shearman, *European Technological Collaboration*, London, Routledge & Kegan Paul, Chatham House Paper 36, 1987, pp. 69–83; A.Y. Portnoff, 'Les 108 projects d'Eurêka', *Sciences et*

Techniques, 1987, 38, pp. 35–41; P.H. Laurent, 'Eureka, or the techno-logical renaissance of Europe', *The Washington Quarterly*, 1987, 10, pp. 55–66. More critical early assessments were offered by A.N. Duff, 'Eureka and the new technology policy of the European Community', *Policy Studies*, 1986, 6, pp. 44–61 and C. Deubner, 'Eureka zwischen nationalen Technologiepolitiken und Europa', *Vierteljahres Berichte*, 1987, 109, pp. 217–29.

39 DRI, *Special Tabulations of International Trade*, Washington DC, National Science Foundation, 1986, pp. 136–7.

40 See U. Hilpert, 'Economic adjustment by techno-industrial innovation and the role of the state' in U. Hilpert (ed.) *State Policies and Techno-Industrial Innovation*, London, Routledge, 1991, pp. 85–9.

41 J. Schumpeter, *Capitalism, Socialism and Democracy*, New York, Harper & Row, 1947. See also R. L. Heilbroner, *The Worldly Philosophers*, New York, Touchstone/Simon & Schuster, 6th edition, 1986, pp. 300–5.

42 Freeman, *The Economics of Industrial Innovation*, pp. 133–44; Roman and Puett, *International Business and Technological Innovation*, pp. 263–6; R. Rothwell, 'Innovation and the smaller firm' in W.S. Brown and R. Rothwell (eds) *Entrepreneurship and Technology: World Experiences and Policies*, Essex, Longman, 1986, p. 45; J. Hagedoorn and F. Prakke, *Barriers to Innovation: the Netherlands*, Delft, TNO Staffgroup Strategic Surveys, 1980, p. 7.

43 F.M. Scherer, *Industrial Market Structure and Economic Performance*, Chicago, Rand McNally & Company, 2nd edition, 1980, p. 438.

44 J. Barber, S. Metcalfe and M. Porteous, 'Barriers to growth: the ACARD study', in J. Barber, S. Metcalfe and M. Porteous (eds) *Barriers to Growth in Small Firms*, London, Routledge, 1989, p. 4.

45 BMFT, 'Facts and figures 1990: update of the report of the Federal Government on Research 1988', Bonn, 1990, p. 101.

46 Acs and Audretsch, 'Innovation in large and small firms', p. 681.

47 See T. Matsuo, 'Japanese R & D policy for techno-industrial innovation' in U. Hilpert (ed.) *State Policies and Techno-Industrial Innovation*, London, Routledge, 1991, pp. 254–7; C. Freeman, 'Diffusion: the spread of new technology to firms, sectors and nations' in A. Heertje (ed.) *Innovation, Technology and Finance*, Oxford, Basil Blackwell for the European Investment Bank, 1988; M. Kenney and R. Florida, 'Beyond mass production: production and the labour process in Japan', *Politics and Society*, 1988, 16, pp. 121–58; K. Yamamura and G. Saxonhouse, 'Technology and the future of the economy' in K. Yamamura and Y. Tasuba (eds) *The Political Economy of Japan: the Domestic Trans-formation*, Palo Alto CA, Stanford University Press, volume 1, 1987; D. Friedman, 'Beyond the age of Ford: the strategic basis of Japanese success in automobiles' in J. Zysman and L. Tyson (eds) *American Industry in International Competition*, Ithaca NY, Cornell University Press, 1983.

48 Rothwell, 'Innovation and the smaller firm', pp. 44–5.

49 P. Dasgupta, 'The theory of technological competition' in D. Encacoua, P. Geroski and A. Jacquemin (eds) *New Developments in the Analysis of Market Structures*, London, Macmillan, 1986, p. 519.

50 L P. Geroski and A. Jacquemin, 'Industrial change, barriers to mobility and European industrial policy', *Economic Policy*, 1987, 1, p. 202.

51 See Rothwell and Zegveld, *Innovation and the Small and Medium-Sized Firm*; J. Barber, S. Metcalfe and M. Porteous (eds) *Barriers to Growth in Small Firms*, London, Routledge, 1989; R. Oakey, *High Technology Small Firms: Regional Development in Britain and the United States*, London, Frances Pinter, 1984; F. Franzmeyer, *Approaches to Industrial Policy within the EC and its Impact on European Integration*, Aldershot, Gower, 1982.

52 Title VI of the Treaty of Rome amended by article 24 of the Single European Act as reproduced in Butterworths European Information Services, *Butterworths Guide to the European Communities*, London, Butterworths, 1989, p. 171.

53 Sharp and Shearman, *European Technological Collaboration*, p. 104; L. Sleuwaegen and H. Yamawaki, 'The formation of the European Common Market: changes in market structure and performance', *European Economic Review*, 1988, 32, pp. 1451–75; G. Locksley and T. Ward, 'Concentration in manufacturing in the European Economic Community', *Cambridge Journal of Economics*, 1979, 3, p. 96.

54 Eureka secretariat, 'Declaration of Principles relating to Eureka', p. 2.

55 See R. Gilpin, *The Political Economy of International Relations*, Princeton NJ, Princeton University Press, 1987, pp. 231–62.

56 F. Prakke, 'The financing of technological innovation' in A. Heertje (ed.) *Innovation, Technology and Finance*, Oxford, Basil Blackwell for European Investment Bank, 1988, p. 95.

57 C. Hood and G.F. Shuppert, 'The study of para-governmental organisations' in C. Hood and G.F. Shuppert (eds) *Delivering Public Services in Western Europe: Sharing Western European Experiences of Para-Government Organization*, London, Sage, 1988, p. 19.

58 Quoted in P.A. Hall, 'The state and the market' in P.A. Hall, J. Hayward and H. Machin (eds) *Developments in French Politics*, London, Macmillan, 1990, p. 183.

59 See C. Hood, *The Tools of Government*, London, Macmillan, 1983; R.L. Merrit and A.J. Merrit (eds) *Innovation in the Public Sector*, London, Sage, 1985.

60 Hood and Shuppert, 'The study of para-governmental organsations', p. 25.

61 J. Pinder, 'The single market: a step towards European Union', in J. Lodge (ed.) *The European Community and the Challenge of the Future*, London, Frances Pinter, 1989, p. 107. See also J. Pelkmans, 'Industrial integration: the core of the European Community rediscovered' in S. Tarditi, K. Thomson, P. Pierani and E. Croci-Angelini (eds) *Agricultural Trade Liberalization in the European Community*, Oxford, Clarendon Press, 1989, pp. 208–10.

62 Duff, 'Eureka and the new technology policy', p. 48.

63 CEC, *The European Community: 1992 and Beyond*, Luxembourg, European documentation series, 1991, pp. 12, 31; Sharp and Shearman, *European Technological Collaboration*, p. 86.

64 P. Defraigne, 'Towards concerted industrial policies in the EC' in A. Jacquemin (ed.) *European Industry: Public Policy and Corporate Strategy*, Oxford, Clarendon Press, 1984, p. 373. The author is a former Commission official.

65 Seminal neo-functionalist works include E. Haas, *The Uniting of Europe*, Palo Alto CA, Stanford University Press, 1958; P. Schmitter, 'Three neo-functionalist hypotheses about international integration', *International*

On revival
of neo-functionalism.

Organization, 1969, 23, pp. 161–6. Calls for its resurrection include R. Pryce and W. Wessels, 'The search for an ever-closer union: a framework for analysis', in R. Pryce (ed.) *The Dynamics of European Union*, London, Croom Helm, 1987, pp. 1–34; P. Taylor, 'The new dynamic of EC integration in the 1980s' in J. Lodge (ed.) *The European Community and the Challenge of the Future*, London, Frances Pinter, 1989, pp. 23–4; S. George, *An Awkward Partner: Britain in the European Community*, Oxford, Oxford University Press, 1990, p. 210. Taylor, George and Keohane and Hoffmann make cases for a refined, eclectic model of integration which retains many neofunctionalist precepts and assumptions. See See P. Taylor, 'The European Community and the state: assumptions, theories and propositions', *Review of International Studies*, 1991, 17, pp. 109–25; S. George, *Politics and Policy in the European Community*, Oxford, Oxford University Press, 2nd edition, 1991, pp. 225–34; R. Keohane and S. Hoffmann, 'Institutional change in Europe in the 1980s' in R. Keohane and S. Hoffmann (eds) *The New European Community: Decisionmaking and Institutional Change*, Boulder CO and London, Westview Press, 1991, pp. 1–39.

66 R. Williams, *European Technology: the Politics of Collaboration*, London, Croom Helm, 1973, p. 143.

67 *Ibid.*, p. 147. On the concept of self-encapsulation, see also E. Haas, 'The study of regional integration' in L. Lindberg and S. Sheingold (eds) *Regional Integration Theory and Research*, Cambridge MA, Harvard University Press, 1971; P. Schmitter, 'Central American integration: spill-over, spill-around or encapsulation?', *Journal of Common Market Studies*, 1971, 9, pp. 1–48.

68 A. Moravcsik, 'Negotiating the Single European Act: national interests and conventional statecraft in the European Community', *International Organization*, 1991, 45, p. 25.

69 S. Hoffmann, 'Obstinate or obsolete? The fate of the nation-state and the case of western Europe', *Daedalus*, 1966, 95, p. 874.

70 See Williams, *European Technology*, p. 144.

71 See R. Keohane and J. Nye, *Power and Interdependence: World Politics in Transition*, Boston, Little & Brown, 1977; R. Keohane, *After Hegemony: Cooperation and Discord in the World Political Economy*, Princeton NJ, Princeton University Press, 1984.

72 See for example CEC, *Europe Without Frontiers: Completing the Internal Market*, Luxembourg, European documentation series, 2, 1989, pp. 11–12, 46–7; CEC, *The European Community: 1992 and Beyond*, pp. 11–12.

73 B. Jessop, *The Capitalist State*, Oxford, Martin Robinson, 1982; P. Berger, *The Capitalist Revolution*, Aldershot, Gower, 1987.

74 F. Duchêne and G. Shepherd (eds) *Managing Industrial Change in Western Europe*, London, Frances Pinter, 1987; P. Hall, *Governing the Economy: the Politics of State Intervention in Britain and France*, Cambridge, Polity Press, 1986; J. Hayward, *The State and the Market Economy: Industrial Patriotism and Economic Intervention in France*, Brighton, Wheatsheaf, 1986; P. Katzenstein, *Small States in World Markets*, Ithaca NY, Cornell University Press, 1985; J. Zysman, *Governments, Markets and Growth: Financial Systems and the Politics of Industrial Change*, Oxford, Martin Robinson, 1983.

75 A. Cawson, K. Morgan, D. Webber, P. Holmes and A. Stevens, *Hostile Brothers: Competition and Closure in the European Electronics Industry*, Oxford, Clarendon Press, 1990; S. Wilks and M. Wright, *Promotion and Regulation of Industry in Japan and her Competitors*, Oxford, Clarendon Press, 1989; S. Wilks and M. Wright (eds) *Comparative Government–Industry Relations: West Europe, the United States and Japan*, Oxford, Clarendon Press, 1987; W. Grant, W. Paterson and C. Whitson, *Government and the Chemical Industry: A Comparative Study of Britain and West Germany*, Oxford, Clarendon Press, 1987.

76 Grant *et al.*, *Government and the Chemical Industry*, p. 314. Emphasis in orginal.

77 Cawson *et al.*, *Hostile Brothers*, p. 7.

78 H. Heclo, 'Issue networks and the executive establishment' in A. King (ed.) *The New American Political System*, Washington DC, American Enterprise Institute, 1978; R.A.W. Rhodes, *Control and Power in Central–Local Relations*, Aldershot, Gower, 1981; R.A.W. Rhodes, 'Power-dependence, policy communities and intergovernmental networks', *Public Administration Bulletin*, 1985, 49, pp. 4–31.

79 Cawson *et al.*, *Hostile Brothers*, p. 318.

80 See M. Wright, 'Policy community, policy network and comparative industrial policies', *Political Studies*, 1988, 36, pp. 593–612; S. Wilks, 'Government–industry relations: progress and findings of the ESRC research initiative', *Public Administration*, 1989, 67, pp. 329–39; R.A.W. Rhodes, 'Policy networks: a British perspective', *Journal of Theoretical Politics*, 1990, 2, pp. 293–317; D. Marsh and R.A.W. Rhodes (eds) *Policy Networks in British Government*, Oxford, Clarendon Press, 1992.

81 J.A. Benson, 'A framework for policy analysis', in D. Rogers, D. Whitten and Associates (eds) *Interorganizational Coordination*, Ames IA, Iowa State University Press, 1982, p. 148.

82 See O. E. Williamson, *Markets and Hierarchies: Analysis and Antitrust Implications*, New York, Free Press, 1975.

83 Håkansson, *Industrial Technological Development*.

84 F. N. Stokman, R. Ziegler and J. Scott (eds) *Networks of Corporate Power: A Comparative Analysis of Ten Countries*, Cambridge, Polity Press, 1988; Cohen and Zysman, 'Manufacturing innovation', pp. 268–9.

85 W.W. Powell, 'Neither market nor hierarchy: network forms of organization' in B.M. Shaw and L. Cummings (eds) *Research in Organizational Behavior*, Greenwich CT, JAI Press, 1989.

86 Keohane and Hoffmann, 'Institutional change in Europe,' pp. 10–15; J. Peterson, 'The European Technology Community: policy networks in a supranational setting' in R.A.W. Rhodes and D. Marsh (eds) *Policy Networks in British Government*, Oxford, Clarendon Press, 1992, pp. 225–48; B.G. Peters, 'Bureaucratic politics and the institutions of the European Community' in A.M. Sbragia (ed.) *Euro-Politics: Institutions and Policymaking in the 'New' European Community*, Washington DC, Brooking Institution, 1992, pp. 75–122; V. Schneider and R. Werle, 'Networks and concertation in European policy making: the cases of chemicals control and telecommunications', paper presented at the joint sessions of the European Consortium for Political Research, Limerick, 30 March-4 April 1992, mimeo.

87 See especially D. Marsh and R.A.W. Rhodes, 'Policy communities and issue networks: beyond typology' in D. Marsh and R.A.W. Rhodes (eds) *Policy Networks in British Government*, Oxford, Clarendon Press.

88 See W. Wallace, 'Less than a federation, more than a regime: the Community as a political system' in H. Wallace, W. Wallace and C. Webb (eds) *Policy-Making in the European Community*, Chichester, Wiley, 1983, pp. 403–36; H. Wallace, 'Implementation across national boundaries' in D. Lewis and H. Wallace (eds) *Politics and Practice*, London, Heinemann, 1984, pp. 193–206; H. Wallace, 'The best is the enemy of the 'could': Bargaining in the EC', in S. Tarditi, K.J. Thomson, P. Pierani and E. Croci-Angelini (eds) *Agricultural Trade Liberalization and the European Community*, Oxford, Clarendon Press, 1989, pp. 403–36.

89 'Declaration of Principles relating to Eureka', p. 7.

90 See J.B. Tucker, 'Partners and rivals: a model of international collaboration in advanced technology' *International Organization*, 1991, 45, pp. 83–120; T.A. Watkins, 'A technological communications costs model of R & D consortia as public policy', *Research Policy*, 1991, 20, pp. 87–107.

91 M. Porter, 'Europe's companies after 1992: don't collaborate, compete', *The Economist*, 9 June 1990, p. 24. This very short article is distilled from Porter's far more developed work on competitive advantage, but it applies his argument more specifically to the EC than does his book, in which the EC does not even rate an entry in the index. More generally, as Strange argues, Porter's argument 'rather [leaves] out the political element, both domestic and global'. See M. Porter, *The Competitive Advantage of Nations*, London, Macmillan, 1990; Strange, 'States, firms and diplomacy', p. 10.

92 R. Reich, *The Work of Nations: Preparing Ourselves for 21st Century Capitalism*, New York, Albert Knopf, 1991, p. 110.

93 For an analysis which argues that promoting collaboration is inappropriate in the context of the 1992 project, see N. Kay, 'Industrial collaborative activity and the completion of the internal market', *Journal of Common Market Studies*, 1991, 28, pp. 347–62.

94 Katzenstein, *Small States in World Markets*, p. 210.

2 PARTNERS, PROCESS AND PROJECTS

1 The author has viewed only parts of this survey. Figures on national public funding levels included in this section were compiled from a variety of sources including other 'internal' Eureka documents and interviews with numerous officials. The precision of these figures varies somewhat, but the section provides a generally reliable survey of national funding policies.

2 British chairmanship, 'Procedures for Eureka projects: note by chairman of the Ministerial Conference', London, 21 May 1986, p. 2.

3 To illustrate the point, when contacted by the author, two individuals whose names appeared in the Eureka central database were unaware that their firm even participated in Eureka!

4 Multiple interviews with French Eureka officials.

5 P.A. Hall, 'The state and the market' in P.A. Hall, J. Hayward and H. Machin (eds) *Developments in French Politics*, London, Macmillan, 1990, p. 177.

6 Author's calculations based on figures in CEC, *Eurostat: Basic Statistics of the Community*, Luxembourg, 28th edition, 1991, pp. 50–1.

7 Interview with Danish Eureka official.

8 Y. Sillard, 'Eurêka: un programme au service de l'innovation technologique européenne', *La Jaune et la Rouge*, 418, October 1986, p. 19.

9 BMFT is the German acronym for *Bundesminister für Forschung und Technologie*.

10 In 1989, the *Länder* share of total German R & D spending was 13.6 per cent compared with the federal government's share of 20.8 per cent. See BMFT, 'Report of the Federal Government on Research', Verlag Deutscher Wirtschaftsdienst, Köln, 1991, p. 29.

11 Interviews with numerous Eureka officials.

12 Author's calculations based on data from Eureka database as of 30 April 1992 and reproduced in Finnish chairmanship, *SMEs: a Challenge to Eureka*, Tampere, 22 May 1992, appendix A.

13 Correspondance from German Eureka official to the author, 17 March 1992.

14 Interview with UK Eureka official.

15 See G. Napolitano, 'European technological co-operation: the Italian participation in Eureka', *Science and Public Policy*, 1988, 6, p. 379.

16 While the special Dutch Eureka budget was only between 8.7 and 11 million ECU in 1992, as much as 150 million ECU was available from a variety of other sources for subsidizing Dutch participants in Eureka. See Finnish chairmanship, *NPC office functions*, Tampere, 22 May 1992, appendix.

17 Total Spanish public funding for R & D increased from 283.7 million ECU in 1987 to 366.1 million ECU in 1991. See OECD, *Innovation Policy: Spain*, Paris, 1987, p. 102; Finnish chairmanship, *SMEs: a Challenge to Eureka*, appendix C.

18 Figures on public funding in Sweden, Denmark and Finland taken from Finnish chairmanship, *NPC Office Functions*, appendix.

19 Finnish chairmanship, *SMEs: a Challenge to Eureka*, appendix C.

20 See Eureka secretariat, *Annual Progress Report 1991*, Brussels, 1992, p. 24; Eureka secretariat, *Annual Project Report 1989*, Brussels, 1990, p. 19; Eureka secretariat, 'Eureka: a golden opportunity for SMEs', *Eureka News*, 2, October 1988, p. 4;

21 Interview with Belgian Eureka official.

22 Numerous interviews with Eureka officials; see also *Agence Europe*, 12 September 1987, 4616, p. 4; European Parliament, 'Draft Report on the European Research Coordination Agency' (The Ford Report), PE 199.362/B, Committee on Energy, Research and Technology, 28 June 1988, p. 7.

23 Interview with representative of 1985–86 British chairmanship.

24 This statement was made at the Copenhagen ministerial conference in June 1988 as presentations on three Eureka projects were about to be made to ministers. The Norwegian minister was aware that journalists were watching the proceedings on closed-circuit television.

25 Official Eureka documents count Turkey as an eighth Member State with earmarked funds, but it appears this money is simply allocated to the staffing of the Turkish Eureka office. See Finnish chairmanship, *NPC Office Functions*, p. 3 and appendix.

26 *Ibid.*, p. 2.

27 Numerous interviews with Eureka officials; *Wall Street Journal*, 16 September 1987; *Hannoverische Allgemeine Zeitung*, 22 April 1988; CEC, 'Reinforcing co-operation in between Eureka and the European Communities', Brussels, (88) 291, 24 June 1988, final, pt. 3.5, p. 5; 'The Ford Report', p. 9. An notably specific estimate made by the Commission in 1990 was that the annual level of public funding had reached approximately 1 billion ECU per year. See CEC, *EC Research Funding: A Guide for Applicants*, Brussels, CEC/DG XII, January 1990, p. 21.

28 Interview with representative of British chairmanship.

29 British chairmanship, 'Memorandum of understanding on the Eureka secretariat between the members of Eureka,' London, 30 June 1986, p. 1.

30 Finnish chairmanship, *NPC Office Functions*, p. 3.

31 *Financial Times*, 18 December 1986; *Wall Street Journal*, 18 December 1986.

32 Swedish Industry Minister Thage Peterson quoted in *Financial Times*, 18 December 1986.

33 See Eureka secretariat, 'Communiqué of the 5th Eureka ministerial conference, Madrid', 15 September 1987, Brussels, p. 2; Eureka secretariat, Communiqué of the 6th Eureka ministerial conference, Copenhagen', 15–16 June 1988, Brussels, p. 1; Coordinateur National Français, 'Eurêka: dossier de presse', Paris, 16 September 1987, p. 1; Danish chairmanship, 'Eureka: goals attained and future development', Copenhagen, 1988, p. 3.

34 The two transport projects, Amadeus and Galileo, were valued at 100 and 273 million ECU respectively. See Eureka secretariat, 'Communiqué of 7th Eureka ministerial conference, Vienna,' 18–19 June 1989, English version, Document Eureka 7MC-8, Brussels; Eureka secretariat, 'Vienna dossier: the '89 vintage', *Eureka News*, 6, 19 October 1989, p.5.

35 Danish chairmanship, 'Goals attained and future development', p. 2; Eureka secretariat, *Annual Progress Report 1991*, p. 17.

36 Eureka secretariat, *Annual Progress Report 1991*, p. 2; Finnish chairmanship, *SMEs: a Challenge to Eureka*, p. 2.

37 Dutch chairmanship, *X-Ray Sessions: a Final Report*, The Hague, 1991, pp. 14–15.

38 OECD, *Science and Technology Policy Outlook*, Paris, 1988, pp. 59–60.

39 See for example CEC, 'The European information technology industry: a short overview', Brussels, June 1983.

40 See S. Woolcock, 'Information technology: the challenge to Europe', *Journal of Common Market Studies*, 1984, 4, pp. 315–31.

41 T.R. Howell, W.A. Noellert, J.H. MacLaughlin and A.W. Wolff, *The Microelectronics Race: the Impact of Government Policy on International Competition*, Boulder Co, Westview Press, 1988, p. 185.

42 Pre-competitive research (also known as 'pre-standardization' or 'pre-normative' research) is defined by the Commission as 'research intended to provide the scientific and technical basis needed for the preparation of standards and technical specifications'. A basic rule of thumb is that pre-competitive R & D implies that commercial production is at least five years away, while 'near-market' R & D is designed to produce a marketable product or process in less than five years. See CEC, 'Eureka and the European Technology Community', Brussels, COM (86) 664 final, 20 November 1986, p. 5.

43 A good and comprehensible review of microelectronics products is OECD, *The Semi-Conductor Industry: Trade-Related Issues*, Paris, 1985, pp. 8–12.

44 M. Hobday, 'The European semiconductor industry: resurgence and rationalization', *Journal of Common Market Studies*, 1989, 28, p. 158.

45 See OECD, *The Semi-Conductor Industry*, pp. 33–4.

46 J.N. Ziegler, 'Semiconductors' in 'Searching for security in a global economy', *Daedalus*, 1991, 120, pp. 168–73; K. Flamm, 'Semiconductors' in G.C. Hufbauer (ed.) *Europe 1992: An American Perspective*, Washington DC, Brookings Institution, 1990, pp. 242–68; Hobday, 'The European semiconductor industry', pp. 177–9.

47 Europe's global market share in semiconductor manufacturing equipment declined from 9 to 4 per cent between 1978 and 1986, while Japan improved increased its share from 10 to 40 per cent. See Dutch chairmanship, *X-Ray Sessions*, p. 25; OECD, *The Semi-Conductor Industry*, pp. 44–5.

48 Hobday, 'The European Semiconductor Industry', p. 169.

49 See *ibid.*, p. 166.

50 Eureka secretariat, 'Jessi Swings Into Action', *Eureka News*, 6, October 1989 p. 9.

51 Eureka Secretariat, *1989 Project Progress Report*, Brussels, 1989, p. 24.

52 Eureka secretariat, 'The four links in the Jessi chain', *Eureka News*, 11, January 1991, p. 8.

53 Eureka secretariat, 'Jessi swings into action', p. 9.

54 Eureka Secretariat, *1989 Project Progress Report*, p. 24.

55 Eureka secretariat, 'Aerospatiale Joins ES2', *Eureka News*, 6, October 1989, p. 2.

56 Eureka secretariat, 'Jessi swings into action', p. 8.

57 These are quotes taken from interviews with British and Scandinavian Eureka officials respectively.

58 OECD, *The Semi-Conductor Industry*, p. 100.

59 Hobday, 'The European Semiconductor Industry', p. 175.

60 See *The Independent*, 5 March 1990; A. Coghlan, 'Europe slams door on 'Japanese company'', *New Scientist*, 6 April 1991.

61 Of fifty projects in this sector, thirty-one carried a total value of less than 10 million ECU in 1990. See Eureka secretariat, *Annual Progress Report 1989*, p. 17.

62 See Eureka secretariat, 'Eureka: a golden opportunity for SMEs', p. 4; Danish chairmanship, 'Progress report on Eureka projects', p. 9.

63 OECD, *Science and Technology Policy Outlook 1988*, p. 63; CEC, 'Towards a European technological community', Brussels, COM (85) 350 final, 1985, p. 1–10.

64 Department of Trade and Industry, *FAMOS: Preliminary Study Report on European Collaboration in the Field of Flexible Automated Assembly Systems*, London, HMSO, 1987, pp. II, 35.

65 P.B. Scott, *The Robotics Revolution*, Oxford, Basil Blackwell, 1984, p. 284.

66 *Ibid.*, p. 284. See also OECD, *Science and Technology Policy Outlook 1988*, p. 64.

67 See Danish Eureka chairmanship, 'Progress report on Eureka projects', p. 9.

68 Department of Trade and Industry, *FAMOS: Preliminary Study Report*, pp. 36–7.

69 *Ibid.*, p. 6.

70 Eureka secretariat, 'FAMOS: reversing Europe's industrial decline', *Eureka News*, 1, June 1988 p. 4.
71 Dutch chairmanship, *X-Ray Sessions: a Final Report*, p. 30.
72 CEC, *EBIS: European Biotechnology Information Service*, 1991, Brussels, DG XII, May, pp. 14–15.
73 Eureka Secretariat, *1989 Project Progress Report*, p. 7; Eureka Secretariat, 'Eureka and medicine', *Eureka News*, 2, October 1988, p. 7.
74 See for example M. Sharp, *The New Biotechnology: European Governments in Search of a Strategy*, Brighton, Sussex Policy Research Institute, 1985; S. Jacobsson, A. Jamison and H. Rothman (eds) *The Biotechnological Challenge*, Cambridge, Cambridge University Press, 1986.
75 Sharp, *The New Biotechnology*, p. 37. See also J. Peterson, 'Hormones, heifers and high politics: biotechnology and the Common Agricultural Policy', *Public Administration*, 1989, 67, pp. 455–71.
76 W. Faulkner and L. Orsenigo, 'Government policies for techno-industrial innovation in weaker economies: the case of biotechnology in the United Kingdom and Italy' in U. Hilpert (ed.) *State Policies and Techno-Industrial Innovation*, London, Routledge, 1991, pp. 134–35.
77 See Dutch chairmanship, *X-Ray Sessions*, p. 18.
78 Strictly speaking, Eurotrac is not an umbrella project, but it has all the essential characteristics of one. See Chapter 7.
79 Dutch chairmanship, *X-Ray Sessions*, p. 23. See also Dutch chairmanship, *Umbrella Projects*, The Hague, Document NPC-9066, 1991.
80 See Dutch chairmanship, *X-Ray Sessions* p. 29.
81 Participants in Prometheus are Daimler-Benz, Volkswagen, BMW, Porsche, Fiat, Alfa Romeo, Renault, Peugeot, Matra, Jaguar, Rolls Royce, Saab-Scania and Volvo. See A. Graves, 'Globalisation of the automobile industry: the challenge for Europe' in C. Freeman, M. Sharp and W. Walker (eds) *Technology and the Future of the Europe: Global Competition and the Environment in the 1990s*, London, Frances Pinter, p. 278.
82 CEC, *Innovation and Technology Transfer*, 1989, Luxembourg, DG XIII-C, 10, 4/89, p. 5.
83 O. Meyer, 'Eureka: living label of quality', *Eureka News*, 1989, no. 6, October, p. 3.
84 Interview with UK Eureka official.
85 *Ibid.*

3 THE WEIGHT OF HISTORY AND ORIGINS OF EUREKA

1 L. Scheinman, 'Euratom: nuclear integration in Europe' *International Conciliation*, 1967, 563, pp. 8–9. See also C. Deubner, 'The expansion of West German capital and the founding of Euratom', *International Organization*, 33, pp. 203–28.
2 R. Williams, *European Technology: the Politics of Collaboration*, London, Croom Helm, 1973, p. 80.
3 M. Sharp and C. Shearman, *European Technological Collaboration*, London, Routledge & Kegan Paul, p. 36; Williams, *European Technology*, pp. 70, 126.
4 J.J. Servan-Schreiber, *Le Défi Américain*, Paris, Denoël, 1967.

5 European Communities Medium Term Economic Policy Committee, *Scientific and Technical Cooperation between European Countries: Possibilities in Seven Sectors*, Brussels, Report of the Working Party on Scientific and Technical Research Policy, 7301/II/69–E, 9 April 1969.

6 M. Sharp, 'The Community and the New Technologies' in J. Lodge (ed.) *The European Community and the Challenge of the Future*, London, Frances Pinter, 1989, p. 204.

7 Sharp and Shearman, *European Technological Collaboration*, p. 28. See also CEC, 'A review of COST cooperation since its beginnings', Luxembourg, 1988.

8 CEC, 'La politique industrielle de la Communauté', Brussels, COM (70) 100 final, 1970.

9 M. Hodges, 'Industrial policy: hard times or great expectations?' in H. Wallace, W. Wallace and C. Webb (eds) *Policy-Making in the European Community*, Chichester, John Wiley & Sons, 2nd edition, 1983, pp. 272–5.

10 Williams, *European Technology*, p. 89.

11 Sharp and Shearman, *European Technological Collaboration*, pp. 46–7.

12 J.P. Contzen, 'The European Community's strategy in science and technology' in M. Smith (ed.) *Technological Change and United States/European Community Relations: Challenges and Responses*, London, University Association for Contemporary European Studies, p. 50–4.

13 See Williams, *European Technology*, pp. 70, 140; Sharp and Shearman, *European Technological Collaboration*, p. 36; K. Pavitt, 'Technology in Western Europe' in R. Mayne (ed.) *Handbooks to the Modern World: Western Europe*, Oxford, Facts on File Publications, 1986, p. 364.

14 *Financial Times*, 22 March 1989.

15 Sharp and Shearman, *European Technological Collaboration*, p. 37.

16 P. Hall, *Great Planning Disasters*, Harmondsworth, Penguin Books, 1980, pp. 87–108; E.J. Feldman, *Concorde and Dissent*, Cambridge, Cambridge University Press, 1985; G. Knight, *Concorde: The Inside Story*, London, Weidenfeld & Nicolson, 1976.

17 Williams, *European Technology*, p. 120.

18 A. May, 'Concorde – bird of harmony or political albatross: an examination in the context of British foreign policy', *International Organization*, 1979, 33, pp. 481–508.

19 Feldman, *Concorde and Dissent*, p. 128.

20 *Ibid.*, p. 112.

21 Sharp and Shearman, *European Technological Collaboration*, pp. 38, 33–4.

22 K. Hayward, 'Airbus: twenty years of European collaboration', *International Affairs*, 64, p. 16.

23 *Ibid.*, p. 16.

24 *Ibid.*, p. 20. See also *International Herald Tribune*, 22 August 1988.

25 See M.A. Rose, 'Airbus industrie and high technology industrial cooperation in Europe: structure, issues, and implications with a view towards Eurofar', paper presented at the Conference on Europe in the 1990s, George Mason University, 24–25 May 1989.

26 See Pavitt, 'Technology in Western Europe', pp. 364–5; Williams, *European Technology*, p. 36; J.C. Rallo, *Defending Europe in the 1990s: the New Divide of High Technology*, Frances Pinter, London, 1986, p. 68.

27 D. Garnham, *The Politics of European Defense Cooperation: Germany, France, Britain and America*, Cambridge MA, Ballinger, 1988, pp. 66–9.

28 See *Le Monde*, 1 March 1989; Ministry of Defence, 'Towards a Stronger Europe: a report by an independent study team established by the Defence Ministers of nations of the Independent European Programme Group to make proposals to improve the competitiveness of Europe's defence equipment industry', London, HMSO, volume I, December 1986.

29 Interview with British delegate to IEPG.

30 P. Lellouche, 'Thinking about the unthinkable: guidelines for a Euro-Defense concept' in J. Alford and K. Hunt (eds) *Europe in the Western Alliance*, London, Macmillan, 1988.

31 J. Hayward, *The State and the Market Economy: Industrial Patriotism and Economic Intervention in France*, Sussex, Wheatsheaf, 1986.

32 Sharp and Shearman, *European Technological Collaboration*, pp. 32–3.

33 Feldman, *Concorde and Dissent*, p. 91.

34 See E. Haas, *The Obsolescence of Regional Integration Theory*, Berkeley CA, University of California Press, 1975, p. 55.

35 Williams, *European Technology*, p. 139.

36 See H. Wallace, 'Negotiation, conflict and compromise: the elusive pursuit of common policies' in H. Wallace, W. Wallace and C. Webb (eds) *Policy-Making in the European Community*, Chichester, John Wiley & Sons, 2nd edition, 1983, pp. 69–71.

37 D. Hickie, 'Airbus Industrie: a case study in European high technology cooperation' in U. Hilpert (ed.) *State Policies and Techno-Industrial Innovation*, London, Routledge, 1991, pp. 209–10.

38 Williams, *European Technology*, p. 155.

39 See for example A.J. Pierre (ed.) *A High Technology Gap? Europe, America, and Japan*, New York, New York University Press and Council on Foreign Relations, 1987; P. Patel and K. Pavitt, 'Is Europe losing the technological race?', *Research Policy*, 16, pp. 3–5; J.M. Marcum, 'The technology gap: Europe at a crossroads', *Issues in Science and Technology*, 1986, Summer, pp. 28–37.

40 W. Sandholtz, 'Esprit and the politics of international collective action', *Journal of Common Market Studies*, 1992, 30, pp. 8–9.

41 OECD, *Science and Technology Policy Outlook*, Paris, 1985, pp. 17–18.

42 L.K. Mytelka and M. Delapierre, 'The alliance strategies of European firms in the information technology industry', *Journal of Common Market Studies*, 1988, 26, p. 231.

43 See M. Kahler, 'The United States and Western Europe: the diplomatic consequences of Mr. Reagan' in K.A. Oye, R.J. Lieber and D. Rothchild (eds) *Eagle Resurgent? The Reagan Era in American Foreign Policy*, Boston, Little Brown & Company, 1987, pp. 312–17.

44 L. Keliher, 'Policy-Making in information technology: a decisional analysis of the Alvey Project', unpublished Ph.D. thesis, London School of Economics, pp. 39–46; G.O. Phillips, *Innovation and Technology Transfer in Japan and Europe: Industry-Academic Interactions*, London, Routledge, 1989, pp. 44–7.

45 Sharp, 'The Community and new technologies', pp. 207–8.

46 See statements by Mitterrand and the West German Chancellor Helmut Kohl at the 1982 Versailles summit of the Group of Seven in Ministère de la Politique Etrangère de la France, 'Rapport du Président de la République au sommet des pays industrialisées: technologie, emploi et croissance', *La Politique Etrangère de la France: Textes et Documents*, juin 1982. Economic

and monetary frictions between the USA and EC during this period are analysed in J. Peterson, *Europe and America in the 1990s: the Prospects for Partnership*, Chelthenham and Brookfield VT, Edward Elgar, 1993, chapter 2.

47 See P. Holmes, 'Broken dreams: economic policies in Mitterrand's France' in S. Mazey & M. Newman (eds) *Mitterrand's France*, London, Croom Helm, 1987; J. Tuppen, *France Under Recession: 1981–86*, Albany, State University of New York Press, 1988; H. Machin and V. Wright (eds) *Economic Policy and Policy-Making under the Mitterrand Presidency 1981–84*, London, Frances Pinter, 1985.

48 V. Wright, 'Socialism and the interdependent economy: industrial policy-making under the Mitterrand presidency', *Government and Opposition*, 1984, 19, p. 295.

49 The final communiqué of Williamsburg Group of Seven summit is reprinted in *Financial Times*, 31 May 1983.

50 *Nature*, 6 June 1985, pp. 443–4.

51 Ministère de la Politique Etrangère de la France, 'Une nouvelle étape pour l'Europe: un espace commun de l'industrie et de la recherche', *Politique Etrangère de la France: Textes et Documents*, 12 September 1983.

52 D. Dickson, 'France proposes joint research channels', *Times Higher Education Supplement*, 9 November 1984; S.F. Wells, 'France and European defence cooperation: implications for United States policy', *Atlantic Community Quarterly*, 1985–86, 23, p. 383.

53 Sharp, 'Europe and new technologies', p. 207–9; Sharp and Shearman, *European Technological Collaboration*, p. 49.

54 The full text of the Reagan's speech which originally proposed the SDI programme is contained in US Department of State, *Department of State Bulletin*, 1983, 2073, pp. 8–14.

55 See *Le Monde*, 25 June 1985; *La Tribune*, 19 April 1985; *Le Soir*, 29 April-5 May 1985; statement by French Senator Guy Cabanelm, 'Le programme Eurêka', *Sénat no. 387 Tome 2*, 1985, p. 120.

56 T. Taylor, 'Britain's response to the Strategic Defense Initiative', *International Affairs*, 1986, 62, p. 217.

57 See C. Bluth, 'SDI: the challenge to West Germany', *International Affairs*, 1986, 62, pp. 247–64.

58 *Le Monde*, 19 April 1985.

59 See J. Fenske, 'France and the Strategic Defense Initiative: speeding up or putting on the brakes?', *International Affairs*, 1986, 62, pp. 243–44; *L'Usine Nouvelle*, 25 April 1985; *Le Monde*, 25 June 1985.

60 *Financial Times*, 18 April 1985.

61 Mitterrand quoted in P. Humphreys, 'The state and telecommunications modernization in Britain, France and West Germany' in U. Hilpert (ed.) *State Policies and Techno-Industrial Innovation*, London, Routledge, 1991, p. 119.

62 I am grateful to Howard Machin for suggesting this point to me.

63 Quoted in *Le Quotidien*, 7 June 1985.

64 Quoted in *Le Monde*, 8 May 1985.

65 *Libération*, 25–26 May 1985.

66 *Le Monde*, 30 May 1985; *L'Humanité*, 29 May 1985.

67 CEC, 'Trends 1974–1991', *Eurobarometer*, Brussels, April 1992, pp. 63, 83; CEC, 'Special issue: Europe 2000 survey', *Eurobarometer*, Brussels, March 1987, pt. 3.6; CEC, *Eurobarometer*, Brussels, 27, June 1987, pt. 5.2.
68 C. Hermant, J.P. Moatti, P. Rolle and E. Barchechath, 'Public acceptance of new technologies: France' in R. Williams and S. Mills (eds) *Public Acceptance of New Technologies: An International Review*, London, Croom Helm, 1986, p. 167.
69 See *New Scientist*, 27 March 1986, p. 12; Fenske, 'France and the Strategic Defence Initiative', pp. 240–1.
70 Interview with French Eureka official.
71 See *Nature*, 28 April 1988.
72 Feldman, *Concorde and Dissent*, pp. 115, 122.
73 See *Le Point*, 17 June 1985; *Financial Times*, 15 July 1985; Ministère de la Recherche et de la Technologie de la France, 'Note de présentation d'Eurêka', *Assises de la Technologie Européenne: Dossier de Presse*, Paris, 19 July 1985.
74 Michel Feldman quoted in *Le Quotidien*, 2 May 1985.
75 Quoted in Bluth, 'SDI: the challenge to West Germany', p. 251.
76 A. Carton, 'Eureka: a west European response to the technological challenge posed the the SDI research programme', in H.G. Brauch (ed.) *Star Wars and European Defence*, New York, St. Martin's Press, 1987, p. 311. See also *Le Quotidien*, 22 May 1985; *La Croix*, 13 June 1985; 'Charles Hernu on Eureka and joint defense with FRG', *Foreign Broadcast Information Service: Western Europe*, German radio interview text, 23 July 1985, p. K1.
77 *L'Express*, 26 April-2 May 1985; *Le Monde*, 30 May 1985.
78 R. Fennell, 'Reform of the CAP: shadow or substance?', *Journal of Common Market Studies*, 1987, 26, p. 65; *Le Quotidien*, 7 June 1985.
79 See *Le Nouvel Economiste*, 23 May 1985.
80 Quoted in *The Times*, 30 April 1985.
81 Quoted in Fenske, 'France and the Strategic Defence Initiative', p. 236.
82 Quoted in *Le Quotidien*, 10 May 1985.
83 Quoted in *La Tribune*, 23 May 1985.
84 Quoted in *Wall Street Journal*, 28 May 1985. See also *Libération*, 22 May 1985.
85 Quoted in *Le Monde*, 31 May 1985. See also *La Tribune*, 31 May 1985.
86 Quoted in *Le Figaro*, 29 May 1985.
87 Quoted in *Wall Street Journal*, 28 May 1985.
88 The left-liberal *Frankfurter Rundschau* suggested 'good personal relations between leaders cannot be a substitute for policy'. The more conservative *Die Welt* urged 'Europe does not have much more time. If we wish that Europe be more than just a community of interests designed to commercialize agricultural projects, we must act'. A survey of German press reaction is contained in *La Croix*, 31 May 1985.
89 See S. Bulmer and W. Paterson, *The Federal Republic of Germany and the European Community*, London, Allen & Unwin, 1987, p. 241; *L'Unité*, 7 June 1985.
90 Quoted in *La Croix* and *La Tribune*, 1 June 1985.
91 Quoted in *Le Monde*, 2–3 June, 1985. See *Le Point*, 3–9 June 1985.
92 *Le Matin*, 3 June 1985; *Le Quotidien*, 3 June 1985; *La Tribune*, 4 June 1985.

93 G. Smith, *Democracy in Western Germany*, Aldershot, Gower, 3rd edition 1986, pp. 58–9; C. Tugendhat, *Making Sense of Europe*, Middlesex, Viking Books, 1986, pp. 95–7.

94 Bulmer and Paterson, *The Federal Republic of Germany*, pp. 230–31 (emphasis in original).

95 Mytelka and Delapierre, 'The alliance strategies of European firms', p. 242.

96 J.M. Cadiou, 'Esprit: un premier bilan', *Bulletin de Liasion de la Recherche en Informatique et Automatique*, 1986, 105, p. 6; A. Danzin, 'La Communauté et le défi de la recherche scientifique et technique', *Journal of European Integration*, 1988, 11, p. 103.

97 Mytelka and Delapierre, 'The alliance strategies of European firms', pp. 244–5; Sharp, 'Europe and the new technologies', p. 209; Sandholtz, 'Esprit and the politics of international collective action', p. 15.

98 J. Pearce and J. Sutton with R. Batcheldor, *Protection and Industrial Policy in Europe*, London, Routledge & Kegan Paul for the Royal Institute of International Affairs, 1985, pp. 53–54; Sharp, 'Europe and the new technologies', p. 208.

99 See CEC, *Official Documents on the Esprit Programme*, Brussels, (86) 269, final, 1986; Sharp, 'Europe and the new technologies', p. 209; Mytelka and Delapierre, 'The alliance strategies of European firms', p. 245–6.

100 *Financial Times*, 7 June 1985; *La Tribune*, 8–9 June 1985.

101 *Le Monde*, 8 June 1985; *Electronique Actualités*, 7 June 1985.

102 Quoted in *Financial Times*, 7 June 1985.

103 *Le Figaro*, 14 June 1985; *La Tribune*, 15–16 June 1985.

104 *Financial Times*, 22 June 1985.

105 Quoted in *International Management*, October 1985, p. 29.

106 Quoted in *Wall Street Journal*, 25 June 1985. The French delegation also revealed that two other agreements were close to fruition, involving Bull, Siemens, Selenia and CGE. See *Financial Times*, 25 June 1985.

107 Moreover, as the Milan summit began, the French attaché Claude Arnaud was in Stockholm to officially invite Sweden into Eureka. The Germans also insisted that Eureka needed to include non-EC Member States in a statement released after a Franco-German meeting of defence, foreign, and technology ministers in Bonn on 26 June. See *Financial Times*, 27 June 1985; 29 June 1985; 5 July 1985.

108 *Le Monde*, 18 April 1985; *Financial Times*, 30 April 1985; 24 June 1985.

109 Quoted in *Financial Times*, 1 July 1985. See also *Wall Street Journal*, 1 July 1985.

110 *Aviation Week and Space Technology*, 15 July 1985, pp. 21–2; *Wall Street Journal*, 5 July 1985; 10 July 1985; *The Times*, 17 July 1985.

111 A.N. Duff, 'Eureka and the new technology policy of the European Community', *Policy Studies*, 1986, 6, p. 58; *Financial Times*, 18 July 1985; *Wall Street Journal*, 18 July 1985.

112 Ministére de la Recherche et de la Technologie de la France, 'Texte du communiqué final', *Assises de la Technologie Européene: Dossier de Presse*, Paris, 19 July 1985, pp. 1–2; *The Times*, 19 July 1985.

113 CESTA, 'La renaissance technology de l'Europe: propositions françaises', Paris, June 1985. See also *Science*, 10 May 1985, p. 694.

114 *Financial Times*, 19 July 1985.

115 Interview with UK Eureka official.

116 *Financial Times*, 14 October 1985.

117 *Wall Street Journal*, 6 September 1985; *Le Monde*, 5 September 1985; *Financial Times*, 18 October 1985.
118 Quoted in *Financial Times*, 20 July 1985.
119 Quoted in *Wall Street Journal*, 4 November 1985.
120 Interview with representative of British chairmanship.
121 Interview with German Eureka official.
122 'Declaration of Principles relating to Eureka', pp. 1–2.
123 Quoted in *International Herald Tribune*, 6 November 1985.
124 *Daily Telegraph*, 7 November 1985.
125 Quoted in *Financial Times*, 8 November 1985. In the event, Thomson withdrew from this project, which never started and was formally abandoned in 1987.
126 *Wall Street Journal*, 6 November 1985.
127 Full details on the projects approved at Hanover are contained in *British Business*, 18 April 1986; *Financial Times*, 7 November 1985; *Wall Street Journal*, 7 November 1985.
128 *Wall Street Journal*, 24 January 1986; *Financial Times*, 24 January 1986.
129 A list of projects approved to this point is detailed in *Aviation Week & Space Technology*, 1 September 1986.
130 British chairmanship, 'Communiqué of the third Eureka ministerial conference', London, 30 June 1986; *Financial Times*, 1 July 1986; *Electronic Engineering Times*, 7 July 1986.
131 10 Downing Street Press Office, 'Text of speech given by the Prime Minister Margaret Thatcher to Eureka ministerial conference,' London, HMSO, 30 June 1986, pp. 20–21.
132 See *Le Monde*, 26–27 January 1986; *Financial Times*, 29 May 1986.
133 *Aviation Week and Space Technology*, 7 July 1986.
134 Interview with representative of British chairmanship.
135 See P. Taylor, 'The new dynamics of EC integration in the 1980s' in J. Lodge (ed.) *The European Community and the Challege of the Future*, London, Frances Pinter, p. 14; Sharp, 'The Community and new technologies', p. 214–15.
136 Quoted in *La Tribune*, 19 April 1985.
137 Phillippe Moreau-Defarges of the French Institute for International Relations quoted in *Wall Street Journal*, 28 May 1985. See also *Les Echos*, 24 April 1985.
138 British chairmanship, 'Memorandum of understanding on the Eureka secretariat between the members of Eureka', London, 30 June 1986, p. 7.

4 HOW EUREKA OPERATES

1 Interview with UK Eureka official.
2 OECD, *Science and Technology Policy Outlook*, Paris, 1985, pp. 17–18; OECD, *Science and Technology Indicators No. 2: R & D, Invention and Competitiveness*, Paris, 1986, p. 78.
3 D.R. Roman and J.F. Puett, Jr, *International Business and Technological Innovation*, Oxford, North-Holland, 1983, p. 90.
4 C. Freeman, *Technology Policy and Economic Peformance: Lessons From Japan*, London, Frances Pinter, 1987, pp. 1–5.

5 See J.J. Salomon, *Le Gaulois, le Cow-boy et le Samuraï: Rapport sur la Politique Française de la Technologie*, Paris, CPE, 1985; OECD, *Science and Technology Policy Outlook*, 1988, pp. 16–17.

6 Freeman, *Technology Policy and Economic Performance*, p. 119.

7 See OECD, *Innovation Policy in France*, Paris, 1986, pp. 24–6.

8 OECD, *The Semi-Conductor Industry: Trade-Related Issues*, Paris, 1985, p. 75.

9 OECD, *Innovation Policy in France*, p. 54; F. Duchêne and G. Shepherd, 'Sources of industrial policy' in F. Duchêne and G. Shepherd (eds) *Managing Industrial Change in Western Europe*, London, Frances Pinter, 1987, p. 36.

10 P. Messerlin, 'France: the ambitious state' in Duchêne and Shepherd, *Managing Industrial Change in Western Europe*, p. 106.

11 R. Nelson, *High-Technology Policies: A Five-Nation Comparison*, Washington DC, American Enterprise Institute for Public Policy Research, 1984, p. 46.

12 See OECD, *Innovation Policy in France*, pp. 27, 216–22, 187–8.

13 *Ibid.*, p. 80; *The Times Higher Education Supplement*, 31 May 1985, p. 8.

14 See T.R. Howell, W.A. Noellert, J.H. MacLaughlin and A.W. Wolff, *The Microelectronics Race: the Impact of Government Policy on International Competition*, Boulder CO, Westview Press, 1988, pp. 169–71.

15 J. de Bandt, 'French industrial policies: successes and failures' in P.R. Beije, J. Groenewegen, I. Kostoulas, J. Paelinck and C. van Paridon (eds) *A Competitive Future for Europe? Towards a New European Industrial Policy*, London, Croom Helm, 1987, pp. 52–53.

16 See R. Gilpin, 'Science, technology and French independence' in T.D. Long and C. Wright (eds) *Science Policies of Industrial Nations*, New York, Praeger Publishers, 1975; Telesis Consultants, *Competing for Prosperity: Business Strategies and Industrial Policies in Modern France*, London, Policy Studies Institute, 1986, pp. 184–94.

17 OECD, *Innovation Policy in France*, p. 18; OECD, *Science and Technology Policy Outlook*, 1988, pp. 60–70.

18 U. Hilpert, 'Economic adjustment by techno-industrial innovation and the role of the state' in U. Hilpert (ed.) *State Policies and Techno-Industrial Innovation*, London, Routledge, 1991, pp. 101–5.

19 See H. Aujac, 'An introduction to French industrial policy' in W.J. Adams and C. Stoffaës (eds) *French Industrial Policy*, Washington DC, Brookings Institution, 1986, p. 25.

20 See *Nature*, 25 January 1990, p. 300.

21 Messerlin, 'France: the ambitious state', pp. 79, 91.

22 Interview with official of regional office of MRT.

23 P.A. Hall, 'The state and the market' in P.A. Hall, J. Hayward and H. Machin (eds) *Developments in French Politics*, London, Macmillan, 1990, pp. 177–78.

24 F. Duchêne, 'Policies for a wider world' in Duchêne and Shepherd (eds) *Managing Industrial Change in Europe*, p. 211.

25 J. Rembser, 'Economic development, the international competitive situation and the framework of federal and state action to promote R & D, technological development and innovation in Germany', paper presented at German–Canadian workshop on 'Promotion of Technology-Based Small and Medium-Size Enterprises and Technology Transfer', Berlin, 2–3

December 1985, pp. 8–13; K. Pavitt and W. Walker, 'Government policies towards industrial innovation: a review', *Research Policy*, 1976, 5, pp. 95–7.

26 D. Webber, 'The framework of government–industry relations and industrial policy making in the Federal Republic of Germany', *University of Sussex Working Papers on Government–Industry Relations*, 1986, Brighton, March, 1, p. 28.

27 Howell *et al.*, *The Microelectronics Race*, p. 172; Roman and Puett, *International Business and Technological Innovation*, p. 90.

28 OECD, *Science and Technology Policy Outlook*, 1988, pp. 94–5, 102–3.

29 See K.P. Friebe, 'Industrial policy in the Federal Republic of Germany' in K.P. Friebe and A. Gerybadze (eds) *Microelectronics in Western Europe*, Berlin, Erich Schmidt Verlag, 1984.

30 E.J. Horn, 'Germany: a market-led process' in Duchêne and Shepherd (eds) *Managing Industrial Change in Western Europe*, p. 63. See also BMFT, *Hochtechnologien und internationale Wettbewerbsfähigkeit der deutschen Wirtschaft*, Bonn, BMWI Dokumentation, p. 263.

31 G. Smith, *Democracy in Western Germany*, Aldershot, Gower, 1986, pp. 123–5; W. Paterson, 'Environmental politics' in G. Smith, W. Paterson and P. Merkl (eds) *Developments in West German Politics*, London, Macmillan, 1989, pp. 267–73.

32 GATT, *International Trade 1984/5*, Geneva, 1985, p. 178.

33 P. Humphreys, 'The state and telecommunications modernization in Britain, France and West Germany' in U. Hilpert (ed.) *State Policies and Techno-Industrial Innovation*, London, Routledge, 1991, p. 119; CEC, 'Government report on information technology: Federal Government scheme to promote the development of microelectronics and the information and communications technologies', Brussels, Information Technologies Task Force, III/2718/84–E, 23 February 1984; *Agence Europe*, 5214, 15 March 1990, p. 11.

34 Howell *et al.*, *The Microelectronics Race*, p. 188.

35 Interview with German Eureka official.

36 Correspondance from German Eureka office to the author, 17 March 1992; BMFT, 'Facts and figures 1990: update of the report of the Federal Government on Research 1988', English version, Verlag Deutscher Wirtschaftsdienst, Köln, 1990, pp. 100–23.

37 Finnish chairmanship, *SMEs: a Challenge to Eureka*, Tampere, 22 May 1992, appendix A.

38 Duchêne and Shepherd, 'Sources of industrial policy', p. 36.

39 Department of Trade and Industry, *A Framework for Government Research and Development*, London, HMSO, 1971; P. Stoneman, *The Economic Analysis of Technology Policy*, Oxford, Clarendon Press, 1987, p. 209.

40 See for example OECD, *Science and Technology Policy Outlook*, 1988, p. 36; D. Edgerton and K. Hughes, 'The poverty of science: a critical analysis of science and industrial policy under Mrs. Thatcher', *Public Administration*, 67, 419–33.

41 P. Hall, *Governing the Economy: the Politics of State Interventionism in Britain and France*, Oxford, Oxford University Press, 1986, pp. 112–13.

42 See Freeman, *Technology Policy and Economic Performance*, pp. 124–6.

43 Department of Trade and Industry, *Evaluation of the Alvey Programme for Advanced Information Technology*, London, HMSO, 1991.

44 See Freeman, *Technology Policy and Economic Performance*, 133; B. Oakley and K. Owen, *Alvey: Britain's Strategic Computing Initiative*, London, MIT Press, 1989.

45 A 1990 survey of British Esprit participants who had previously received grants through the Alvey project found that 70 per cent were making use of results or experience gained from their past participation in Alvey in their present Esprit project. See PREST, 'Results of telephone survey of UK industrial participants in Esprit II', University of Manchester, Policy Research in Engineering, Science and Technology, 1990. See also W. Sandholtz, 'Esprit and the politics of international collective action', *Journal of Common Market Studies*, 1992, 30, p. 13; L. Keliher, 'Policy-making in information technology: a decisional analysis of the Alvey project', unpublished Ph.D. thesis, London School of Economics, 1987, p. 257; Danish Chairmanship, 'Eureka: goals attained and future development', Copenhagen, 1988.

46 Department of Trade and Industry, *Information Technology: A Plan for Concerted Action – the Report of the IT 86 Committee*, London, HMSO, 1986, pp. 10–11.

47 Freeman, *Technology Policy and Economic Performance*, p. 131.

48 Press conference, Copenhagen, 16 June 1988.

49 Sharp, *The Community and the New Technologies*, p. 215; S. George, *An Awkward Partner: Britain in the European Community*, Oxford, Oxford University Press, 1990, p. 201.

50 See A.N. Duff, 'Eureka and the new technology policy of the European Community', *Policy Studies*, 1986, 6, p. 48; Stoneman, *The Economic Analysis of Technology Policy*, p. 209.

51 Interviews with numerous German and Dutch Eureka officials.

52 R. van Tulder, 'Small countries and the global innovation race: the role of the state in the Netherlands, Belgium and Switzerland' in U. Hilpert (ed.) *State Policies and Techno-Industrial Innovation*, London, Routledge, 1991, p. 301.

53 OECD, *Science and Technology Policy Outlook*, 1988, p. 19.

54 P. Ranci, 'Italy: the weak state' in Duchêne and Shepherd, *Managing Industrial Change in Europe*, 1987, p. 141.

55 S. Hinder, 'Eureka: a UK perspective', unpublished M.Phil. thesis, University of Manchester, 1987, p. 29.

56 See Duchêne, 'Policies for a Wider World', p. 220.

57 Danish Eureka chairmanship, 'Eureka: goals attained', table 1.

58 See CEC, *Bulletin of the European Communities*, 1989, Brussels, 20, 6, p. 40.

59 See *Wall Street Journal*, 18 December 1986; *Financial Times*, 18 December 1986.

60 Danish chairmanship, 'Eureka Management Research Initiative (EMRI)', Eureka document 626, 15 June 1988, p. 2.

61 *Ibid.*, p. 4; correspondance from Dr Kristian Kreiner, Director of EMRI, Institute of Organisation and Industrial Sociology, Copenhagen School of Economics and Social Science to the author, 16 June 1990.

62 Interview with CEC official.

63 Danish chairmanship, 'Eureka: goals attained', p. 6.

64 Austrian chairmanship, 'Proposals for the work programme and tentative calendar of meetings during the Austrian chairmanship', Eureka document 652, 16 June 1988, p. 1.

65 The author attended a meeting in Vienna on 17 October 1988 of the HLG's *Groupe de Réflexion*, which was formed to debate the plan. The quotations and impressions contained in this paragraph are from notes taken during this meeting. As the meeting was not open to the public, all quotations are unattributed.

66 Interview with UK Eureka official.

67 Interview with Danish Eureka official.

68 Interview with representative of Eureka secretariat.

69 Interview with UK Eureka official.

70 Numerous interviews with Eureka officials; British chairmanship, 'Memorandum of understanding on the Eureka secretariat between the members of Eureka,' London, 30 June 1986, p. 4.

71 Interview with representative of Eureka secretariat.

72 *Ibid.*

73 Interview with CEC official.

74 Eureka secretariat, 'Progress report on Eureka projects', Brussels, 16 June 1988, p. 8; Eureka secretariat, 'Communiqué of the 6th Eureka ministerial conference, Brussels, Copenhagen, 15–16 June 1988, p. 2.

75 Danish chairmanship, 'Some statistical data about Eureka projects', Copenhagen, 16 June 1988, p. 1.

76 Eureka secretariat, *Eureka Annual Project Report*, 1988, p. 3.

77 Eureka secretariat, 'Programme of work under the Austrian chairmanship', Brussels, Eureka document 705, 3 October 1988, p. 3.

78 Interview with representative of Eureka secretariat.

79 Interview with UK Eureka official.

80 Interview with Danish Eureka official.

81 Interview with UK Eureka official.

82 Interview with Danish Eureka official.

83 Eureka secretariat, 'Declaration of Principles relating to Eureka adopted at Hanover, 6 November 1985', Brussels, p. 1.

84 Interview with UK Eureka official.

85 A powerful piece of interactive software is used by national Famos resource teams to monitor projects, share information on new projects needed to support or complement existing ones, and avoid duplication by comparing new project proposals with existing ones. Numerous interviews with Eureka officials and industrialists involved in Famos.

86 Finnish chairmanship, *NPC Office Functions*, Tampere, 22 May 1992, p. and appendix; interview with Dutch Eureka official.

87 This refers to a report system undertaken throughout the British civil service before public expenditure is released for any purpose. ROAM is an acronym for a Rationale, Objectives (how success or failure is measured), Appraisal (criteria for deciding whether to make the expenditure or not), and Monitoring. Numerous interviews with UK Eureka officials.

88 Interview with UK Eureka official.

89 The author was provided with a copy of the internal Keddie Group report in confidence and thus statements about its contents are general and not cited.

90 Interview with UK Eureka official.

91 Interview with CEC official.

92 Interview with CEC official.

93 Finnish chairmanship, *NPC Office Functions*, p. 3.

94 Interview with Swedish Eureka official.
95 Interview with Danish Eureka official.
96 Interview with Dutch Eureka official.
97 Interview with UK Eureka official.
98 Numerous interviews with Eureka officials.
99 Interview with UK Eureka official.
100 Eureka secretariat, 'Spotlight on Vienne', *Eureka News*, 6, October 1989, p. 6.
101 Interview with UK Eureka official.
102 Interview with representative of Eureka secretariat.
103 European Bankers Round Table, 'Declaration to the Eureka Conference of Ministers', Madrid, 15 September 1987, p. 2.
104 *Ibid.*, p. 6.
105 Interview with UK Eureka official.
106 Interview with Dutch Eureka official.
107 Interview with UK Eureka official.
108 Interview with UK Eureka official.
109 Finnish chairmanship, *NPC Office Functions*, appendix; numerous interviews with Eureka officials.
110 Interview with CEC official.
111 Interview with UK Eureka official.
112 P. Van den Bergen, Dutch Eureka NPC quoted in Eureka secretariat, 'Supportive measures: Eureka value-added input', *Eureka News*, 4, April 1989, p. 2.
113 Interview with UK Eureka official.
114 Dutch Eureka Office, *Industrial HP Lasers: a Survey on Hazards and Safety Regulations*, Eureka bulletin special issue The Hague, July 1989.
115 CEN and CENELEC are French acronyms for *Comité Européen de Normalisation* and *Comité Européen de Normalisation Electrotechnique*. See Eureka secretariat, 'Standardisation: first come, first served', *Eureka News*, 1, June 1988, p. 8.
116 Interview with UK Eureka official.
117 Dutch chairmanship, *Eureka and Supportive Measures*, The Hague, Document NPC-9067, 1991, p. 5.
118 Interview with CEC official.
119 Interview with UK Eureka official.
120 Interview with UK Eureka official.
121 *Ibid.*
122 British chairmanship, 'Procedures for Eureka projects', note by the chairman of the ministerial conference, London, 21 May 1986.
123 Apparently, only a handful of such queries were tabled between 1985 and 1989. Numerous interviews with Eureka officials.
124 IDS Consultants, 'Audit opérationnel du programme Eurêka en France: point clés de la synthèse', Levallois, 1989.
125 Dutch chairmanship, *The Report of the Eureka Assessment Panel*, The Hague, 1991, pp. 12–13.
126 The author was provided with a copy of this report in confidence, so it is not referenced. However, it suffices to note that the report concluded that any assessment of the economic impact of Eureka was impossible without substantially improved information-gathering procedures.
127 Interview with UK Eureka official.

128 Interview with representative of Eureka secretariat.
129 Interview with UK Eureka official.
130 Interview with Danish Eureka official.
131 'Programme of work under the Austrian chairmanship', p. 6.
132 Eureka secretariat, 'Eureka and the environment: an overview – the scientific and technological stakes', *Eureka News*, 1, June 1989, p. 7; Eureka secretariat, 'Surge in environmental awareness', *Eureka News*, 6, October 1989, p. 9.
133 Numerous interviews with Eureka officials.
134 Interview with UK Eureka official.

5 EUREKA AND THE EUROPEAN COMMUNITY

1 Interview with representative of Eureka secretariat.
2 CEC, 'Towards a European technology community', Brussels, COM (85) 350 final, 1985, p. 3.
3 See *Le Monde*, 27 July 1985.
4 A proposal to create an EC agency to coordinate all European R & D programmes including Eureka was voted down by the EP in 1986 on a vote of 156 in favour and 152 opposed, with 17 abstentions. See P. Braillard and A. Demant, *Eurêka et l'Europe Technologique*, Brussels, Emile Bruylant, 1991, p. 87.
5 British chairmanship, 'Memorandum of understanding on the Eureka secretariat between the members of Eureka', London, Annex, 1986, p. 8.
6 CEC, 'Eureka and the European Technology Community', Brussels, Communication from the Commission to the Council, COM (86) 664 final, 1986.
7 CEC, 'Reinforcing cooperation between Eureka and the European Community', Brussels, Communication from the Commission to the Council, COM (88), 291 final, 1988.
8 Quoted in *Financial Times*, 16 September 1987.
9 CEC, 'Declaration by Mr K.H. Narjes, Vice-President of the European Commission before the 6th Eureka conference in Copenhagen', Brussels, 18 June 1988, pp. 1–2.
10 Press conference, Copenhagen, 16 June 1988.
11 Secretariat of the European Council of Ministers, 'Ways for increasing the participation of the Community in Eureka Projects: memorandum of the government of the Federal Republic of Germany', Brussels, English translation, 4 February 1988, p. 4.
12 Quoted in *Financial Times*, 30 June 1988.
13 Anonymous CEC official quoted in *Wall Street Journal*, 4 November 1985.
14 Interview with CEC official.
15 CEC, 'Reinforcing cooperation', pts 12–13.
16 Interview with CEC official.
17 Interview with Danish Eureka official.
18 Interview with CEC official.
19 Interview with CEC official.
20 Numerous interviews with Eureka officials and industrialists. See also *Financial Times*, 9 November 1989.
21 CEC, Eureka and the European Technology Community, pp. 3, 5.

22 Pandolfi quoted in Eureka Secretariat, 'Spotlight on Vienne', *Eureka News*, 6, October 1989, p. 7. See also Eureka secretariat, 'Formentor: European Commission joins the fray', *Eureka News*, 5, June 1989, p. 2; CEC, *The Commission Programme for 1990*, Luxembourg, Bull. Supplement 1/90, 1990, p. 23; Eureka secretariat, 'New opportunities for developing environmental technologies: Euroenviron – the green umbrella', Brussels, 1990, p. 2.

23 Interview with CEC official.

24 See CEC, 'Eureka and the European Technology Community'.

25 Interview with representative of Eureka secretariat.

26 CEC, *Innovation and Technology Transfer*, 1990, 11/3, p. 18. See also CEC, *Bulletin of the European Communities*, 1989, Luxembourg, 22 (6), pt. 2.1.62; Eureka secretariat, 'JESSI swings into action', *Eureka News*, 6, October 1989, p. 9.

27 See CEC, 'Reinforcing cooperation between Eureka and the European Community', p. 8.

28 Interview with CEC official.

29 Eureka secretariat, *Annual Progress Report 1991*, Brussels, 1992, p. 26.

30 Eureka secretariat, *Annual Project Report 1989*, Brussels, 1990, p. 7.

31 Interview with representative of CEN/CENELEC.

32 Interview with CEC official.

33 Eureka Secretariat, 'Interview with Jos Peeters, chairman of EVCA', *Eureka News*, 5, June 1989, pp. 6–7.

34 ECVA chairman Neil Cross quoted in *New Scientist*, 8 October 1987, p. 17. See also CEC, *Eurotech Capital*, Luxembourg, DG XVIII, 1990; EVCA, *Venture Consort: Innovation Finance Scheme*, Zaventem, 1990; Eureka Secretariat, "Eurotech-Capital" pilot programme for high-tech projects', *Eureka News*, 4, April 1989, p. 8.

35 EVCA chairman K. Nathusius quoted in CEC, *Innovation and Technology Transfer*, 1989, 10/1, May 1989, p. 34. See also CEC, *Innovation and Technology Transfer*, 1989, 10/4, p. 32; *New Scientist*, 11 August 1988.

36 CEC, *Eurotech Capital*, p. 2.

37 Address by Fabia Manunta, DG XXIII of European Commission to Eureka NPCs, Amsterdam, 10 April 1990.

38 Interview with French Eureka official.

39 Interview with UK Eureka official.

40 Interview with CEC official.

41 This quotation paraphrases comments made by a member of the Austrian delegation at a meeting of Eureka NPCs, 10 April 1991, Amsterdam.

42 Interview with CEC official.

43 CEC, 'Reinforcing cooperation', p. 5.

44 CEC, *The Commission's programme for 1990: address by Jacques Delors, President of the Commission, to the European Parliament*, Luxembourg, Bull. supplement 1/90, 1990, p. 10.

45 J. Pelkmans and A. Winters, *Europe's Domestic Market*, London, Routledge & Kegan Paul, 1988, pp. 32–3.

46 CEC, *Sixteenth Report on Competition Policy*, Brussels/Luxembourg, pt. 247, 1987, p. 167 (emphasis in original).

47 *Ibid.*, p. 167.

48 CEC, *Seventeenth Report on Competition Policy*, Brussels/Luxembourg, pt. 176, 1988, p. 143.

49 CEC, *Eighteenth Report on Competition Policy*, Brussels/Luxembourg, Pt. 172, 1989, pp. 151–2.
50 CEC, *Bulletin of the European Communities*, 1989, 22, p. 46; *Agence Europe*, 5110, 13 October 1989, p. 12; *Agence Europe*, 5114, 19 October 1989, p. 12; *Agence Europe*, 5171, 13 January 1990, p. 14; *Agence Europe*, 5195, 16 February 1990, p. 13.
51 Interview with CEC official.
52 J. Gilchrist and D. Deacon, 'Curbing subsidies' in P. Montagnon (ed.) *European Competition Policy*, London, Frances Pinter Publishers for the Royal Institute of International Affairs, 1990, pp. 48–9. The authors are both officials of DG IV.
53 *Ibid.*, p. 44.
54 Interview with CEC official.
55 CEC, 'Completing the internal market: white paper from the Commission to the European Council', Luxembourg, 1985, para. 82.
56 P. Cecchini with M. Catinat and A. Jacquemin, *The European Challenge: 1992 – the Benefits of a Single Market*, Aldershot, Wildwood House, 1988, p. 17.
57 J. Pinder, 'The single market: a step towards European Union' in J. Lodge (ed.) *The European Community and the Challenge of the Future*, London, Frances Pinter, 1989, p. 99.
58 'Declaration of Principles relating to Eureka', p. 3.
59 Pinder, 'The single market', p. 100.
60 CEC, 'Completing the internal market', paras. 133–49.
61 P.L Thoft, 'Promotion of innovation: a new direction for national patent offices' in U. Täger and A. von Witzleben (eds) *Patinnova '90: Strategies for the Protection of Innovation*, London, Kluwer Academic, 1991, p. 44.
62 C.C. Twitchett, *Harmonisation in the EEC*, London, Macmillan, 1991, p. 3.
63 A. Schäfers, 'The Luxembourg patent convention: the best option for the internal market', *Journal of Common Market Studies*, 1987, 25, pp. 193–207.
64 See CEC, 'Patents, trade marks and copyright in the European Community', *European File*, 1989, 17, December, pp. 4–6.
65 See Department of Trade and Industry, *Company Law Harmonisation*, London, HMSO, February, 1992; CEC, *Euro-Info*, 1990, 30, p. 1; *The Company Lawyer Digest*, 1990, 11, February, pp. 1–2.
66 HDTV secretariat, 'Vision 1250 established', *HDTV Report*, 2 June 1990, p. 12; Eureka secretariat, 'HDTV: EEC promises promotion body', *Eureka News*, 4, April 1989, p. 8; *Agence Europe*, 5217, 19–20 March 1990, p. 10.
67 CEC, 'Proposal for a Council Regulation on a statute for a European Company', Brussels, COM (89) 268 final, 1989.
68 Numerous interviews with Eureka officials.
69 Quoted in *New Scientist*, 6 April 1991.
70 Correspondence from member of Eurotrac international scientific secretariat to the author, 31 August 1990.
71 Dutch chairmanship, *X-Ray Sessions: a Final Report*, The Hague, 1991, pp. 10–24.
72 European Parliament, 'Draft Report on the European Research Coordination Agency' (The Ford Report), PE 199.362/B, Committee on Energy, Research and Technology, 28 June 1988, p. 7.

252 *High Technology and the Competition State*

Brewin and D. McAllister, 'Annual review of the activities of the
European Community in 1989', *Journal of Common Market Studies*, 1990,
28, p. 466; P. Aigrain, G. Allen, E. de Arantes e Oliveira, U. Colombo and
H. Markl, *The Report of the Framework Review Board*, Brussels, June 1989;
TRN Groep/Volder & Vis, *Analysis of and Comments on the Organisation of
DG XII, DG XIII and the Joint Research Centre*, Brussels, 1989.
74 CEC, *Innovation and Technology Transfer*, 1989, 10/3, July, p. 5.
75 See CEC, 'The Community and business: the action programme for small
and medium-sized enterprises', *European File*, Luxembourg, 3/88, 1988;
CEC, 'The European Community and cooperation among small and
medium-sized enterprises', *European File*, Luxembourg, 11/88, 1988, p. 3.
76 See CEC, 'Council decision on the improvement of the business
environment and the promotion of the development of enterprises, and in
particular small and medium-sized enterprises in the Community', *Official
Journal of the European Communities*, 1989, Brussels, No. L 239/33, 89/490/
EEC; CEC, *Innovation and Technology Transfer*, 1990, Brussels, 11/3, p. 20.
77 Interview with UK Eureka official.
78 See *Nature*, 21 March 1991, p. 177; 25 April 1991, p. 641.
79 See P.G. Nell, 'EFTA in the 1990s: the search for a new identity', *Journal of
Common Market Studies*, 1990, 28, June, pp. 332–3.
80 F. Laursen, 'The Community's policy towards EFTA: regime formation in
the European Economic Space', *Journal of Common Market Studies*, 1990,
28, p. 312.
81 See CEC, 'Implementation of the R & D cooperation with EFTA
countries', *Innovation and Technology Transfer*, 1990, 10/2, p. 4.
82 'Declaration of Principles relating to Eureka', p. 3.
83 Interview with CEC official.
84 CEC, *Innovation and Technology Transfer*, 1990, 11/1, p. 2.
85 *Agence Europe*, 5201, 24 February 1990, p. 5.
86 *Agence Europe*, 5242, 26 April 1990, p. 7; *Agence Europe*, 5274, 14 June
1990, p. 9.
87 Interview with CEC official; *Agence Europe*, 5234, 12 April 1990, p. 9.
88 Interview with representative of Eureka secretariat.
89 Raad van Advies voor het Wetenschapsbeleid, *Advies Inzake Eureka*, Den
Haag, 72, May 1990, p. 19.
90 See Eureka secretariat, 'Eureka meets the East', *Eureka News*, 12, 1991, p.
12; Dutch chairmanship, *Eureka: Exploring Cooperation Between East and
West*, The Hague, Final Programme for Eureka Congress, Budapest,
Hungary, 1–3 May 1991.
91 Dutch chairmanship, 'The Hague statement: extending cooperation with
partners from European non-member countries', The Hague, Document
Eureka 9MC-3, Rev. 1, 17 June 1991.
92 CEC, 'Towards a European technological community', pp. 23–5.
93 Interview with CEC official.
94 See Aigrain *et al.*, *The Report of the Framework Programme Review Board*,
pp. 8–10.
95 T. Watkins, 'Research collaboration in the EC: innovation, technology
diffusion and political support', paper presented at the Inaugural
Conference of the European Community Studies Association, Fairfax,
1989, p. 8.
96 Interview with CEC official.

97 Quoted in *New Scientist*, 8 October 1987, p. 25.
98 Quoted in *Agence Europe*, 5195, 16 February 1990, p. 13.
99 Interview with CEC official.
100 Interview with CEC official.
101 Laursen, 'The Community's policy toward EFTA', p. 317.
102 Quoted in *Agence Europe*, 5244, 28 April 1990, p. 8
103 See Pelkmans and Winters, *Europe's Domestic Market*, pp. 22, 30–1.
104 CEC, 'Reinforcing co-operation between Eureka and the European Communities', p. 6.

6 THE PARTICIPANTS' VIEW

1 See S. Hinder, 'Eureka: a UK perspective', unpublished M.Phil. thesis, University of Manchester, 1987; European Foundation for Management Development, *Eureka: the Management of Collaboration*, Brussels, 1987; IDS Consultants, 'Audit opérationnel du programme Eurêka en France: point clés de la synthèse', Levallois, 1989; IFT Marketing for UK Department of Trade and Industry, *Eureka Survey*, HMSO, London, 1989; Science and Engineering Policy Studies Unit, *European Collaboration in Science and Technology II: Pointers to the Future for Policymakers*, The Royal Society and Fellowship of Engineers, London, 1989.

2 The independent survey data were reported previously in J. Peterson, 'Assessing the performance of European collaborative R & D policy: the case of Eureka', *Research Policy*, 1993. A more detailed analysis of these data may be found in J. Peterson, 'The politics of European technological collaboration: an analysis of the Eureka initiative', unpublished Ph.D. thesis, London School of Economics, 1992, pp. 239–89.

3 It should be noted that after the Vienna ministerial conference of June 1989, the official total of announced Eureka projects was 297. However, 24 projects apparently were dropped from the database between June and November 1989. Moreover, eleven independent survey questionnaires were 'returned to sender' because the project had been abandoned, individual addressees had left their organization, or the address in the database was incomplete. Clearly, there either exist flaws in Eureka's systems for gathering accurate information on projects, or its project list is in a constant state of flux, or both.

4 The questionnaire was pre-tested by sending an early version to two project leaders, who were then contacted for feedback on its structure, clarity and the amount of time required to complete it. A revised version was shown to a Eureka official who suggested further changes, several of which were implemented in the final version.

5 Dutch chairmanship, *The Report of the Eureka Assessment Panel*, The Hague, 1991, p. 49. This report is the source for all data listed in tables labelled 'official survey'.

6 Discrepancies exist in the official estimates of Eureka's total number of participants. At one point, the assessment panel report includes an estimate of 2300 'total partners', but elsewhere it claims that 1935 questionnaires were mailed to 'all participants in all Eureka countries'. At the approximate time when the official survey was being conducted, the Eureka secretariat estimated that 'some 2000 participants' were involved. Part of the

explanation is that some organizations participate in more than one Eureka
project, but certainly not enough to account for such large discrepancies.
See *ibid.*, pp. 12,49; Dutch chairmanship, 'Communiqué of the IX Eureka
ministerial conference', The Hague, 19 June 1991, p. 2; Eureka secretariat,
Annual Progress Report 1990, Brussels, 1991, p. 2.

7 Independent survey data on the number of respondents with previous
experience in EC-funded R & D are reported in Table 6.6.

8 The breakdown of responses to the independent survey question, 'Did any
of your current partners contact you during the 45 day period,' were 47
'yes', 57 'no', 14 'unsure', and three gave no response.

9 Dutch chairmanship, *The Report of the Eureka Assessment Panel*, pp.
26,59.

10 Dutch chairmanship, *X-Ray Sessions: Final Report*, The Hague, 1991, p.
15.

11 Project results were expected within two years by eight per cent of
respondents and within two to five years by 49 per cent. The panel adds the
caveat that, on average, respondents already have participated in Eureka
for about two-and-a-half years. See Dutch chairmanship, *The Report of the
Eureka Assessment Panel*, pp. 30–1.

12 *Ibid.*, p. 63

13 *Ibid.*, p. 38.

14 The independent survey posed the question 'Would the project have been
launched if Eureka did not exist?' The assessment panel survey asked,
'Would the project have been continued if Eureka status had not been
granted?' See *ibid.*, p. 57.

15 *Ibid.*, p. 57.

16 More than 40 per cent of all those who had never received EC R & D funds
said their project would definitely exist even if Eureka did not. See Peterson,
'The politics of European technological collaboration', pp. 258.

17 *Ibid.*, p. 257.

18 A large number of respondents – 31 per cent of the total – chose not to rank
the choices offered and instead simply 'ticked' as many as they deemed
relevant. Since these thirty-eight respondents ticked a total of 254 choices
(or an average of 6.68 choices each), these choices have each been assigned a
value of 13, corresponding to the median value for all choices had each of
these respondents actually ranked seven choices.

19 This point in borne out in a study of nearly 2000 collaborative R & D
agreements in information technology, biotechnology and new materials
which showed 'technological complementarity' to be the most important
motive for joint R & D in each of these sectors. See J. Hagedoorn and J.
Schakenraad, 'Inter-firm partnerships and co-operative strategies in core
technologies' in C. Freeman and L. Soete (eds) *New Explorations in the
Economics of Technical Change*, London, Frances Pinter, 1990, pp. 11–12.

20 Additional choices offered were 'new process technologies', 'long-term
cooperation with foreign partners', 'acceleration of product introductions'
and 'patents or patents pending'. See Dutch chairmanship, *The Report of
the Eureka Assessment Panel*, p. 62.

21 *Ibid.*, p. 58.

22 More than 40 per cent of French project leaders had never engaged in
international collaborative R & D compared with about 30 per cent of
Italian, British and German leaders and 13 per cent of Dutch leaders. Only

about half of all French respondents had previously collaborated with at least one of their current Eureka partners, compared with two-thirds of the total sample.

23 More than 40 per cent of French-led projects include two or three partners, compared with less than 30 per cent of Italian and Dutch-led projects and about 10 per cent of German and British-led projects.

24 To illustrate, 72 per cent of German respondents led projects with six or more participants, compared with 36 per cent of non-German respondents.

25 Only 22 per cent of German respondents proposed their projects compared with 61 per cent of all others. Meanwhile, 17 per cent of German respondents cited 'expanded potential market' as a primary effect of Eureka, as opposed to 34 per cent of all others.

26 For example, one-third of German respondents said a primary effect of Eureka was to delay the start of the project compared with 17 per cent of all others, and 28 per cent reported language problems compared with 9 per cent of all others.

27 Only about one-quarter Dutch leaders suggested their governments could be more helpful by eliminating delays in funding, compared with well over half of all other respondents.

28 For example, 43 per cent of Italian respondents want more help from their national Eureka office with standards, compared with 13 per cent of all other respondents.

29 More than one-third of Italian respondents cited problems with both IPRs and the risk of exploitation by competitors as problems of Eureka, compared with 24 per cent and 13 per cent of the rest of the sample.

30 The shares of British leaders who say primary effects of Eureka are to expand their potential market and produce a prototype sooner were 70 and 60 per cent respectively, while corresponding totals for all others were 28 and 38 per cent.

31 Most British respondents (70 per cent) reported delays in their project's schedule as a problem of Eureka compared with 35 per cent of all others. Most (60 per cent) cited difficulty with administration as a primary effect of Eureka, compared with 32 per cent of all others.

32 Author's calculation based on data in Eureka cental database, November 1989.

33 Dutch chairmanship, *Report of the Eureka Assessment Panel*, p. 31.

34 *Ibid.* p. 15. It might be noted that previous surveys tended to second the asssessment panel's greater emphasis on the problem of getting projects started, as opposed to managing once they are approved. See EFMD, *Eureka: the Management of Collaboration*, p. 14; IFT Marketing Research, *Eureka Survey*, p. 32.

35 Dutch chairmanship, *The Report of the Eureka Assessment Panel*, p. 15.

36 This point was seconded by what was probably the most comprehensive survey of Eureka participants previous to the two reported in this chapter. Conducted in 1987 by the European Foundation for Management Development (EFMD), it surveyed about twenty firms and eighteen projects involving six Member States and focused on management problems related to Eureka. The study's authors stressed that the problems faced and risks taken by SMEs in Eureka were 'substantially greater than those taken by a large company'. See EFMD, *Eureka: the Management of Collaboration*, p. 14.

37 The lack of any correlation between the amount of public funding received
    and the likelihood that projects would exist without Eureka may be seen,
    for example, in the responses of the 53 per cent share of the independent
    survey sample who receive 26–50 per cent of their project's total R & D
    costs in the form of public funding. The breakdown of responses to the
    question 'would your project exist without Eureka' was: 15 per cent
    definitely; 27 per cent probably; 40 per cent unlikely; and 14 per cent
    definitely not. These percentages differ only marginally from those in Table
    6.13 for the sample as a whole.
38 Dutch chairmanship, *The Report of the Eureka Assessment Panel*, p. 32.
39 The survey collected data on participants in about half of the 127 projects
    which included French partners in 1989. See IDS Consultants, 'Audit
    opérationnel du programme Eurêka', pp. 2–3; *Nature*, 25 January 1990, p.
    300.
40 To illustrate the point, six of fourteen Italian respondents to the
    independent survey were SMEs, compared with only two of fifteen Dutch
    respondents.
41 See IFT Marketing Research, *Eureka Survey*, pp. 7, 31–4 (quote on p. 32);
    SEPSU, *European Collaboration in Science and Technology*, p. 15; Hinder,
    'Eureka: a UK perspective', pp. 67–69.
42 Dutch chairmanship, *The Report of the Eureka Assessment Panel*, p. 35.
43 *Ibid.*, p. 28.
44 *Ibid.*, pp. 15–16. Evidence that disharmonized funding procedures is
    Eureka's greatest weakness in the eyes of its participants is overwhelming.
    See IFT Marketing Research, *Eureka Survey*, p. 32; SEPSU, *European
    Collaboration in Science and Technology*, p. 15; EFMD, *Eureka: the
    Management of Collaboration*, p. 14; IDS Consultants, 'Audit Opérationnel
    du Programme Eurêka', p. 3.
45 See IDS Consultants, 'Audit opérationnel du programme Eurêka', pp. 4–5;
    IFT Consultants, *Eureka Survey*, pp. 31–4.
46 Dutch chairmanship, *The Report of the Eureka Assessment Panel*, p. 9.
47 *Ibid.*, p. 46.
48 Several previous surveys found rather clear evidence that Eureka was
    generally viewed less favourably than the EC's programmes by its industrial
    participants. See SEPSU, *European Collaboration in Science and
    Technology*, pp. 15, 18; EFMD, *Eureka: the Management of Collaboration*,
    p. 10.

7 INSIDE THE PROJECTS: CASE STUDIES

1 MITHRA is a French acronym for *Matérials Intertechnologique de Haute
   Robot Avancée*. The Eureka database lists the project title in the loose
   translation 'Mobile Robots for Remote Surveillance'.
2 Project details obtained from Eureka central project database, 5 June 1990.
3 Interview with representative of the Grenoble robotics firm, AID.
4 Interview with regional delegate to MRT, Lyon.
5 Interview with representative of Grenoble consultancy, ITT.
6 *Le Monde*, Rhône–Alpes supplement, 7 July 1987.
7 The two partners which completed survey questionnaires (and voluntary
   identified themselves) were Bossard Consultants, a consultancy firm with

no industrial or R & D activity which coordinates the project, and Société Bertin, a large French industrial group which has interests in both robotics and surveillance and security.

8 Interview with representative of AID.
9 *Ibid.*
10 Written response of representative of Bossard Consultants to survey questionnaire.
11 One partner claimed 'off the record' that the French MRT wanted Dutch and Austrian firms be brought into MITHRA when the proposal was first circulated and demurred only after several partners resisted the idea.
12 Interview with representative of AID.
13 Ironically, one of the specialties of the company became consulting other French firms on how to participate in Eureka! Interview with French Eureka official.
14 *Le Monde*, supplement Rhône–Alpes, 8 September 1987.
15 Interview with representative of AID.
16 Project details obtained from Eureka central project database, 13 December 1990.
17 Interview with British Eureka official.
18 See G.K. Wilson, *Business and Politics: A Comparative Introduction*, London, Macmillan, 2nd edition, 1990, pp. 166–7; A.F. Havighurst, *Britain in Transition: the Twentieth Century*, Chicago, University of Chicago Press, 4th edition, 1985, pp. 571–72.
19 Interview with representative of Strachan and Henshaw.
20 *Ibid.*
21 *Ibid.*
22 *Ibid.*
23 *Ibid.*
24 *Ibid.*
25 *Ibid.*
26 *Ibid.*
27 See Eurotrac International Scientific Secretariat, *Annual Report Part 1: General Report*, Garmisch-Partenkirchen, Fraunhofer Institute, 1990, pp. 6, 17; speech by Dr Wolfgang Seiler, Director of International Scientific Secretariat of Eurotrac, 6th Eureka Ministerial Conference, Copenhagen, 16 June 1988.
28 Interview with German Eureka official.
29 Eurotrac International Scientific Secretariat, *Annual Report Part 1*, p. 18.
30 Correspondence from member of Eurotrac Scientific Secretariat to the author, 31 August 1990.
31 *Ibid.*
32 Eurotrac International Scientific Secretariat, *Annual Report*, p. 21.
33 Eurotrac International Scientific Secretariat, *Eurotrac: Eureka Enviromental Project*, Garmisch-Partenkirchen, Fraunhofer Institute, 1988, p. 4
34 Eurotrac International Scientific Secretariat, *Annual Report*, p. 6.
35 See CEC, *EC Research Funding: A Guide for Applicants*, Brussels, DG XII, January 1990, pp. 59–60.
36 Eurotrac International Scientific Secretariat, *Annual Report*, pp. 7, 15, 20.
37 Fabio Pistella, Italian representative to Eureka High Level Group, quoted in D. Clery, 'The greening of Eureka', *New Scientist*, 9 June 1990, p. 38.

38 Tom Salusbury of the British DTI quoted in 'The green umbrella goes up in Britain', *Eureka News*, 8, April 1990, p. 10–11.
39 Eurotrac International Scientific Secretariat, *Annual Report*, p. 16.
40 *Ibid.*, p. 6.
41 Interview with representative of Eurotrac International Scientific Secretariat.
42 Interview with Dutch Eureka official.
43 See M. Sharp and C. Shearman, *European Technological Collaboration*, London, Routledge & Kegan Paul, 1987, pp. 54–6. The way in which the OSI model 'federates' networks based on different communications media and coding programmes is explained in *The Economist*, 20 June 1992, pp. 129–32.
44 See RARE, 'Cosine – Eureka Project 8: Final Specification Phase Overview Report', Luxembourg, CEC for Réseaux Associés pour la Recherche Européenne, 3.2.2., 1989, p. 13.
45 J. Pelkmans and A. Winters, *Europe's Domestic Market*, London, Routledge & Kegan Paul, 1988, p. 52.
46 M. Sharp, 'Review of Fast Report: the Challenges of Innovation', *Journal of Common Market Studies*, 1986, 25, p. 169.
47 The general thrust of the Commission's strategy is outlined in CEC, 'Towards a dynamic European economy: Green Paper on the development of the common market for telecommunications services and equipment', Brussels, COM (87) 290 final, 30 June 1987.
48 Interview with CEC official.
49 See P. Tindemans, 'Cosine: ready to move into implementation phase', *Computer Networks and ISDN Systems*, 1989, 17, p. 345. The author is a deputy High Level Group member for the Netherlands and Chair of the Cosine Policy Group.
50 Cosine Policy Group, 'Cosine implementation phase project proposal', CPG/89/0083, final version, Annex B, August 1989b, pp. 55–6.
51 *Ibid.*, p. 7.
52 See A. Cawson, K. Morgan, D. Webber, P. Holmes and A. Stevens, *Hostile Brothers: Competition and Closure in the European Electronics Industry*, Oxford, Clarendon Press, 1990, pp. 188–9.
53 See RARE, *RARE Information Bulletin*, 1989, 3, Amsterdam.
54 CEC, *IES News*, 1990, 28, pp. 1, pp. 13–15.
55 Cosine Policy Group, 'Project status information: Eureka project no. 8 – Cosine', Brussels, 14 June 1989, p. 5.
56 Interview with CEC official.
57 See P. Humphreys, 'The state and telecommunications modernization in Britain, France and West Germany' in U. Hilpert (ed.) *State Policies and Techno-Industrial Innovation*, London, Routledge, 1991, pp. 109–32.
58 R. Mansell and K. Morgan, 'Evolving telecommunication infrastructures: organising the new European Community marketplace' in C. Freeman, M. Sharp and W. Walker (eds) *Technology and the Future of Europe: Global Competition and the Environment in the 1990s*, London, Frances Pinter, pp. 141–45.
59 Interview with CEC official.
60 H. Ungerer with N. Costello, *Telecommunications in Europe: Free Choices for the User in Europe's 1992 Market*, CEC, Brussels, European Perspectives Series, 1988, p. 98; J. Capel, *Special Report on the Impact of*

1992 on European Industrial and Financial Markets, CEC, Brussels, September 1988, p. 18.

61 Interview with CEC official.

62 See A. Cawson, 'Interests, groups and public policy-making: the case of the European consumer electronics industry' in J. Greenwood, J. Grote and K. Ronit (eds) *Organised Interests and the European Community*, London, Sage, 1992.

63 Dutch chairmanship, *The Report of the Eureka Assessment Panel*, The Hague, 1991, pp. 6–7.

64 A lucid and comprehensible discussion of the interaction of the technical and political in the development of CTV is Cawson *et al.*, *Hostile Brothers*, pp. 223–7; 331–2.

65 *Ibid.*, p. 321.

66 See Eureka secretariat, 'HDTV: the standard approaches', *Eureka News*, 13, 1991, pp. 10–11; M. Carpentier, 'High Definition Television: Its Impact on the European Information Technologies Sector', paper presented at European Forum Seminar, Brussels, 22 September 1989.

67 See CEC, 'Towards a large European audio-visual market,' *European File*, 1988, Brussels, 4, February, pp. 2–4.

68 The HDTV project has ten different 'project groups', with Thomson and Philips each leading two. Details of each project group are included in Eureka HDTV Directorate, *A Challenge Born in Europe: To Reach HDTV in a Compatible World*, Eindhoven, 1988, pp. 1–31. A complete list of all project participants is contained in Eureka HDTV Directorate, *HDTV Report*, 1990, Eindhoven, 2, p. 12.

69 Cawson *et al.*, *Hostile Brothers*, p. 322; G.C Lodge, *Comparing Business-Government Relations*, Englewood Cliffs NJ, Prentice Hall, 1990, p. 350; *Financial Times*, 15 May 1990.

70 Cawson *et al.*, *Hostile Brothers*, p. 323.

71 Interview with representative of Eureka HDTV Directorate.

72 See CEC, *Official Journal of the European Communities*, 1989, Brussels, OJ L 363, 13 December; CEC, *Innovation and Technology Transfer*, 1989, 9, p. 4; *Agence Europe*, 5128, 9 November 1989, p. 6.

73 Interview with representative of Philips consumer electronics division.

74 See K. Dyson, 'The nature and relevance of state policy for techno-industrial innovation' in U. Hilpert (ed.) *State Policies and Techno-Industrial Innovation*, London, Routledge, 1991, pp. 43–8; CEC, 'Towards a large European audio-visual market,' pp. 2–4.

75 See interview with Mitterrand in *The Independent*, 27 July 1989.

76 *Agence Europe*, 5753, 19 June 1992, p. 15.

77 See *Agence Europe*, 5106, 7 October 1989, p. 13.

78 Cawson *et al.*, *Hostile Brothers*, pp. 328–9.

79 Eureka HDTV Secretariat, *HDTV Report*, 1990, Eindhoven, 2, June, p. 12.

80 Interview with representative of Philips consumer electronics division.

81 The Italian consortium, *Consorzio Italiano per lo Sviluppo della televisione ad Alta definizione Europea* (CISAE), contains seven Italian companies doing R & D on HDTV equipment. Eureka HDTV Directorate, *HDTV Report*, p. 4; interview with secretary of HDTV directorate.

82 *New Scientist*, 29 June 1991; 3 Feburary 1990; Cawson *et al.*, *Hostile Brothers*, p. 331–2.

83 Philips chairman Jan Timmer quoted in *Financial Times*, 15 May 1990. See also *The Independent*, 2 February 1991; 1 March 1991.
84 See *The Economist*, 13 April 1991, p. 4; Lodge, *Comparative Business-Government Relations*, p. 340.
85 Quoted in Eureka secretariat, 'Jessi has got what it takes to succeed,' *Eureka News*, 11, January 1991, p. 5.
86 *New Scientist*, 7 November 1991; 28 November 1991.
87 US Congress Office of Technology Assessment, *The Big Picture: HDTV and High Resolution Systems*, Washington DC, USGPO, OTA BP CIT 64, June 1990, p. 7.
88 Eureka secretariat, 'HDTV: the standard approaches', p. 11; Dutch chairmanship, 'HDTV related supportive measures: draft recommendations', The Hague, Eureka Document 9 MC-4, rev 1, 19 June 1991, p. 4.
89 *New Scientist*, 7 September 1991; 28 October 1989.
90 US OTA, *The Big Picture*, pp. 7–8; T.A. Watkins, 'A technological communications costs model of R & D consortia as public policy', *Research Policy*, April 1991, 20, p. 101; B.R. Inman and D.F. Burton, 'Technology and Competitiveness: the New Policy Frontier', *Foreign Affairs*, Spring 1990, pp. 124–6; J.S. Yudken and M. Black, 'Targeting National Needs: A New Direction for Science and Technology Policy', *World Policy Journal*, 1990, 8, pp. 251–4.
91 See Eureka HDTV Directorate, *High-Definition Television Update* (Eindhoven), Summer 1988; Eureka secretariat, 'The unknown factor', *Eureka News*, 3, January 1989, p. 8.
92 See *The Economist*, 23 February 1991.
93 See Cawson, 'Interests, groups and public policy-making', p. 116.
94 *New Scientist*, 15 June 1991; *The Economist*, 11 May 1991.
95 *New Scientist*, 7 September 1991.
96 Report of EC HDTV Working Group quoted in *New Scientist*, 15 June 1991.
97 Quoted in *Agence Europe*, 5611, 18–19 November 1991, p. 12.
98 *New Scientist*, 11 January 1992.
99 Interview with Dutch Eureka official.
100 *Agence Europe*, 5751, 17 June 1992, p. 12.
101 The UK Secretary of State for Telecommunications, Edward Leigh, quoted in *Agence Europe*, 5750, 15–16 June 1992, p. 11. Later developments, including the Commission's decision to abandon the proposal and thus accept the 'death' of the Eureka HDTV project in early 1993, are covered in J. Peterson, 'Towards a common European industrial policy? The case of high definition television', *Government and Opposition*, 28, 3, 1993.
102 See for example speech by P.W. Bögels, Chairman of HDTV Directorate, Eureka Conference of Ministers, Copenhagen, 16 June 1988.
103 Eureka Secretariat, 'Evolution not revolution', *Eureka News*, 3, January 1990, p. 6.
104 Finnish chairmanship, *Report of EU 95/HDTV Supportive Measures*, Tampere, 22 May 1992.
105 *Ibid.*, p. 14.
106 Interview with representative of Eureka HDTV Directorate.
107 Interview with representative of AID.

108 The number of firms who participate in Famos has grown exponentially since it was first formed and numerous protagonists in Famos claim that it now encompasses a far more diverse array of firms than when it first was launched. Numerous interviews with Eureka officials and industrialists involved in Famos.

109 Interview with member of Eurotrac scientific secretariat.

110 See D. Vogel, *National Styles of Regulation: Environmental Policing in Great Britain and the United States*, Ithaca NY, Cornell University Press, 1986.

111 Interview with representative of Eurotrac scientific secretariat.

8 CONCLUSION

1 See P.A. Hall, 'The state and the market' in P.A. Hall, J. Hayward and H. Machin (eds) *Developments in French Politics*, London, Macmillan, 1990, pp. 185–7; M. Giles, 'Second thoughts: a survey of business in Europe', *The Economist*, 8 June 1991.

2 Eureka secretariat, 'Declaration of Principles relating to Eureka adopted at Hanover, 6 November 1985', Brussels, p. 3.

3 Interviews with CEC officials in DGs IV and XIII which, coincidentally, were both conducted in one afternoon.

4 A. Cawson, 'Interests, groups and public policy-making: the case of the European consumer electronics industry' in J. Greenwood, J. Grote and K. Ronit (eds) *Organised Interests and the European Community*, London, Sage, 1992, p. 116.

5 G. Dosi, K. Pavitt and L. Soete, *The Economics of Technical Change and International Trade*, London, Harvester Wheatsheaf, 1990, p. 11.

6 M. Sharp and C. Shearman, *European Technological Collaboration*, London, Routledge & Kegan Paul, Chatham House Paper 36, 1987, p. 102.

7 P. Cerny, 'The limits of deregulation: transnational interpenetration and policy change', *European Journal of Political Research*, 1991, 19, p. 182 (emphasis in original).

8 A. Cawson, K. Morgan, D. Webber, P. Holmes and A. Stevens, *Hostile Brothers: Competition and Closure in the European Electronics Industry*, Oxford, Clarendon Press, 1990, chapters 1 and 2.

9 See M. Sharp, 'The single market and European technology policies' in C. Freeman, M. Sharp and W. Walker (eds) *Technology and the Future of Europe: Global Competition and the Environment in the 1990s*, London, Frances Pinter, 1991, pp. 59–76; M. Sharp, 'Tides of change: the world economy and Europe in 1992', *International Affairs*, 1992, 68, pp. 17–35.

10 G. Dosi *et al.*, *The Economics of Technical Change*, p. 267..

11 See A. Shonfield, *Modern Capitalism*, Oxford, Oxford University Press, 1965; C. Crouch, *The Politics of Industrial Relations*, London, Fontana, 1982.

12 A. Cawson, 'Varieties of corporatism: the importance of the meso-level of interest intermediation' in A. Cawson (ed.) *Organized Interests and the State: Studies in Meso-Corporatism*, London, Sage, 1985, p. 5. See also A. Cawson and P. Saunders, 'Corporatism, competitive policies, and class struggle' in R. King (ed.) *Capital and Politics* London, Routledge & Kegan Paul, 1983.

13 Cawson, 'Varieties of corporatism', p. 11.
14 U. Hilpert, 'The state, science and techno-industrial innovation: a new model of state policy and a changing role of the state' in U. Hilpert (ed.) *State Policies and Techno-Industrial Innovation*, London, Routledge, 1991, p. 4.
15 Cawson *et al.*, *Hostile Brothers*, p. 358.
16 *Ibid.*, p. 358.
17 I am grateful to Wayne Sandholtz for suggesting this typology to me.
18 See E. Nordlinger, *The Autonomy of the Democratic State*, Cambridge MA, Harvard University Press, 1981, pp. 171–2; A. Diamant, 'Bureaucracy and public policy in neocorporatist settings', *Comparative Politics*, 1981, 14, pp. 101–24; P. Dunleavy and B. O'Leary, *Theories of the State: the Politics of Liberal Democracy*, London, Macmillan, 1987, pp. 195–7.
19 Interview with member of Eureka secretariat.
20 M. Hilf, 'PGOs and the European Community' in C. Hood and G.F. Shuppert (eds) *Delivering Public Services in Western Europe: Sharing Western European Experiences of Para-Government Organization*, London, Sage, p. 221.
21 See G.C. Lodge, *Comparative Business-Government Relations*, Englewood Cliffs NJ, Prentice Hall, 1990, pp. 17–23; A. Gamble, *The Free Economy and the Strong State: the Politics of Thatcherism*, London, Macmillan, 1988; D. Lam, 'Evaluating the strong state thesis: the origins of electronics manufacturing in Taiwan', paper presented to the annual meeting of Western Political Science Association, 23 March 1991.
22 R. Paletto quoted in *Eureka News*, 11, January 1991, p. 5.
23 A. Coghlan, 'Europe slams door on 'Japanese Company'', *New Scientist*, 6 April 1991, p. 9. See also M. Fagan, 'Unravelling the ICL conundrum', *The Independent*, 20 May 1991; W. Münchau, 'Nokia sale to ICL boosts Japan's hold on computers', *The Times*, 30 May 1991; 'Spare the rod and spoil the child', *The Economist*, 20 April 1991.
24 Interview with representative of ICL.
25 Cawson, 'Interests, groups and public policy-making'; Cawson *et al.*, *Hostile Brothers*, pp. 355–6.
26 See for example J.K. Benson, 'A framework for policy analysis' in D. Rogers, D. Whitten and associates (eds) *Interorganizational Coordination*, Ames IA, Iowa State University Press, 1982, pp. 161–76; R.A.W. Rhodes, 'Policy networks: a British perspective', *Journal of Theoretical Politics*, 1990, 2, pp. 296–301.
27 V. Schneider and R. Werle, 'Networks and concertation in European policy making: the cases of chemicals control and telecommunications', paper presented at the joint sessions of the European Consortium for Political Research,, Limerick, 30 March-4 April 1992, p. 19.
28 Cawson, 'Interests, groups and public policy-making'.
29 Interview with UK Eureka official.
30 See CEC, *Value: Community Programme for the Diffusion and Utilization of Scientific and Technological Results*, Luxembourg, 1991.
31 Dutch chairmanship, *The Report of the Eureka Assessment Panel*, The Hague, 1991, p. 18.
32 Quoted in D. MacKenize, 'Delors to push science funds into arms of commerce', *New Scientist*, 8 February 1992, p. 16.
33 Pandolfi quoted in *Agence Europe*, 5751, 17 June 1992, p. 12.

34 Dutch chairmanship, *X-Ray Sessions: Final Report*, The Hague, 1991, p. 39.

35 Dutch chairmanship, *Eureka and Supportive Measures*, The Hague, document NPC-9067, 1991, p. 5.

36 Dutch chairmanship, *Report of the Eureka Assessment Panel*, pp. 42–3.

37 Dutch chairmanship, *X-Ray Sessions*, p. 9.

38 *Ibid.*, p. 9.

39 Dutch chairmanship, *Umbrella Projects*, The Hague, document NPC-9066, 1991, p. 3.

40 Interviews with numerous Eureka officials, in which the Eurocare and Euromar umbrella projects were mentioned most often in this context.

41 Dutch chairmanship, *Umbrella Projects*, p. 5.

42 *Ibid.*, p 5.

43 Dutch chairmanship, *X-Ray Sessions*, p. 5.

44 Dutch chairmanship, *Report of the Eureka Assessment Panel*, p. 7.

45 Dutch chairmanship, *X-Ray Sessions*, pp. 9, 38.

46 F. Prakke, 'The financing of technological innovation' in A. Heertje (ed.) *Innovation, Technology and Finance*, Oxford, Basil Blackwell for European Investment Bank, 1988, p. 95.

47 See M. Lampola and S. Gstöhl, 'A dynamic Europe needs wide R & D co-operation', *EFTA Bulletin*, 1990, 4, pp. 21–4.

48 Dutch chairmanship, *Report of the Eureka Assessment Panel*, p. 8.

49 Cawson *et al.*, *Hostile Brothers*, p. 363.

50 This paraphrases comments made by a member of the Austrian delegation during a question and answer session which followed the author's presentation.

51 Dutch chairmanship, *X-Ray Sessions: Final Report*, p. 38.

52 In particular, the French took the lead on this initiative after the 1989 IDS survey recommended that project approval and funding decisions should be synchronized. An interministerial committee chaired by Curien unveiled a series of new measures in early 1990 which included strengthening ANVAR's role in coordinating multinational funding commitments. The French then approached a range of other Member States about synchronizing their approval and funding procedures with those of France for a one-year trial period. See IDS Consultants, 'Audit opérationnel du programme Eurêka: point clés de la synthèse', Levallois, 1989, pp. 4–5; P. Coles, 'Still a step from 'Eureka'', *Nature*, 25 January 1990, p. 300.

Bibliography

GENERAL WORKS

Acs, Z.J. and Audretsch, D.B., 'Innovation in large and small firms: an empirical analysis', *American Economic Review*, 1988, 78: 678–90.

Aigrain, P., Allen, G., de Arantes e Oliveira, E., Colombo, U. and Markl, H., *The Report of the Framework Review Board*, Brussels, June 1989.

Aubert, J., 'Innovation policies: a three way contrast', *OECD Observer*, 1984, 131: 6–11.

Aujac, H., 'An introduction to French industrial policy' in W.J. Adams and C. Stoffaës (eds) *French Industrial Policy*, Washington DC, Brookings Institution, 1986.

Balassa, B., *The Theory of Economic Integration*, London, Allen & Unwin, 1961.

Barber, J., Metcalfe S. and Porteous, M., (eds), *Barriers to Growth in Small Firms*, London, Routledge, 1989.

Benson, J.A., 'A framework for policy analysis' in D. Rogers, D. Whitten and associates (eds) *Interorganizational Coordination*, Ames, Iowa State University Press, 1982.

Berger, P., *The Capitalist Revolution*, Aldershot, Gower, 1987.

Bluth, C., 'SDI: the challenge to West Germany', *International Affairs*, 1986, 62: 247–64.

Braillard, P. and Demant, A., *Eurêka et l'Europe Technologique*, Brussels, Emile Bruylant, 1991.

Brewin, C. and McAllister, R., 'Annual review of the activities of the European Community in 1989', *Journal of Common Market Studies*, 1990, 28: 451–96.

Brown, M. and Conrad, A.H., 'The influence of research and CES production relations' in M. Brown (ed.) *The Theory and Empirical Analysis of Production*, New York, Columbia University Press, 1967.

Bulmer, S. and Paterson, W. *The Federal Republic of Germany and the European Community*, London, Allen & Unwin, 1987.

Butterworths European Information Services, *Butterworths Guide to the European Communities*, London, Butterworths, 1989.

Cabanelm, G., 'Le programme Eurêka', *Sénat no. 387 Tome 2*, France, 1985.

Cadiou, J.M., 'Esprit: un premier bilan', *Bulletin de Liasion de la Recherche en Informatique et Automatique*, 1986, 105: 3–6.

Capel, J., *Special Report on the Impact of 1992 on European Industrial and Financial Markets*, Brussels, Commission of the European Communities, September 1988.

Carpentier, M., 'High Definition Television: its impact on the European information technologies sector,' paper presented at European Forum Seminar, Brussels, 22 September 1989.

Carton, A., 'Eureka: a west European response to the technological challenge posed the the SDI research programme' in H.G. Brauch (ed.) *Star Wars and European Defence*, New York, St. Martin's Press, 1987.

Cawson, A. and Saunders, P., 'Corporatism, competitive policies, and class struggle' in R. King (ed.) *Capital and Politics*, London, Routledge & Kegan Paul, 1983.

Cawson, A. 'Varieties of corporatism: the importance of the meso-level of interest intermediation' in A. Cawson (ed.) *Organized Interests and the State: Studies in Meso-Corporatism*, London, Sage, 1985.

A. Cawson, K. Morgan, D. Webber, P. Holmes and A. Stevens, *Hostile Brothers: Competition and Closure in the European Electronics Industry*, Oxford, Clarendon Press, 1990.

Cawson, A. and Holmes, P., 'The new consumer electronics' in C. Freeman, M. Sharp and W. Walker (eds) *Technology and the Future of Europe: Global Competition and the Environment in the 1990s*, London, Frances Pinter, 1991.

Cawson, A., 'Interests, groups and public policy-making: the case of the European consumer electronics industry' in J. Greenwood, J. Grote and K. Ronit (eds) *Organised Interests and the European Community*, London, Sage, 1992.

Cecchini, P. with Catinat, M. and Jacquemin, A., *The European Challenge 1992: the Benefits of a Single Market*, Aldershot, Wildwood House, 1988.

Cerny, P., *The Changing Architecture of Politics: Structure, Agency, and the Future of the State*, London, Sage, 1990.

Cerny, P., 'The limits of deregulation: transnational interpenetration and policy change', *European Journal of Political Research*, 1991, 19: 173–96.

Chandler, A.D., *Scale and Scope: the Dynamics of Industrial Capitalism*, Cambridge MA, Harvard University Press, 1990.

Cohen, S., Teece, D., Tyson, L. and Zysman, J., 'Competitiveness', *BRIE Working Papers*, 8, 1984.

Cohen, S. and Zysman, J., 'Manufacturing innovation and industrial competitiveness' in U. Hilpert (ed.) *State Policies and Techno-Industrial Innovation*, London, Routledge, 1991.

Contzen, J.P., 'The European Community's strategy in science and technology' in M. Smith (ed.) *Technological Change and United States–European Community Relations: Challenges and Responses*, London, University Association for Contemporary European Studies, 1985.

Crouch, C., *The Politics of Industrial Relations*, London, Fontana, 1982.

Danzin, A., 'La Communauté et le défi de la recherche scientifique et technique', *Journal of European Integration*, 1988, 11: 91–106.

Dasgupta, P., 'The theory of technological competition' in D. Encacoua, P. Geroski and A. Jacquemin (eds) *New Developments in the Analysis of Market Structures*, London, Macmillan, 1986.

de Bandt, J., 'French industrial policies: successes and failures' in P.R. Beije, J. Groenewegen, I. Kostoulas, J. Paelinck and C. van Paridon (eds) *A Competitive Future for Europe? Towards a New European Industrial Policy*, London, Croom Helm, 1987

266   *High Technology and the Competition State*

Defraigne, P., 'Towards concerted industrial policies in the EC' in A. Jacquemin (ed.) *European Industry: Public Policy and Corporate Strategy*, Oxford, Clarendon Press, 1984.
Deubner, C., 'The expansion of West German capital and the founding of Euratom', *International Organization*, 1979, 33: 203–28.
Deubner, C., 'Eureka zwischen nationalen Technologiepolitiken und Europa', *Vierteljahres Berichte*, 1987, 109: 217–29.
Diamant, A. 'Bureaucracy and public policy in neocorporatist settings', *Comparative Politics*, 1981, 14: 101–24.
Dorfman, N.S., *Innovation and Market Structure: Lessons from the Computer and Semiconductor Industries*, Cambridge MA, Ballinger, 1987.
Dosi, G., Pavitt, K. and Soete, L., *The Economics of Technical Change and International Trade*, London, Harvester Wheatsheaf, 1990.
Duchêne, F., 'Policies for a wider world' in F. Duchêne and G. Shepherd (eds) *Managing Industrial Change in Western Europe*, London, Frances Pinter, 1987.
Duchêne F. and Shepherd, G., 'Sources of industrial policy' in F. Duchêne and G. Shepherd (eds) *Managing Industrial Change in Western Europe*, London, Frances Pinter, 1987.
Duff, A.N., 'Eureka and the new technology policy of the European Community', *Policy Studies*, 1986, 6: 44–61.
Dunleavy P. and O'Leary, B., *Theories of the State: the Politics of Liberal Democracy*, London, Macmillan, 1987.
Dyson, K., 'The nature and relevance of state policy for techno-industrial innovation' in U. Hilpert (ed.) *State Policies and Techno-Industrial Innovation*, London, Routledge, 1991.
Edgerton, D. and Hughes, K., 'The poverty of science: a critical analysis of science and industrial policy under Mrs. Thatcher', *Public Administration*, 1989, 67: 419–33.
Elliot, R.F. and Wood, P., *The International Transfer of Technology and Western European Integration*, University of Aberdeen, Department of Political Economy, occasional paper 79–07, 1987.
English, M., 'The European information technology industry' in A. Jacquemin (ed.) *European Industry: Public Policy and Corporate Strategy*, Oxford, Clarendon Press, 1984.
European Foundation for Management Development, *Eureka: the Management of Collaboration*, Brussels, 1987.
EVCA, *Venture Consort: Innovation Finance Scheme*, Zaventem, 1990.
Faulkner, W. and Orsenigo, L., 'Government policies for techno-industrial innovation in weaker economies: the case of biotechnology in the United Kingdom and Italy' in U. Hilpert (ed.) *State Policies and Techno-Industrial Innovation*, London, Routledge, 1991.
Feldman, E.J., *Concorde and Dissent*, Cambridge, Cambridge University Press, 1985.
Fennell, R., 'Reform of the CAP: shadow or substance?', *Journal of Common Market Studies*, 1987, 26: 61–77.
Fenske, J., 'France and the Strategic Defense Initiative: speeding up or putting on the brakes?', *International Affairs*, 1986, 62: 231–46.
Flamm, K., 'Semiconductors' in G.C. Hufbauer (ed.) *Europe 1992: An American Perspective*, Washington DC, Brookings Institution, 1990.

Franzmeyer, F., *Approaches to Industrial Policy within the EC and its Impact on European Integration*, Aldershot, Gower, 1982.

Freeman, C., *The Economics of Industrial Innovation*, 2nd edition, London, Frances Pinter, 1982.

Freeman, C., *Technology Policy and Economic Peformance: Lessons From Japan*, London, Frances Pinter, 1987.

Freeman, C., 'Diffusion: the spread of new technology to firms, sectors and nations' in A. Heertje (ed.) *Innovation, Technology and Finance*, Oxford, Basil Blackwell for the European Investment Bank, 1988.

Freeman, C. and L.L.G., Soete, *Technological Change and Full Employment*, Oxford, Basil Blackwell, 1987.

Friebe, K.P., 'Industrial policy in the Federal Republic of Germany' in K.P. Friebe and A. Gerybadze (eds) *Microelectronics in Western Europe*, Berlin, Erich Schmidt Verlag, 1984.

Friedman, D., 'Beyond the age of Ford: the strategic basis of Japanese success in automobiles' in J. Zysman and L. Tyson (eds) *American Industry in International Competition*, Ithaca NY, Cornell University Press, 1983.

Gamble, A., *The Free Economy and the Strong State: the Politics of Thatcherism*, London, Macmillan, 1988.

Garnham, D., *The Politics of European Defense Cooperaiton: Germany, France, Britain and America*, Cambridge MA, Ballinger, 1988.

George, S., *An Awkward Partner: Britain in the European Community*, Oxford, Oxford University Press, 1990.

George, S., *Politics and Policy in the European Community*, Oxford, Oxford University Press, 2nd edition, 1991

Geroski, P. and Jacquemin, A., 'Industrial change, barriers to mobility and European industrial policy', *Economic Policy*, 1987, 1: 170–218.

Gilchrist, J. and Deacon, D., 'Curbing subsidies' in P. Montagnon (ed.) *European Competition Policy*, London, Frances Pinter for the Royal Institute of International Affairs, 1990.

Gilpin, R., 'Science, technology and French independence' in T.D. Long and C. Wright (eds) *Science Policies of Industrial Nations*, New York, Praeger Publishers, 1975.

Gilpin, R., *The Political Economy of International Relations*, Princeton, Princeton University Press, 1987.

Grant, W., Paterson, W. and Whitson, C., *Government and the Chemical Industry: A Comparative Study of Britain and West Germany*, Oxford, Clarendon Press, 1987.

Graves, A.P., 'Globalisation of the automobile industry: the challenge for Europe' in C. Freeman, M. Sharp and W. Walker (eds.) *Technology and the Future of Europe: Global Competition and the Environment in the 1990s*, London, Frances Pinter, 1991.

Grewlich, K.W., 'EUREKA – eureka?', *Aussenpolitick*, 1986, 37: 24–36.

Haas, E., *The Uniting of Europe*, Palo Alto CA, Stanford University Press, 1958.

Haas, E., 'The study of regional integration' in L. Lindberg and S. Sheingold (eds) *Regional Integration Theory and Research*, Cambridge MA, Harvard University Press, 1971.

Haas, E., *The Obsolescence of Regional Integration Theory*, Berkeley, University of California Press, 1975.

Hagedoorn, J. and Prakke, F., *Barriers to Innovation: the Netherlands*, Delft, TNO Staffgroup Strategic Surveys, 1980.

Hagedoorn, J. and Schakenraad, J., 'Inter-firm partnerships and co-operative strategies in core technologies' in C. Freeman and L. Soete (eds) *New Explorations in the Economics of Technical Change*, London, Frances Pinter, 1990.

Håkansson, H., *Industrial Technological Development*, London, Croom Helm, 1987.

Hall, P., *Great Planning Disasters*, Harmondsworth, Penguin Books, 1980.

Hall, P., *Governing the Economy: the Politics of State Intervention in Britain and France*, Cambridge, Polity Press, 1986.

Hall, P.A., 'The state and the market' in P.A. Hall, J. Hayward and H. Machin (eds) *Developments in French Politics*, London, Macmillan, 1990.

Havighurst, A.F., *Britain in Transition: the Twentieth Century*, Chicago, University of Chicago Press, 4th edition, 1985.

Hayward, J., *The State and the Market Economy: Industrial Patriotism and Economic Intervention in France*, Brighton, Wheatsheaf, 1986.

Hayward, K., 'Airbus: twenty years of European collaboration', *International Affairs*, 1988, 64: 11–26.

Heclo, H., 'Issue networks and the executive establishment' in A. King (ed.) *The New American Political System*, Washington DC, American Enterprise Institute, 1978.

Heertje, A., 'Can we explain technical change?', in S. MacDonald, D. McL. Lamberton, and T. Mandeville (eds) *The Trouble with Technology: Explorations in the Process of Technological Change*, London, Frances Pinter, 1983.

Heilbroner, R. L., *The Worldly Philosophers*, New York, Touchstone/Simon & Schuster, 6th edition, 1986.

Hermant, C., Moatti, J.P., Rolle, P. and Barchechath, E., 'Public acceptance of new technologies: France' in R. Williams and S. Mills (eds) *Public Acceptance of New Technologies: An International Review*, London, Croom Helm, 1986.

Hilf, M., 'PGOs and the European Community' in C. Hood and G.F. Shuppert (eds) *Delivering Public Services in Western Europe: Sharing Western European Experiences of Para-Government Organization*, London, Sage, 1988.

Hilpert, U., 'Economic adjustment by techno-industrial innovation and the role of the state' in U. Hilpert (ed.) *State Policies and Techno-Industrial Innovation*, London, Routledge, 1991.

Hilpert, U., 'The state, science and techno-industrial innovation: a new model of state policy and a changing role of the state' in U. Hilpert (ed.) *State Policies and Techno-Industrial Innovation*, London, Routledge, 1991.

Hinder, S., 'Eureka: a UK perspective', unpublished M.Phil. thesis, University of Manchester, 1987.

Hobday, M., 'The European semiconductor industry: resurgence and rationalization', *Journal of Common Market Studies*, 1989, 28: 155–86.

Hodges, M., 'Industrial policy: hard times or great expectations?' in H. Wallace, W. Wallace and C. Webb (eds) *Policy-Making in the European Community*, Chichester, John Wiley & Sons, 2nd edition, 1983.

Hoffmann, S., 'Obstinate or obsolete? The fate of the nation-state and the case of western Europe', *Daedalus*, 1966, 95: 862–915.

Holmes, P., 'Broken dreams: economic policies in Mitterrand's France' in S. Mazey and M. Newman (eds) *Mitterrand's France*, London, Croom Helm, 1987.

Hood, C., *The Tools of Government*, London, Macmillan, 1983.

Hood, C. and Shuppert, G.F., 'The study of para-government organisations' in C. Hood and G.F. Shuppert (eds) *Delivering Public Services in Western Europe: Sharing Western European Experiences of Para-Government Organization*, London, Sage, 1988.

Horn, E.J., 'Germany: a market-led process' in F. Duchêne and G. Shepherd (eds) *Managing Industrial Change in Western Europe*, London, Frances Pinter, 1987.

Howell, T.R., Noellert, W.A., MacLaughlin, J.H. and Wolff, A.W., *The Microelectronics Race: the Impact of Government Policy on International Competition*, Boulder CO, Westview Press, 1988.

Humphreys, P., 'The state and telecommunications modernization in Britain, France and West Germany' in U. Hilpert (ed.) *State Policies and Techno-Industrial Innovation*, London, Routledge, 1991.

IDS Consultants, 'Audit opérationnel du programme Eurêka en France: point clés de la synthèse', Levallois, 1989.

Inman, B.R. and Burton, D.F., 'Technology and competitiveness: the new policy frontier', *Foreign Affairs*, 1990, Spring: 116–34.

Jacobsson, S., Jamison, A. and Rothman, H. (eds), *The Biotechnological Challenge*, Cambridge, Cambridge University Press, 1986.

Jacquemin, A. and DeJong, H., *European Industrial Organizations*, London, Macmillan, 1977.

Jacquemin, A., *Collusive Behavior, R & D and European Policy*, Brussels, Commission of the European Communities, EC Economic Paper 61, 1987.

Jaikumur, R., 'Post-industrial manufacturing', *Harvard Business Review*, 1986, 64: 69–76.

Jessop, B., *The Capitalist State*, Oxford, Martin Robinson, 1982.

Jessop, B., 'Neo-conservative regimes and the transition to post-Fordism: the cases of Great Britain and West Germany' in M. Gottdiener and N. Komninos (eds) *Modern Capitalism and Spatial Development: Accumulation, Regulation and Crisis Theory*, London, Macmillan, 1989.

Jessop, B., *State Theory: Putting Capitalist States in Their Place*, Cambridge, Polity Press, 1990.

Jessop, B., 'Thatcherism: the British road to post-Fordism?', *Essex Papers in Politics and Government*, 1990, 68.

Kahler, M., 'The United States and Western Europe: the diplomatic consequences of Mr. Reagan', in K.A. Oye, R.J. Lieber and D. Rothchild (eds) *Eagle Resurgent? The Reagan Era in American Foreign Policy*, Boston, Little Brown & Company, 1987.

Katzenstein, P., *Small States in World Markets*, Ithaca NY, Cornell University Press, 1985.

Kay, N., 'Industrial collaborative activity and the completion of the internal market', *Journal of Common Market Studies*, 1991, 28: 347–62.

Keliher, L., 'Policy-Making in information technology: a decisional analysis of the Alvey project', unpublished Ph.D. thesis, London School of Economics, 1987.

Kenney, M. and Florida, R., 'Beyond mass production: production and the labour process in Japan', *Politics and Society*, 1988, 16: 121–58.

Keohane, R., *After Hegemony: Cooperation and Discord in the World Political Economy*, Princeton NJ, Princeton University Press, 1984.

Keohane R. and Nye, J., *Power and Interdependence: World Politics in Transition*, Boston, Little & Brown, 1977.

Keohane, R. and Hoffmann, S., 'Institutional change in Europe in the 1980s' in R. Keohane and S. Hoffmann (eds) *The New European Community: Decisionmaking and Institutional Change*, Boulder CO and London, Westview Press, 1991.

King, A., 'The problem of overload' in A. King (ed.) *Why is Britain Becoming Harder to Govern?*, London, BBC, 1975.

Kirzner, I.M., *Discovery and the Capitalist Process*, Chicago, University of Chicago Press, 1985.

Kline, S.J. and Rosenburg, N., 'An overview of innovation' in R. Landau and N. Rosenburg (eds) *The Positive-Sum Strategy: Harnessing Technology for Economic Growth*, Washington DC, National Academy Press, 1986.

Knight, G., *Concorde: The Inside Story*, London, Weidenfeld & Nicolson, 1976.

Lampola, M. and Gstöhl, S., 'A dynamic Europe needs wide R&D co-operation', *EFTA Bulletin*, 1990, 4: 21–4.

LAREA/CEREM, *Les Strategies d'Accordes des Groupes Européennes: Entre La Cohesion et l'Eclatement*, Nanterre, Université de Paris X, 1985.

Laurent, P.H., 'Eureka, or the technological renaissance of Europe', *The Washington Quarterly*, 1987, 10: 55–66.

Laursen, F., 'The Community's policy towards EFTA: regime formation in the European Economic Space', *Journal of Common Market Studies*, 1990, 28: 327–58.

Lellouche, P., 'Thinking about the unthinkable: guidelines for a Euro-Defense concept' in J. Alford and K. Hunt (eds) *Europe in the Western Alliance*, London, Macmillan, 1988.

Lesourne, J., 'The changing context of industrial policy: external and internal developments' in A. Jacquemin (ed.) *European Industry: Public Policy and Corporate Strategy*, Oxford, Clarendon Press, 1984.

Levinsen, J. and Kristensen, P.H., *Small Country Squeeze*, Copenhagen, Forlaget fur Samfunds-konomi og Planlaegning, 1983.

Locksley, G. and Ward, T., 'Concentration in manufacturing in the EEC', *Cambridge Journal of Economics*, 1979, 3: 91–7.

Lodge, G.C., *Comparative Business–Government Relations*, Englewood Cliffs NJ, Prentice Hall, 1990.

Machin, H. and Wright, V. (eds), *Economic Policy and Policy-Making under the Mitterrand Presidency 1981–84*, London, Frances Pinter, 1985.

Mansell, R. and Morgan, K., 'Evolving telecommunication infrastructures: organising the new European Community marketplace' in C. Freeman, M. Sharp and W. Walker (eds) *Technology and the Future of Europe: Global Competition and the Environment in the 1990s*, London, Frances Pinter, 1991.

Mansfield, E., 'Rates of return from industrial research and development', *American Economic Review*, 1965, 55: 310–22.

Marcum, J.M., 'The technology gap: Europe at a crossroads', *Issues in Science and Technology*, 1986, Summer: 28–37.

Marsh, D. and Rhodes, R.A.W. (eds) *Policy Networks in British Government*, Oxford, Oxford University Press, 1992.

Marsh, D. and Rhodes, R.A.W., 'Policy communities and issue networks: beyond typology' in D. Marsh and R.A.W. Rhodes (eds) *Policy Networks in British Government*, Oxford, Clarendon Press, 1992.

T. Matsuo, 'Japanese R & D policy for techno-industrial innovation' in U. Hilpert (ed.) *State Policies and Techno-Industrial Innovation*, London, Routledge, 1991.

May, A., 'Concorde – bird of harmony or political albatross: an examination in the context of British foreign policy', *International Organization*, 1979, 33: 481–508.

Merrit, R.L. and Merrit, A.J. (eds), *Innovation in the Public Sector*, London, Sage, 1985.

Messerlin, P., 'France: the ambitious state' in F. Duchêne and G. Shepherd (eds) *Managing Industrial Change in Western Europe*, London, Frances Pinter, 1987.

Meyer, F., *International Trade Policy*, London, Croom Helm, 1978.

Minasian, J., 'Research and development, production functions, and rates of return', *American Economic Review*, 1969, 59: 80–5.

Moravcsik, A., 'Negotiating the Single European Act: national interests and conventional statecraft in the European Community', 1991, *International Organization*, 45: 651–88.

Mowery, G.C. and Rosenberg, N., *Technology and the Pursuit of Economic Growth*, Cambridge and New York, Cambridge University Press, 1989.

Mytelka, L.K. and Delapierre, M., 'The alliance strategies of European firms in the information technology industry', *Journal of Common Market Studies*, 1987, 26: 231–53.

Napolitano, G., 'European technological co-operation: the Italian participation in Eureka', *Science and Public Policy*, 1988, 15: 376–82.

Nell, P.G., 'EFTA in the 1990s: the search for a new identity', *Journal of Common Market Studies*, 1990, 28: 327–58.

Nelson, R., *High-Technology Policies: A Five-Nation Comparison*, Washington DC, American Enterprise Institute for Public Policy Research, 1984.

Nordlinger, E., *The Autonomy of the Democratic State*, Cambridge MA, Harvard University Press, 1981.

Oakey, R., *High Technology Small Firms: Regional Development in Britain and the United States*, London, Frances Pinter, 1984.

Oakley, B. and Owen, K., *Alvey: Britain's Strategic Computing Initiative*, London, MIT Press, 1989.

Olson, M., *The Rise and Decline of Nations*, New Haven CT, Yale University Press, 1982.

Patel, P. and Pavitt, K., 'Is Europe losing the technological race?', *Research Policy*, 1987, 16: 3–5.

Paterson, W., 'Environmental politics' in G. Smith, W. Paterson and P. Merkl (eds) *Developments in West German Politics*, London, Macmillan, 1989.

Pavitt, K. and Walker, W., 'Government policies towards industrial innovation: a review', *Research Policy*, 1976, 5: 87–104.

Pavitt, K., 'Technology in Western Europe' in R. Mayne (ed.) *Handbooks to the Modern World: Western Europe*, Oxford, Facts on File Publications, 1986.

Pearce, J. and Sutton, J. with Batcheldor, R., *Protection and Industrial Policy in Europe*, London, Routledge & Kegan Paul for the Royal Institute of International Affairs, 1985.

Pelkmans, J. and Winters, A. *Europe's Domestic Market*, London, Routledge & Kegan Paul, 1988.

Pelkmans, J., 'Industrial integration: the core of the European Community rediscovered' in S. Tarditi, K. Thomson, P. Pierani and E. Croci-Angelini (eds) *Agricultural Trade Liberalization in the European Community*, Oxford, Clarendon Press, 1989.

Peters, B.G., 'Bureaucratic politics and the institutions of the European Community' in A.M. Sbragia (ed.) *Euro-Politics: Institutions and Policy-making in the 'New' European Community*, Washington DC, Brooking Institution, 1992, 75–122.

Peterson, J., 'Hormones, heifers and high politics: biotechnology and the Common Agricultural Policy', *Public Administration*, 1989, 67: 455–71.

Peterson, J. 'The European Technology Community: policy networks in a supranational setting' in R.A.W. Rhodes and D. Marsh (eds) *Policy Networks in British Government*, Oxford, Clarendon Press, 1992.

Peterson, J., 'The politics of European technological collaboration: an analysis of the Eureka initiative', unpublished Ph.D. thesis, London School of Economics, 1992.

Peterson, J., 'Assessing the performance of European collaborative R & D policy: the case of Eureka', *Research Policy*, forthcoming, 1993.

Peterson, J., *Europe and America in the 1990s: the Prospects for Partnership*, Cheltenham and Brookfield VT, Edward Elgar, 1993.

Peterson, J., 'Towards a common European industrial policy? The case of high definition television', *Government and Opposition*, 28, 3, 1993.

Phillips, G.O., *Innovation and Technology Transfer in Japan and Europe: Industry-Academic Interactions*, London, Routledge, 1989.

Pierre, A.J. (ed.), *A High Technology Gap? Europe, America, and Japan*, New York, New York University Press and Council on Foreign Relations, 1987.

Pinder, J., 'The single market: a step towards European Union' in J. Lodge (ed.) *The European Community and the Challenge of the Future*, London, Frances Pinter, 1989.

Piore, M. and Sabel, C., *The Second Industrial Divide*, New York, Basic Books, 1984.

Porter, M., *The Competitive Advantage of Nations*, London, Macmillan, 1990.

Porter, M., 'Europe's companies after 1992: don't collaborate, compete', *The Economist*, 9 June 1990: 23–26.

Portnoff, A.Y., 'Les 108 projets d'Eurêka', *Sciences et Techniques*, 1987, 38: 35–41.

Powell, W.W., 'Neither market nor hierarchy: network forms of organization' in B.M. Shaw and L. Cummings (eds) *Research in Organizational Behavior*, 12, Greenwich CT, JAI Press, 1989.

Prakke, F., 'The financing of technological innovation' in A. Heertje (ed.) *Innovation, Technology and Finance*, Oxford, Basil Blackwell for European Investment Bank, 1988.

PREST, 'Results of telephone survey of UK industrial participants in Esprit II', University of Manchester, Policy Research in Engineering, Science and Technology, 1990.

Pryce, R. and Wessels, W., 'The search for an ever-closer union: a framework for analysis' in R. Pryce (ed.) *The Dynamics of European Union*, London, Croom Helm, 1987.

Rallo, J.C., *Defending Europe in the 1990s: the New Divide of High Technology*, Frances Pinter, London, 1986.

Ranci, P., 'Italy: the weak state' in F. Duchêne and G. Shepherd (eds) *Managing Industrial Change in Western Europe*, London, Frances Pinter, 1987.

Reich, R., *The Work of Nations: Preparing Ourselves for 21st Century Capitalism*, New York, Albert Knopf, 1991.

Rembser, J., 'Economic development, the international competitive situation and the framework of federal and state action to promote R & D, technological development and innovation in Germany', paper presented at German-Canadian workshop on 'Promotion of Technology-Based Small and Medium-Size Enterprises and Technology Transfer', Berlin, 2–3 December 1985, mimeo.

Rhodes, R.A.W., *Control and Power in Central–Local Relations*, Aldershot, Gower, 1981.

Rhodes, R.A.W., 'Power-dependence, policy communities and intergovernmental networks', *Public Administration Bulletin*, 1985, 49: 4–31.

Rhodes, R.A.W., 'Policy networks: a British perspective', *Journal of Theoretical Politics*, 1990, 2: 293–317.

Roman, D.R. and Puett, J.F., Jr, *International Business and Technological Innovation*, Oxford, North-Holland, 1983.

Roobeck, A., 'The Crisis in Fordism and the rise of a new technological paradigm', *Futures*, 1987, 19: 129–54.

Rose, M.A., 'Airbus industrie and high technology industrial cooperation in Europe: structure, issues, and implications with a view towards Eurofar', paper presented at the Conference on Europe in the 1990s, George Mason University, 24–25 May 1989.

Rothwell, R. and Zegveld, W., *Industrial Innovation and Public Policy: Preparing for the 1980s and 1990s*, London, Frances Pinter, 1981.

Rothwell R., and Zegveld, W., *Innovation and the Small and Medium-sized Firm*, London, Frances Pinter, 1982.,

Rothwell, R., 'The difficulties of national innovation policies' in S. MacDonald, D. McL. Lamberton and T. Mandeville (eds) *The Trouble with Technology: Explorations in the Process of Technological Change*, London, Frances Pinter, 1983.

Rothwell, R., 'Innovation and the smaller firm' in W.S. Brown and R. Rothwell (eds) *Entrepreneurship and Technology: World Experiences and Policies*, Essex, Longman, 1986.

Salomon, J.J., *Le Gaulois, le Cow-boy et le Samurai: Rapport sur la Politique Française de la Technologie*, Paris, CPE, 1985.

Sandholtz, W., 'Esprit and the politics of international collective action', *Journal of Common Market Studies*, 1992, 30: 1–21.

Schäfers, A., 'The Luxembourg patent convention: the best option for the internal market', *Journal of Common Market Studies*, 1987, 25: 193–207.

Scheinman, L., 'Euratom: nuclear integration in Europe' *International Conciliation*, 1967, 563: 8–9.

Scherer, F.M., *Industrial Market Structure and Economic Performance*, Chicago, Rand McNally & Company, 2nd edition, 1980.

Schmitter, P., 'Three neo-functional hypotheses about international integration', *International Organization*, 1969, 23: 161–6.

Schmitter, P., 'Central American integration: spill-over, spill-around or encapsulation?', *Journal of Common Market Studies*, 1971, 9: 1–48.

Schneider, V. and Werle, R., 'Networks and concertation in European policy making: the cases of chemicals control and telecommunications', paper presented at the joint sessions of the European Consortium for Political Research, Limerick, 30 March–4 April 1992, mimeo.

Schumpeter, J., *Capitalism, Socialism and Democracy*, New York, Harper & Row, 1947.

Scott, P.B., *The Robotics Revolution*, Oxford, Basil Blackwell, 1984.

SEPSU, *European Collaboration in Science and Technology II: Pointers to the Future for Policymakers*, London, The Royal Society/Fellowship of Engineers, 1989.

Servan-Schreiber, J.J., *Le Défi Américain*, Paris, Denoël, 1967.

Sharp, M., *The New Biotechnology: European Governments in Search of a Strategy*, Brighton, Sussex Policy Research Institute, 1985.

Sharp, M., 'Review of Fast Report: the Challenges of Innovation', *Journal of Common Market Studies*, 1986, 25: 169.

Sharp, M., 'The Community and the New Technologies' in J. Lodge (ed.) *The European Community and the Challenge of the Future*, London, Frances Pinter, 1989.

Sharp, M., 'The single market and European technology policies' in C. Freeman, Sharp, M. and W. Walker (eds) *Technology and the Future of Europe: Global Competition and the Environment in the 1990s*, London, Frances Pinter, 1991.

Sharp, M., 'Tides of change: the world economy and Europe in 1992', *International Affairs*, 1992, 68: 17–35.

Sharp, M. and Shearman, C., *European Technological Collaboration*, London, Routledge & Kegan Paul, 1987.

Shonfield, A., *Modern Capitalism*, Oxford, Oxford University Press, 1965.

Sillard, Y., 'Eurêka: un programme au service de l'innovation technologique européenne', *La Jaune et la Rouge*, 418, octobre 1986: 97–112.

Sleuwaegen, L. and Yamawaki, H., 'The formation of the European Common Market: changes in market structure and performance', *European Economic Review*, 1988, 32: 1451–75.

Smith, B.L.R., 'A new 'technology gap' in Europe?', *SAIS Review*, 1986, 6, 1: 219–36.

Smith, G., *Democracy in Western Germany*, Aldershot, Gower, 1986.

Stokman, F. N., Ziegler, R. and Scott, J. (eds), *Networks of Corporate Power: A Comparative Analysis of Ten Countries*, Cambridge, Polity Press, 1988.

Stoneman, P., *The Economic Analysis of Technology Policy*, Oxford, Clarendon Press, 1987.

Strange, S., *States and Markets*, London, Frances Pinter, 1988.

Strange, S., 'States, firms and diplomacy', *International Affairs*, 1992, 68: 1–15

Taylor, P., 'The new dynamic of EC integration in the 1980s' in J. Lodge (ed.) *The European Community and the Challenge of the Future*, London, Frances Pinter, 1989.

Taylor, P., 'The European Community and the state: assumptions, theories and propositions', *Review of International Studies*, 1991, 17: 109–25.

Taylor, T., 'Britain's response to the Strategic Defense Initiative', *International Affairs*, 1986, 62: 217–30.

Telesis Consultants, *Competing for Prosperity: Business Strategies and Industrial Policies in Modern France*, London, Policy Studies Institute, 1986.

Thoft, P.L., 'Promotion of innovation: a new direction for national patent offices' in U. Täger and A. von Witzleben (eds) *Patinnova '90: Strategies for the Protection of Innovation*, London, Kluwer Academic, 1991.

Thomas, E., 'Recent research on R & D and productivity growth', paper presented to OECD conference on science and technology indicators, 1980, Paris, May, mimeo.

Tindemans, P., 'Cosine: ready to move into implementation phase', *Computer Networks and ISDN Systems*, 1989, 17: 344–5.

TRN Groep/Volder & Vis, *Analysis of and Comments on the Organisation of DG XII, DG XIII and the Joint Research Centre*, Brussels, 1989.

Tucker, J.B., 'Partners and rivals: a model of international collaboration in advanced technology', *International Organization*, 1991, 45: 83–120.

Tugendhat, C., *Making Sense of Europe*, Middlesex, Viking Books, 1986.

Tuppen, J., *France Under Recession: 1981–86*, Albany NY, State University of New York Press, 1988.

Twitchett, C.C., *Harmonisation in the EEC*, London, Macmillan, 1981.

Tyson, L. and Zysman, J., 'American industry in international competition' in L. Tyson and J. Zysman (eds) *American Industry in International Competition*, Ithaca NY, Cornell University Press, 1983.

Ungerer, H. with Costello, N., *Telecommunications in Europe: Free Choices for the User in Europe's 1992 Market*, Brussels, Commission of the European Communities, European Perspectives Series, 1988.

van der Straaten, J., 'The Dutch national environmental policy plan', *Environmental Politics*, 1, 1992: 45–71.

van Tulder, R., 'Small countries and the global innovation race: the role of the state in the Netherlands, Belgium and Switzerland' in U. Hilpert (ed.) *State Policies and Techno-Industrial Innovation*, London, Routledge, 1991.

Vogel, D., *National Styles of Regulation: Environmental Policing in Great Britain and the United States*, Ithaca NY, Cornell University Press, 1986.

Wallace, H., 'Negotiation, conflict and compromise: the elusive pursuit of common policies' in H. Wallace, W. Wallace and C. Webb (eds) *Policy-Making in the European Community*, Chichester, John Wiley & Sons, 2nd edition, 1983.

Wallace, H., 'Implementation across national boundaries' in D. Lewis and H. Wallace (eds) *Politics and Practice*, London, Heinemann, 1984.

Wallace, H., 'The best is the enemy of the 'could': bargaining in the EC' in S. Tarditi, K.J. Thomson, P. Pierani and E. Croci-Angelini (eds) *Agricultural Trade Liberalization and the European Community*, Oxford, Clarendon Press, 1989.

Wallace, W., 'Less than a federation, more than a regime: the Community as a political system' in H. Wallace, W. Wallace and C. Webb (eds) *Policy-Making in the European Community*, Chichester, John Wiley & Sons, 2nd edition, 1983.

Ward, H. and Edwards, G., 'Chicken and technology: the politics of the EC's budget for research and development', *Review of International Studies*, 1990, 16: 37–54.

Watkins, T., 'Research collaboration in the EC: innovation, technology diffusion and political support', paper presented at the Inaugural Conference of the European Community Studies Association, Fairfax, VA, May 1989.

Watkins, T.A., 'A technological communications costs model of R & D consortia as public policy', *Research Policy*, 1991, 20: 87–107.

Webber, D., 'The framework of government-industry relations and industrial policy making in the Federal Republic of Germany', *University of Sussex Working Papers on Government-Industry Relations*, March 1986, Brighton, 1.

Wells, S.F., 'France and European defence cooperation: implications for United States policy', *Atlantic Community Quarterly*, 1985–86, 23: 379–388.

Wilks, S. and Wright, M. (eds), *Comparative Government–Industry Relations: West Europe, the United States and Japan*, Oxford, Clarendon Press, 1987.

Wilks S. and Wright, M., *Promotion and Regulation of Industry in Japan and her Competitors*, Oxford, Clarendon Press, 1989.

Wilks, S., 'Government-industry relations: progress and findings of the ESRC research initiative', *Public Administration*, 1989, 67: 329–39.

Williams, R., *European Technology: the Politics of Collaboration*, London, Croom Helm, 1973.

Williamson, O. E., *Markets and Hierarchies: Analysis and Antitrust Implications*, New York, Free Press, 1975.

Wilson, G.K., *Business and Politics: A Comparative Introduction*, London, Macmillan, 2nd edition, 1990.

Woolcock, S., 'Information technology: the challenge to Europe', *Journal of Common Market Studies*, 1984, 22: 315–31.

Wright, M., 'Policy community, policy network and comparative industrial policies', *Political Studies*, 1988, 36: 593–612.

Wright, V., 'Socialism and the interdependent economy: industrial policy-making under the Mitterrand presidency', *Government and Opposition*, 1984, 19: 287–303.

Yamamura, K. and Saxonhouse, G., 'Technology and the future of the economy' in K. Yamamura and Y. Tasuba (eds) *The Political Economy of Japan: the Domestic Transformation*, Palo Alto CA, Stanford University Press, vol. 1, 1987.

Yudken, J.S. and Black, M., 'Targeting National Needs: A New Direction for Science and Technology Policy', *World Policy Journal*, 1990, 8: 251–88.

Ziegler, J.N., 'Semiconductors' in 'Searching for security in a global economy', *Daedalus*, 1991, Proceedings of the American Academy of Arts and Sciences, 120: 155–82.

Zysman, J., *Governments, Markets and Growth: Financial Systems and the Politics of Industrial Change*, Oxford, Martin Robinson, 1983.

OFFICIAL EUREKA PUBLICATIONS

Austrian chairmanship, 'Proposals for the work programme and tentative calendar of meetings during the Austrian chairmanship', Document Eureka 652, 16 June 1988.

British chairmanship, 'Procedures for Eureka projects: note by chairman of the Ministerial Conference', London, 21 May 1986.

British chairmanship, 'Communiqué of the third Eureka ministerial conference', London, 30 June 1986.

British chairmanship, 'Memorandum of understanding on the Eureka secretariat between the members of Eureka,' London, 30 June 1986.

Coordinateur National Français, 'Eurêka: dossier de presse', Paris, 16 September 1987.

Danish chairmanship, 'Eureka: goals attained and future development', Copenhagen, 1988.

Danish chairmanship, 'Progress report on Eureka projects', Copenhagen, 15 May 1988.

Danish chairmanship, 'Eureka Management Research Initiative (EMRI)', Eureka document 626, 15 June 1988.

Danish chairmanship, 'Some statistical data about Eureka projects', Copenhagen, 16 June 1988.

Dutch chairmanship, *Eureka and Supportive Measures*, The Hague, document NPC-9067, 1991.

Dutch chairmanship, *Eureka: Exploring Cooperation Between East and West*, The Hague, final programme for Eureka congress, Budapest, Hungary, 1–3 May 1991.

Dutch chairmanship, 'The Hague statement: extending cooperation with partners from European non-member countries', The Hague, Document Eureka 9MC-3, Rev. 1, 17 June 1991.

Dutch chairmanship, 'HDTV related supportive measures: draft recommendations', The Hague, Eureka Document 9 MC-4, Rev. 1, 19 June 1991.

Dutch chairmanship, *The Report of the Eureka Assessment Panel*, The Hague, 1991.

Dutch chairmanship, *Umbrella Projects*, The Hague, document NPC-9066, 1991.

Dutch chairmanship, *X-Ray Sessions: a Final Report*, The Hague, 1991.

Dutch Eureka Office, *Industrial HP Lasers: a Survey on Hazards and Safety Regulations*, Eureka bulletin special issue, The Hague, July 1989.

Eureka HDTV Directorate, *A Challenge Born in Europe: To Reach HDTV in a Compatible World*, Eindhoven, 1988.

Eureka HDTV Directorate, *High-Definition Television Update*, Eindhoven, Summer 1988.

Eureka secretariat, 'Declaration of Principles relating to Eureka adopted at Hanover, 6 November 1985', Brussels.

Eureka secretariat, 'Communiqué of the 5th Eureka ministerial conference, Madrid', Brussels, 15 September 1987.

Eureka secretariat, 'The Eureka projects: an overview', Brussels, October 1987.

Eureka secretariat, 'Communiqué of the 6th Eureka ministerial conference, Copenhagen, Brussels,' 15–16 June 1988.

Eureka secretariat, 'Programme of work under the Austrian chairmanship', Brussels, Eureka document 705, 3 October 1988.

Eureka secretariat, 'Progress report on Eureka projects', Brussels, 16 June 1988.

Eureka secretariat, *1989 Project Progress Report*, Brussels, 1989.

Eureka secretariat, 'Communiqué of 7th Eureka ministerial conference, Vienna,' English version, Document Eureka 7MC-8, 18–19 June 1989.

Eureka secretariat, *Annual Project Report 1989*, Brussels, 1990.

Eureka secretariat, 'New opportunities for developing environmental technologies: Euroenviron – the green umbrella', Brussels, 1990.

Eureka secretariat, *Annual Progress Report 1990*, Brussels, 1991.

Eureka secretariat, *Annual Progress Report 1991*, Brussels, 1992.

Eurotrac International Scientific Secretariat, *Eurotrac: Eureka Enviromental Project*, Garmisch-Partenkirchen, Fraunhofer Institute, 1988.

Eurotrac International Scientific Secretariat, *Annual Report Part 1: General Report*, Garmisch-Partenkirchen, Fraunhofer Institute, 1990.

Eurotrac International Scientific Secretariat, text of speech by Dr Wolfgang Seiler, Director of International Scientific Secretariat of Eurotrac, 6th Eureka Ministerial Conference, Copenhagen, 16 June 1990, mimeo.

Finnish chairmanship, *NPC office functions*, Tampere, 22 May 1992.

Finnish chairmanship, *Report of EU 95/HDTV Supportive Measures*, Tampere, 22 May 1992.

Finnish chairmanship, *SMEs: a Challenge to Eureka*, Tampere, 22 May 1992.

OTHER OFFICIAL EUROPEAN COMMUNITY PUBLICATIONS

BMFT, *Hochtechnologien und internationale Wettbewerbsfähigkeit der deutschen Wirtschaft*, Bonn, BMWI Dokumentation, 1986.

BMFT, 'Facts and figures 1990: update of the report of the Federal Government on Research 1988', English version, Verlag Deutscher Wirtschaftsdienst, Köln, 1990.

BMFT, 'Report of the Federal Government on Research', Verlag Deutscher Wirtschaftsdienst, Köln, 1991.

CEC, 'La politique industrielle de la Communauté', Brussels, COM (70) 100 final, 1970.

CEC, 'The European information technology industry: a short overview', Brussels, June 1983.

CEC, 'Government report on information technology: Federal Government scheme to promote the development of microelectronics and the information and communications technologies', Brussels, Information Technologies Task Force, III/2718/84–E, 23 February 1984.

CEC, 'Completing the internal market: white paper from the Commission to the European Council', Luxembourg, 1985.

CEC, 'Towards a European technological community', Brussels, COM (85) 350 final, 1985.

CEC, 'Eureka and the European Technology Community', Brussels, Communication from the Commission to the Council, COM (86) 664 final, 1986.

CEC, *Official Documents on the Esprit Programme*, Brussels, COM (86) 269 final, 1986.

CEC, 'Special issue: Europe 2000 survey', *Eurobarometer*, Brussels, March 1987.

CEC, *Eurobarometer*, Brussels, 27 June 1987.

CEC, *Sixteenth Report on Competition Policy*, Brussels/Luxembourg, pt. 247, 1987.

CEC, 'Towards a dynamic European economy: Green Paper of the development of the common market for telecommunications services and equipment', Brussels, COM (87) 290 final, 30 June 1987.

CEC, 'Declaration by Mr K.H. Narjes, Vice-President of the European Commission before the 6th Eureka conference in Copenhagen', Brussels, 18 June 1988.

CEC, 'Reinforcing co-operation between Eureka and the European Communities', Brussels, COM (88) 291 final, 24 June 1988.

CEC, 'A review of COST cooperation since its beginnings', Luxembourg, 1988.

CEC, *Seventeenth Report on Competition Policy*, Brussels/Luxembourg, 1988.

CEC, *Eighteenth Report on Competition Policy*, Brussels/Luxembourg, 1989.

CEC, *Europe Without Frontiers: Completing the Internal Market*, Luxembourg, European documentation series, 2, 1989.

CEC, 'Proposal for a Council Regulation on a statute for a European Company', Brussels, COM (89) 268 final, 1989.

CEC, *The Commission's programme for 1990: address by Jacques Delors, President of the Commission, to the European Parliament*, Luxembourg, bull. supplement 1/90, 1990.

CEC, *EC Research Funding: A Guide for Applicants*, Brussels, CEC/DG XII, January 1990.

CEC, *Eurotech Capital*, Luxembourg, DG XXIII, 1990.

CEC, *The European Community: 1992 and Beyond*, Luxembourg, European documentation series, 1991.

CEC, *Eurostat: Basic Statistics of the Community*, Luxembourg, 28th edition, 1991.

CEC, *Value: Community Programme for the Diffusion and Utilization of Scientific and Technological Results*, Luxembourg, 1991.

CEC, 'Trends 1974–1991', *Eurobarometer*, Brussels, April 1992.

CESTA, 'La renaissance technology de l'Europe: propositions françaises', Paris, June 1985.

Cosine Policy Group, 'Project status information: Eureka project no. 8 – Cosine', Brussels, 14 June 1989.

Cosine Policy Group, 'Cosine implementation phase project proposal', CPG/ 89/0083, final version, Annex B, August 1989.

Department of Trade and Industry, *A Framework for Government Research and Development*, London, HMSO, 1971.

Department of Trade and Industry, *Information Technology: A Plan for Concerted Action – the Report of the IT 86 Committee*, London, HMSO, 1986.

Department of Trade and Industry, *FAMOS: Preliminary Study Report on European Collaboration in the Field of Flexible Automated Assembly Systems*, London, HMSO, 1987.

Department of Trade and Industry, *Evaluation of the Alvey Programme for Advanced Information Technology*, London, HMSO, 1991.

Department of Trade and Industry, *Company Law Harmonisation*, London, HMSO, 1992.

DRI, *Special Tabulations of International Trade*, Washington D.C., National Science Foundation, 1986.

European Bankers Round Table, 'Declaration to the Eureka Conference of Ministers', Madrid, 15 September 1987.

European Communities Medium Term Economic Policy Committee, *Scientific and Technical Cooperation between European Countries: Possibilities in Seven Sectors*, Brussels, Report of the Working Party on Scientific and Technical Research Policy, 7301/II/69–E, 9 April 1969.

European Parliament, 'Draft Report on the European Research Coordination Agency' (The Ford Report), PE 199.362/B, Committee on Energy, Research and Technology, 28 June 1988.

GATT, *International Trade 1984/5*, Geneva, 1985.

IFT Marketing for UK Department of Trade and Industry, *Eureka Survey*, HMSO, London, 1989.

Ministère de la Politique Etrangère de la France, 'Rapport du Président de la République au sommet des pays industrialisées: technologie, emploi et croissance', *La Politique Etrangère de la France: Textes et Documents*, Paris, June 1982.

Ministère de la Politique Etrangère de la France, 'Une nouvelle étape pour l'Europe: un espace commun de l'industrie et de la recherche', *Politique Etrangère de la France: Textes et Documents*, Paris, 12 September 1983.

Ministére de la Recherche et de la Technologie de la France, 'Note de présentation d'Eurêka', *Assises de la Technologie Européenne: Dossier de Presse*, Paris, 19 July 1985.

Ministére de la Recherche et de la Technologie de la France, 'Texte du communiqué final', *Assises de la Technologie Européene: Dossier de Presse*, Paris, 19 July 1985.

Ministry of Defence, 'Towards a Stronger Europe: a report by an independent study team established by the Defence Ministers of nations of the Independent European Programme Group to make proposals to improve the competitiveness of Europe's defence equipment industry', London, HMSO, volume I, December 1986.

OECD, *The Semi-Conductor Industry: Trade-Related Issues*, Paris, 1985.

OECD, *Science and Technology Policy Outlook*, Paris, 1985.

OECD, *Innovation Policy in France*, Paris, 1986.

OECD, *Science and Technology Indicators No. 2: R&D, Invention and Competitiveness*, Paris, 1986.

OECD, *Innovation Policy: Spain*, Paris, 1987.

OECD, *Science and Technology Policy Outlook*, Paris, 1988.

Raad van Advies voor het Wetenschapsbeleid, *Advies Inzake Eureka*, Den Haag, 72, May 1990.

RARE, 'Cosine – Eureka Project 8: Final Specification Phase Overview Report', Luxembourg, CEC for Réseaux Associés pour la Recherche Européenne, 3.2.2, 1989.

Secretariat of the European Council of Ministers, 'Ways for increasing the participation of the Community in Eureka Projects: memorandum of the government of the Federal Republic of Germany', Brussels, English translation, 4 February 1988.

10 Downing Street Press Office, 'Text of speech given by the Prime Minister Margaret Thatcher to Eureka ministerial conference', London, HMSO, 30 June 1986.

US Congress Office of Technology Assessment, *The Big Picture: HDTV and High Resolution Systems*, Washington DC, USGPO, OTA BP CIT 64, June 1990.

PERIODICALS

Aviation Week and Space Technology
Bulletin of the European Communities
The Company Lawyer Digest
Department of State Bulletin (USA)
The Economist
Electronic Engineering Times

Electronique Actualités
Eureka News
Euro-Info
European Biotechnology Information Service
(Agence) Europe
European File
HDTV Report
IES News
Innovation and Technology Transfer
International Management
Nature
New Scientist
Le Nouvel Economiste
Le Nouvel Observateur
Official Journal of the European Communities
RARE Information Bulletin
Science
Sciences et Techniques
The Times Higher Education Supplement
L'Usine Nouvelle

NEWSPAPERS

Christian Science Monitor
Le Croix
Daily Telegraph
Les Echos
L'Express
Le Figaro
Financial Times
The Guardian
Hannoverische Allgemeine Zeitung
L'Humanité
The Independent
International Herald Tribune
Libération
Le Matin de Paris
Le Monde
Le Monde Diplomatique
The Observer
Le Point
Le Quotidien de Paris
Le Soir
The Times (of London)
La Tribune
L'Unité
Wall Street Journal

INTERVIEWS

A total of fifty-one interviews were conducted between 1987 and 1992 for this study. The institutions represented by interviewees were:

AID, Grenoble
Belgian Eureka office
CEC, DG I
CEC, DG III
CEC, DG IV
CEC, DG XII
CEC, DG XIII
CEC, Secretariat General
CEN/CENELEC
Danish Eureka chairmanship
Danish Eureka office
Dutch Eureka projects office
Eureka secretariat
Eurotrac International Scientific Secretariat
Famos steering committee
French Eureka office
French Ministry of Industry
French Ministry of Research and Technology, Lyon
German BMFT
German Eureka referat
HDTV directorate
ICL, London
MBB, Munich
Norwegian Eureka office
OECD secretariat, Paris
Philips consumer electronics, Eindhoven
Science et Techniques, Paris
Strachan and Henshaw, Bristol
Swedish Eureka office
Taylor HiTech Limited, Chorley (UK)
TTY France, Grenoble
UK delegate to IEPG
UK Department of Trade and Industry
UK Eureka office
UK Foreign and Commonwealth Office

Index

Abrahamson, Lt. Gen. J. 58
acid rain 168–72
added value: defined 10; and Eureka
    97–102, 143–9, 155–6, 163, 170,
    175, 218–19
additionality: defined 10; and Eureka
    141–3, 152, 155–6, 157–8, 160
AID 164
Airbus 52, 53, 55, 72, 200
Alvey project 82
Ariane 55, 200
Arianespace 52
assessment panel (Eureka) 127–60
    passim
Austria 29, 85, 110, 139
aviation 52–5, 72, 200

Belgium 29, 30, 31, 124
biotechnology 43, 117, 211, 216
BMFT (Germany) 27, 31, 79, 80–1,
    94, 168, 173, 212
Britain: *see* Clarke, K.; Howe, G.;
    Thatcher, M.; UK
Brite 42, 108, 116, 119, 123, 193, 209,
    211, 216
BSB 183
BSkyB 184, 186, 187
Bulmer, S.: and Paterson, W. 64
Bush, G. 62

Cawson, A. *et al.* 205, 213, 215, 221
Caudron, G. 187
CEPT 174
CERD 50
CERN 50

Cerny, P. 5
chairmanship of Eureka, reforms to
    223–4
Chandernagor, A. 57
Chandler, A. D. 4
Chirac, J. 59, 60
Clarke, K. 82–3, 105
Colonna Report 50
communications 40–1
Concorde 52, 54, 55, 60, 72, 200
Copenhagen ministerial conference
    (1988) 32, 86, 89, 96, 104–5
corporatism 204–14; meso-
    corporatism 204–8
Cosine 40, 108, 114, 116, 122, 162,
    172–7, 191, 192, 194, 195, 196, 201
COST 50, 54, 120, 159, 169
Council of Ministers (EC) 16, 57,
    117, 187–8; Council of Science
    Ministers 50
CSCE 120–1, 207
CTV 177–81, 182, 183, 188, 189, 195;
    PAL 177–8, 184, 186, 187;
    SECAM 177–8: *see* HDTV
Curien, H. 65, 66, 71, 162

Davignon, E. 57, 64, 70, 103
Declaration of Principles (Eureka) 1,
    13, 22, 68–9, 84, 87, 90, 105, 114, 201
DeGaulle, C. 49, 50, 53, 77
Dekker, W. 129
Delors, J. 66, 67, 104, 105, 111, 122,
    125, 216
Denmark 28–9, 30, 32, 74, 85, 86, 87,
    96, 105, 124, 222

DTI (UK) 31, 82, 83, 166, 171, 172, 193, 212
Duff, A. N. 15
Dumas, R. 60, 62

Eastern Europe (and EC) 121–2
EC 1, 18, 134; CAP 202; and Eureka 15–19, 103–26; institutional jealousy (with Eureka) 103–7: *see* Council of Ministers; Eastern Europe; European Commission; European Parliament; industrial policy; innovation; internal market; Member States; R & D; SEA
EEIGs 115–16
EFA 53
EFTA 1, 85, 118–21, 125–6, 152–3, 156, 158, 170, 173, 191, 219
ELDO 50, 52
Elliott, R. F.: and Wood, P. 9
EMRI 86
environmental technology 44–5, 102, 114, 170, 210, 213
ERDA 50
ESA 51–2, 72
Esprit 35, 37, 57, 65, 66, 79, 82, 91, 106, 108, 116, 119, 123, 125, 163, 174, 193, 211, 212
ESRO 51
ES2 38
Euratom 49, 53, 54, 55, 72
Eurocare 45
Eurodata 51
European Bankers Round Table 94
European Commission 1, 15, 16, 18, 20, 22, 30, 31, 50, 55, 57, 58, 65, 66, 67, 70, 71, 72, 83, 96, 97, 98, 103–26, 160, 168, 169, 170, 172–7, 181, 183, 186–91 *passim*, 194–5, 196–7, 200–8 *passim*, 211–16 *passim*; DGs 176; III 122–3; IV 113, 122, 202; XII 123, 224; XIII 123, 183, 202, 224; XXIII 117
European Parliament 15, 104, 111, 187, 214
Eurotrac 45, 108, 116, 162, 168–72, 191, 192, 194, 210, 218
EVCA 109–10

Fabius, L. 76
Famos 42–3, 45, 46, 91, 108, 116,

193, 201, 206, 209–12 *passim*, 216, 218
Finland 29, 35, 74, 75, 85, 92, 100
FMS 41–3, 44, 210
Framework programme 15–16, 17, 18, 22, 30, 55–64, 66, 67, 70, 71, 72, 83, 103, 104, 105, 106, 107, 116, 117, 118, 119, 121, 123, 124, 125, 126, 133, 159, 170, 174, 176, 181, 200–3 *passim*, 208–12 *passim*, 215–16; Framework II programme 107; Framework III programme 107, 111, 117–18, 120, 124, 170, 216
France 14, 15, 26–7, 30, 35, 42, 47–8, 49, 50, 51, 52, 53, 55–61, 63, 64, 65, 66, 67–8, 69, 70–1, 72, 74, 75–9, 79–81 *passim*, 93, 95, 96, 100, 103, 105, 110, 113, 139, 149, 154, 157, 162, 182–3, 210, 212, 222; ANVAR 78; *Filière Electronique* programme 76, 77, 222; MRT 75–6, 77, 78, 162: *see* Chirac, J.; Delors, J.; Mitterrand, F.
Freeman, C. 5, 82

Genscher, H.-D. 60, 61, 62, 64, 120
Germany 11, 15, 27, 30, 31, 42, 47, 49, 50, 51, 53, 55, 57, 60–4, 66, 68–9, 70–1, 79–81, 87, 92, 93, 94, 105, 112, 113, 117, 124, 139, 149, 157, 168, 172, 183, 187, 194, 210: *see* BMFT; Genscher, H.-D.; Kohl, H.; Reisenhuber, H.; Schmidt, H.
Geroski, L. P.: and Jacquemin, A. 12
Giraud, A. 59
Grant, W. *et al.* 19
Greece 29, 30, 92, 98, 210
Group of Seven 56, 58, 61–2
Gyllenhammer group 65, 71, 122

Hague ministerial conference, the (1991) 34, 121
Håkansson, H. 6–7
Hall, P. A. 78–9
Hanover ministerial conference (1985) 69
Hayward, J. 54
HDTV 40, 96, 108, 109, 114, 115,

122, 162, 177–91, 192, 193, 195, 201, 202, 206, 212, 216, 217, 218; MAC standard 96, 179–80, 183, 184–91 *passim*, 195: *see* CTV
Hilbert, U. 205
Hilf, M. 207
HLG 31, 32, 69, 86, 87, 88, 89, 91, 94, 97, 98, 99, 100, 105, 124
Hoffmann, S. 17
Howe, G. 62, 63
Hungary 1, 29, 121

Iceland 29
industrial policy 111–14, 188, 198, 200, 203, 210–11, 214
information technology 35–40, 202
infrastructure 46
innovation: 5; 'Big Science' innovations 11, 13, 77, 79; EC policy and 7–10, 12–13, 15–16, 54–5, 68, 75, 79, 101, 116–18, 122–6, 173, 182, 190, 198–222; 'external factors' affecting 14; Schumpeterian model 10–12; *see* national innovation policies; R & D
interdependence 19
internal market 7–10, 15, 18, 36, 40, 85, 100, 115, 122–3, 124, 126, 199–204
IPRs 32, 115, 133, 147–8, 150, 154, 155, 158, 164, 224
Ireland 29, 74, 210
Italy 28, 30, 32, 67, 69, 70, 84–5, 86, 95, 96, 112, 150, 157, 162, 210

Jacquemin, A., *see* Geroski, L. P.
Japan 7, 10, 11, 12, 35, 36, 37, 39, 41–2, 44, 45, 56, 74, 75, 80, 82, 100, 119, 162, 178–9, 185–6, 188–9, 197, 199, 202; MITI 37, 56, 183; VLSI programme 37
Jessi 37, 38, 39, 40, 108, 122, 125, 177, 185, 188, 201, 206, 210, 212–13, 216, 217, 218
JRC 169, 170, 171

Katzenstein, P. 23
Keddie Group 92, 94, 100

Keohane, R.: and Nye, R. 18
Keynesianism 3, 4, 78, 205
knowledge, state power and 6, 198, 207–8
Kohl, H. 60–1, 62, 63, 64, 79

London ministerial conference (1986) 69, 88, 99
Luxembourg 29
Luxembourg Accord 119, 120, 170

Maastricht summit 118
Madrid ministerial conference (1987) 32, 104, 122
Maire, E. 59
Mauroy, P. 76
Medium-term Plan 100, 102
Megaproject II 37, 80
Meyer, O. 47
Milan summit (1985) 66–7, 104, 122
ministerial conferences 96–7: *see* Copenhagen; the Hague; Hanover; London; Madrid; Paris; Rome; Stockholm; Vienna
MITHRA 161–5, 191, 192, 193, 196
MITI: *see* Japan
Mitterrand, F. 26, 56, 57, 58, 59, 60, 62, 63, 67, 68, 70, 119–20, 182
MNCs 13, 35, 38, 39, 50, 67, 71, 76, 84, 122, 162, 201
MRCA (Tornado) 53
Murdoch, R. 184, 187

Narjes, K.-H. 58, 71, 104–5, 106, 107, 108, 122
national innovation policies 73–85, 199–222: *see also* individual nations; R & D
NATO 53, 57
Netherlands 11, 28, 30, 69, 75, 83–4, 91, 100, 102, 105, 112, 117, 124, 149–50, 157, 210, 216–18, 222: *see* assessment panel
new materials 45–6
'New Right' 3
Norway 29, 30, 63, 66, 85, 165–7, 191–2
NPCs 31, 32, 91–3, 98, 100, 110, 111, 118, 162, 215, 217–18, 219, 221, 223
Nye, J., *see* Keohane, R.

OECD 35, 74, 77
OSI 172–7, 195

Pandolfi, F. M. 106, 107, 108, 116, 117, 123, 125, 187, 188, 215, 216
Paris ministerial conference (1985) 48, 55, 67–8
patents 115–16
Patterson, W., *see* Bulmer, S.
Pattie, G. 63, 65, 68, 69
PGOs 206–8
Philips 177–82 *passim*, 184–5, 188–9, 190, 195, 199, 202
PHOXA 168
policy networks 19–24, 208–14, 225
Poniatowski, M. 104
Porter, M. 23
Portugal 29, 30, 92, 98, 124
'post-Fordism' 3–7, 11, 193, 206
Prakke, F. 13–14, 219
precursors to Eureka 49–55: *see* Airbus; Ariane; Arianespace; CERD; Concorde; CERN; COST; EFA; ERDA; ESA; ESRO; MRCA; Unidata
1992 Project 111–21, 123, 125, 153, 199–204, 219
projects, Eureka 69, 90–7; definition phase 90; implementation phase 90; overview 32–4: *see* biotechnology; communications; environmental technology; information technology; infrastructure; new materials; robotics and production automation
PTTs 173–6 *passim*, 181, 194, 195

RA-D 162, 165–7, 191, 192, 193, 194, 196
RARE 174–5, 176, 194
R & D: collaborative 2–19, 21–2, 41, 56, 65, 66, 67–8, 70, 71, 90–2, 94, 110, 111–16, 117, 124, 141–9, 159, 202; EC and individual Member State spending 15, 28, 51, 53, 73–4, 93–9, 103, 107, 112, 122, 126, 130, 191, 200, 207, 210–11, 212; legal framework 115–16; 'near market' 1, 23, 46–8, 116, 121, 133–7, 147,

150, 154, 165, 171, 193, 194, 198, 200; spending levels before Eureka 73–5, 131, 132, 133: *see* innovation interdependence; national innovation policies; projects; technological change
Reagan administration 3, 55, 56, 57, 58, 60, 61–2
Reich, R. 23
resource dependencies 20, 214
Rhodes, R. A. W. 20–1
Riesenhuber, H. 62, 65, 67, 94, 105
robotics and production automation 41–3, 202, 210, 212
Rome ministerial conference (1990) 34, 121
Rothschild Report 81

Scherer, F. M. 11
Schmidt, H. 62, 64
Schneider, V., and Werle, R. 214
SDI 22, 55–64, 65, 67, 70, 71, 125, 208, 209
SEA 3, 12, 15, 16, 18, 77, 112, 114, 115, 182, 199, 203
secretariat (of Eureka): need for 87–90, 92, 93, 94, 99, 103, 108, 121, 224–5
semi-conductors: Aerospatiale 32, 38, 67; ASICs 37–9; DRAM 37; ES2 38–9; IBM 37, 39; ICs 36–37, 38, 39, 56, 179, 184; JRC 169, 170, 171: *see* Esprit; Jessi; Megaproject II
Servan-Schreiber, J.-J. 50
Sharp, M. 173: and Shearman, C. 52, 202
Shearman, C.: *see* Sharp, M.
Sillard, Y. 27, 53
SMEs 11–13, 28, 29, 32, 33, 36–44 *passim*, 78, 79, 80–9 *passim*, 109, 110, 111, 116, 117, 118, 124, 128–39 *passim*, 141, 144–9 *passim*, 153–4, 157, 161–5, 171, 193, 194, 196, 200, 210–15 *passim*, 217–25 *passim*
Spain 28, 32, 85, 117, 139, 222
Stern, J. 123
Stockholm ministerial conference (1986), 86, 87, 96
Strange, S. 4, 6

surveys of Eureka: methodology
127–30; participant attitudes 149–
53; participants 130–3; project
funding 137–41: projects 133–7
Sweden 28, 30, 32, 42, 69, 74, 85, 222
Switzerland 29, 30, 67, 69, 87, 91,
163, 210

technological change 12, 11–12, 207,
211; 'network' approach 6–7: *see*
innovation; R & D
'technology gap' 55–6
technology transfer 2–3, 77, 78, 85
telecommunications 194–5, 205, 214
Thatcher, M. 3, 70, 81–2, 83, 102
theories of regional integration;
intergovernmental theories of
European integration 15–19, 70–
72, 86–90; neofunctionalism 16–17
Tornado; *see* MRCA
Treaty of Rome 12, 71, 104, 111, 112,
114, 115
Turkey 1, 29, 30, 210

UK 1, 3, 11, 15, 19, 28, 30–1, 47, 48,
52, 53, 55, 57, 66, 67, 68, 69, 81–3,

91–3, 98, 105, 117, 150, 157, 165–7,
183, 187, 188, 193–4, 208, 210;
Department of Energy 166, 193;
Department of the Environment
172: *see* Clarke, K.; DTI; Howe,
G.; Thatcher, M.
Unidata 55
universities and research institutes,
participation in Eureka 127–31,
141, 168, 193, 194, 211
USA 3, 10, 19, 22, 35, 36, 37, 39, 41–
2, 44, 45, 50, 55–7, 61–2, 74, 162,
197, 199, 202: *see* Reagan
administration; Weinberger, C.

Veil, S. 58
venture capital 95, 109, 166, 221, 224;
see EVCA
Vienna ministerial conference 33

Weinberger, C. 57
Williams, R. 16, 54, 55
Williamsburg summit (1983) 56: *see*
Group of Seven
Wood, P., see Elliott, R.

But really until
the discussion of , verific
Eureka Projects (last chapter)
does he bring into play the
policy network framework
version sketched in chap. 1

and
not properly
realize the
conclusion,

A meaty read! Flashes of inspiration, but generally
very stolid.

Full of pithy quotes of/similarly quotable one-liners.
The usage of interviews, plus a survey based
chapter.

and its anti-
bureaucratic char.
It offers a bit of 'Seattle, not utopia' prescription
to improve Eureka's operation. There are penalties
to the intergovernmental politics of Eureka, which
are at once its raison d'être, a source of its hostilities,
not also and a source of its weaknesses too.
a source of its rigor

Refreshingly
(Confirms Key
analysis by Moravan,
vote Moravcsik . p. 17
Lack of development of 'policy network'
approach (p. 20-21)